IT's WAKE-UP TIME

IT'S WAKE-UP TIME

Angela Skelley

Matador
9 Priory Business Park,
Wistow Road, Kibworth Beauchamp,
Leicestershire. LE8 0RX
Tel: 0116 279 2299
Email: books@troubador.co.uk
Web: www.troubador.co.uk/matador
Twitter: @matadorbooks

ISBN 978 1789013 627

British Library Cataloguing in Publication Data.
A catalogue record for this book is available from the British Library.

Printed on FSC accredited paper
Printed and bound in Great Britain by 4edge Limited
Typeset in 11pt Minion Pro by Troubador Publishing Ltd, Leicester, UK

Matador is an imprint of Troubador Publishing Ltd

This is my story about growing up in Bristol
in the 1960s and 70s. It is dedicated to everyone who appears
here: you have all helped make me who I am!

In loving memory of my brother Dave.

PANGE
OLD MISERY GUTS

I've decided not to kill myself after all. Last night, though, I almost did it. I went to bed feeling lonely, missing Ben so much. Even to hug my hot water bottle tight, trying to imagine I was cuddling him, failed to be of comfort. I wet the bed yet again with bucketfuls of tears. I flooded my earholes with them too which will probably start up an internal itch, and I thought "Yes, I really will do it this time and put myself out of misery once and for all." I didn't exactly chicken out. Lying in the dark, on my sodden pillow, I worked out my plan of action to end it all down to the minutest detail. I would wait until everyone was in bed of course, then up I would get very gingerly, trying not to creak the bed or the floorboards, rummage in the dressing table for my lady razor, because naturally I couldn't put the light on, get back into bed in the warmth with it and just do it. I would be dead and gone without any trouble at all – simply a few quick slashes across the wrists, nothing more. I expect I would have screwed up my eyes and gritted my teeth, but it wouldn't have hurt because nicks don't. I wouldn't even have been able to see blood gushing. I'd shut my peepers, snuggle down beneath the blankets and drift up to heaven; leastways I would have hoped to put down roots there. It would have been a perfect way to go. I most definitely would have been a corpse, no doubt about it, when discovered this morning. I mean to say, the family wouldn't have begun to worry that they hadn't seen me until lunchtime, because I usually have an extremely long lie-in on Sunday mornings, and by the time a knock came on my door accompanied by "You getting up today or tomorrow?" I would have been stone cold.

Why, you may be wondering, wasn't the deed accomplished then? Well, as I was going back over my plan, and at the same time doing my best not to cry noisily in case a member of the household heard and came to investigate the horrible row, I suddenly thought of Blossom, my old china-pie Mum. There she was downstairs, odds-on with bent head and arms folded, stockings rolled down to her ankles, asleep in the chair, absolutely unaware that she would have to clean up a bloody, ghastly mess in the morning. Sure as eggs she would have fainted off too at the sight of me, and it is possible Dad, and brothers Dave and Al might have had queasy stomachs. I couldn't do it to them, not that way, and other ways I've thought of don't appeal to me. Maybe I should have fizzed a bottle of Disprin in a glass of water and taken it before going to bed. I wouldn't have had time to think then, once I had climbed the stairs. On second thoughts that would have been gassy and filled me with wind. I should imagine that was an uncomfortable way to die, feeling burpy and bloated. And besides I have never made it clear to Dad that when I go I don't wish to be locked up in a coffin. I would get awful claustrophobia and the beetles and woodworm would be bound to get me eventually. Oh no, that's not for me. I want to be burnt and my ashes scattered haphazardly. That is, preferably over countryside and near to the sea. (A bluebell wood would do nicely.) Rather different to what Mrs. Batter has in store for her husband. His ashes are going into an egg timer. She told me she is going to give him a headache, and make him work, if it's the last thing she ever does.

So when tears and morbid thoughts wore me out, I suppose I fell asleep. Not before Blossom created a disturbance. She had a shrieking nightmare and told us this morning, beaming all over her 'cherubs', she could remember burglars kidnapping her. Dad slept on and didn't put up a fight. As Mum was telling us the story, she stepped back onto a saucepan she had put on the floor and squashed it. Pop wouldn't even have dented it, had it been him. Actually, it's Dad who usually wakes me up in the night, not Mum. His snores are loud certainly, but he also calls out "Oh dear, oh dear, oh dear" over and over again in his sleep.

So there we are. I woke up this morning remembering the gory details of the night before, gave myself a stern talking to and here I am, still in the land of the living. I will be honest and tell you that yesterday morning I also thought I might do away with myself. When I left home to go shopping I informed the family they would never see me again, because I was going under a bus, but I forgot to do said deed and on my return Dave's first words were "Weren't they running Pange?" So how to cure myself of acute heartache? There are plenty more fish in the sea so I'm led to believe.

Excuse me while I adjust. My movements are restricted today on account of my bra strap breaking, and it's too cold and I'm too lazy to do anything about it. I really don't have the right to feel downhearted. There are those far worse off than me. Prunella went to the dentist last week for a check-up. She thought she needed a filling, which was correct. Also she was told she would have to have all four wisdom teeth out, and at the same time the hospital would see to her clicking jaw as well. If I think about it, most days my spirits do get a boost and there are occasions when I find myself chuckling – a good sign I'm recovering from my loss and my broken heart is on the mend. I bet if I think back over the past week I can think of a dozen things whereupon I smiled without force. Now let's see.

Last Saturday Peggy from the office spent a day in town wearing a black shoe and a navy shoe, not realising she was odd. The heels weren't on the same level either. Sunday I did find one or two things to chortle about too. Tea-time we had a power cut when Dave was making toast under the grill and he ended up with Frizzled Dick, because he only managed to do the one side. "Dang" he said, but munched nonetheless. Later Dad took a candle upstairs to have a bath with and next minute was thumping down for Mum to take up the matches. He had accidentally blown it out. Mum went upstairs with crossed legs, laughing at the thought of Pop's predicament, but she had to compose herself before going in to him, and make sure she had the straightest of faces, as they were in a huff with one another that day and not speaking. The rest of the evening was spent by firelight and I had the pleasure of listening to my dear brothers joining in with songs on Radio Lux. Dave, the versatile member of the family, could stretch his notes either way, to falsetto or bass. Al made do with his tenor. The neighbours must be used to plugging their ears by now. We did too play creatures on the wall with hand shadows, but I declined participating in a game of murder in the dark. I was happy enough. It was better than going to bed early and not sleeping, which I find myself doing most nights, because no-one has thought to buy me a truncheon to keep beside the bed.

Then Monday evening I walked out of the house arm in arm with Al, on our way to beginners' dancing class, carrying my hairwash stethoscope instead of my brolly. They are both hung up in the same corner of the kitchen so it wasn't such a dumb thing to do. On Wednesday morning the Baker came early, before I went to work, and caught Mum on the hop. She wasn't dressed and had to swiftly don Dad's mackintosh over her nightgown before running to the door. I wouldn't go because I had only one eye made up. Mum was so flustered she asked for a loaf and some faggots. She meant to say crumpets. The Baker did laugh and Mum did too, although she didn't want to, because she didn't have her teeth in. Thursday another happening occurred and laughter even began to hurt. Des and I went to the pictures that evening. It was so draughty round our feet I tucked mine under my bottom, whereas Des put her woolly mittens on her cold tootsies. Heavens above, she hastily removed them, on our way to the bar in the intermission, when I glanced down and saw thick socks on her feet in high-heeled shoes. Again at work on Friday Peggy, Dafty Daphne and I couldn't help but chuckle at crestfallen Mattie, or Haggis as she is more commonly known. She went home lunchtime and returned to say she had just had a bereavement in the family. I thought oh no, was it her horse. I knew it had warts. But it was her cockerel. He had suddenly collapsed and died of a heart attack. You see, only the day before she had added to her menagerie a flea-bitten Afghan hound. During lunchbreak the hound went woof and made a playful pass at her two whippets. They scarpered instantly, and the old cockerel was so flabbergasted he dropped dead on the spot without so much as a final utterance. Poor Mattie, what with this and losing face with her husband, because she cleaned parts of the new family car with a brillo pad, she hasn't been herself. Hubby insulted her too by saying she was the shape of a milk bottle. She also walked into our boss's office, when he rang through at a minute to five, wearing her tea cosy hat. She forgot she had put it on in readiness to flee the premises as soon as she called "Time". Old P raised an eyebrow, but didn't say a dicky-bird. I too caused a frivolous scene on Friday. Lunchtime, as usual, I was sat in Lin's front parlour with her family, eating my sandwiches and drinking my second cup of tea. I was feeling

4

full up afterwards, so undid my two kilt buttons. I had a job to control my two godchildren, Annie and Katie, sat beside me on the settee. They are going through a stage of wanting to press women's chests (stomachs they call them) to see if they squeak like their dollies. Half an hour later I got up to go back to work and whoosh my skirt was down round my ankles. "Typical" the Hibbs' said. Lin's Mum disgraced herself as well as me. She went to the door when the shop-van-man called flogging his goods, either Rollicky Bill or Day-oh, wearing a face pack. Green it was. Oh, that day I know I had walked out of work, and down to Lin's, carrying a coat hanger. I had grabbed my coat on the way out and wondered why I couldn't get it on properly in the lift. I had the coat hanger sticking up the back of my neck. If I had returned it there and then to the cloakroom, I would have had a cold cup of tea waiting for me at Lin's.

GOOD GRIEF,
THE SIGHT OF ME!

Then yesterday and today the blues came back. But here I am on this Sunday afternoon determined to rid myself of them. I'm plonked on the bed corner and upon looking out of the window I declare the day to be a beautiful one. It may be goose pimply weather, damp and windy, but we have blue skies, the sun is wedged between two tree branches and everything outside is glistening with droplets. Our fried egg flowers look nice. I can see swiping golfers dotted about the course, with a few more trapped in the bunkers no doubt.

My God! What a sight for sore eyes. I've caught a glimpse of my image in the mirror. I'm definitely a peaky 'pasty-face' today. I need a cold sloosh. There, a dunking has worked wonders. No wonder Al has renamed me Bloodhound. I've had that droopy look just lately. Mmm, eyebrows are coming along nicely. I'm growing them again, and have been watching them closely and tending to their needs: Vaseline, wet finger and regular combing. I wish I had never messed with them in the first place. I shouldn't have experimented with shapes. Gosh, the agony I went through, tugging out clumps of hairs that first time. I got carried away and couldn't believe it when I surveyed myself properly after the deed was done. I found a couple of half brows instead of whole ones. Now though, I have stopped my daily plucking and hope the downward slopes will sprout out and grow quite quickly. I'm looking forward to being naturally curvy again, so long as they grow flat and in the right direction. I mustn't think of worn toothbrushes or tufty hedgehog balls. That reminds me, I must sharpen my brow pencil or I'll have them thick as nanas.

The other day, upon scrutiny in the mirror, and I told myself not to frown, I could count a number of fine mesh forehead wrinkles in waves across my brow. No use kidding myself it was laughter lines, not up there. Perhaps I'm coming up to an early change of life, because I often experience hot flushes at work and have to partly disrobe or stick my head out of the window. Peggy might stand over me flapping with a file if she can spare a minute or two. Mr. Ede, my nice boss, says I'm hot stuff. I do too get the whirling pits when I stand up after bending down. I reckon I've got more symptoms than Mum. I've only got to say "Phew, a hot flush" at home and Dave remarks "Pull it quick then."

Yes, definitely mousy hair, but I do get golden hues in summer. I'm insanely jealous of our Rish's copper nob. What was it that boy at school wrote on her Valentine's card, "To the most gorgeous Belisha Beacon in the world". I wonder if she still adds vinegar or light ale to her final hair wash rinse? When I first left school I changed my hair colour every few weeks. It was a dicey business, as I could have turned green like that girl Angela did. It was merely a fad. Hair is growing quite rapidly, split ends as well, even though I spent an hour yesterday morning snipping off those I could see. It was either that or spend a detestable hour sewing up moth-holes in a couple of cardigans. Serves me right for removing the mothballs Mum slyly put in the wardrobe ages ago. Bloss annoys me when she does that. To counteract the smell, I pluck a handful of Quince from the garden and pop them amongst my clothing. Hair is long, but I want it longer. The last time I went for a trim Frederick banged my chest. He probably didn't notice I had one, but I knew they had been manhandled and I turned pink. He made me stand too, because he couldn't get the scissors down the back of the chair. I've got squiggly waves. I make them appear by straining my hair back in a tight, bulbous stump round an elastic band. 'Our boys' have got my hairnets. Their need is greater than mine. Dave has a pink one and Al's is brown. Al especially needs to flatten 'stickups'. His thatch always was unruly, what with his double crown and his horn in the front. It's a quiff that just would not stay down when he was a littlun. He plasters it with something now, says

"Down boy" and down it stays. Dave is forever going off to work forgetting to take the clips out of his hair. He tries to train waves without much success. I've got the dreaded lurgi, as I cannot defeat the druff or danders. We never have called it dandruff in our family. Pity, because I do like wearing black. I suffer from an itchy drake too. My hairpiece isn't any use now. My own tresses are longer. I'll keep it on my bedpost though. A long mane, however, does have its drawbacks. I find I'm eating hair often. It gets gummy then stiff after it has fallen into gravy. It sticks to lipstick. It has given me the fright of my life when it was whipped into the blades of the hair-drier, and wound and twisted into a matted ball. Scissors had to be summoned to cut me free. It has blinded me to lamp posts. But for all its faults, I'll keep my locks lengthy because, so I'm told, it makes me look younger. Occasionally I bundle it up on top in a cat's ears style. "Make the most of your hair while you've got it" Mum says, because she is positive at the rate I moult I shall be bald by the time I'm thirty.

Why do I look like death warmed up without make-up? If I don't wear any, friends, full of concern, enquire whether I'm feeling all right or have I been crying?

Mum got in a right muddle over Dave's and my eyebrows. Mine are black and Dave's are fair, yet his hair is black, well very dark brown, black when it's dirty, and my hair is pale. That's what comes of having us on top of one another. All four of us turned out wrong in parts. Not long ago Al was really upset and saying he was a freak and Mum shouldn't have had him. He is lopsided in his legs. He went for treatment and poor devil was put on a rack and stretched. I thought that only happened in X rated films, not in real life. He was down in the dumps though, because he thought his cricket career playing for Somerset 2nd XI would be at an end. We told him "rubbish" and that everybody's leg stalks differ slightly.

Dave I have renamed Monkhead. Thanks to me he has got a square cut for a square head. To my mind he looks exactly like a Monk in an outsize sloppy-Joe jumper. He has this enormous old maroon thing that hangs loosely about him. It would even be ten sizes too big for Bloss. He came downstairs in it the other day and frightened us to death. He had pulled it up over his head and inserted in the neck hole my balsa wood head with the short wig on top. It was totally unexpected to see this pimple on a rock suddenly appear in the doorway. Then he came simpering in like Fifi the male model. He's funny peculiar. I have proof. He recently went to be measured for a suit and the assistant asked him where the hell had he picked up such shoulders. Although Dave is so slim, his shoulders are massive. He told Dave, "You're unbalanced mate". That's exactly what I've been saying for yonks.

I have to use lashings of mascara for allure. Eyes have been tired and worn lately, but I can't keep my specs on for long before they fall off. They have expanded. I shall have to Sellotape them to my ears like Susan does, because it is dangerous the way they are at present. The other day in work they crash-landed into the ink-pad and again in the loo as I was about to hoist up my coms. Both times, luckily, they didn't have far to drop. It's merely my arms that need heating up and moulding to fit properly. Yesterday I asked Al to go and get my glasses for me and he returned with two. Dave says the only time I look remotely intelligent is when I've got my specs on. I reckon wearing them affects my hearing, so I take them off to answer the phone. I have to be honest though; they have helped soothe my nut when the gremlins are in there having a conker match. Dave doesn't believe I get headaches. He says how can I, when there is nothing inside to ache. Huh, the other day a bus conductor said, "Do you know what your eyes remind me of?" I gave him a dazzling smile, expecting a reply like emeralds. Instead I got mildew. With regard to my coal scuttles I dab white goo underneath the eyeballs. Good stuff that.

My nose! To add to the problem I have to keep snipping at a long black whisker that keeps growing down through the right ventricle. I'm not likely to forget somebody once said Rish and I looked like sisters, except that Rish's nose turned up, kind of cute, and mine, well mine turned down. I do have a big freckle on it riding side-saddle, which I prefer to call a beauty spot. I suppose I've got fat lips, but I wouldn't want them to be the pencil straight, thin kind, which is a sign of meanness Mum says. Ally boy has the rosebud mouth of the family. He used to get so riled when Rish, Dave and I sang "Baby Face" to him, just because he was the youngest and the one most vulnerable to torment. We dare not do it now, with him being the biggest member of the family.

I have a slightly protruding front tooth, which is yellow. I've worn the enamel away, and there are patches of yellowness appearing on others too.

Not to worry. I'm into cheese so I shouldn't develop rot or gum trouble. The inconvenience that tooth caused me. I had to be equipped with a dreadful brace in my school-days, which meant either no toffee or difficulties. The brace helped to reverse the offending tooth into its rightful parking slot, but the silly thing gave up the ghost before it should have and stopped a fraction short. Of course my front teeth are quite notched on the ends. They were smooth in my younger days, until I received an uppercut from one of my lovely brothers in a friendly fight. What a crunch! My jaws locked tight together, top teeth slammed down onto the bottom set, and when I opened up dozens of smashed molar filings shot out my mouth. I truly did laugh at the time, because I was like a cannon firing ground tusks. Naturally the second I stopped laughing I bashed dear brother. Muggins wondered if an Emily board, those nail-file doofers, would be able to even them up. Well I was extremely young and had no sense. One rasp was enough to make my timbers shiver. The zig-zaggedness took forever to wear down. Crusts helped, Mum constantly repeated.

What I like on my face is my little mole set in my right cheek. It has got three curly long hairs growing out of it. It's a good job they don't grow half an inch a month like topknots. That would be hysterical. Dave wants to pull them out, but I'll bleed to death if he does, and besides Mum said pull one hair out and two will grow in its place.

I loathe and detest my skin. I get pus-filled ugly spots forcing their way through the epidermis to lie brazenly basking on the surface. Oh, I attack and kill a few of the yellowheads to be sure, but they call up reinforcements. It makes me livid. At my age I should be passed puberty and have outgrown pimples, but they still crop up to reap a full harvest at a certain time of the month. What is it I've got that others haven't which makes the poxy varmints thrive so? No wonder Dave and Al call me Pimp. I'm strict too. Chocolate is taboo. I only eat chips when Mum does them the way I like them, and then it's purely by luck rather than judgment. I can't abide sugar except for a teaspoonful of crystals on Weetabix, and the same pinch of brown sprinklings on porridge. I have used every blemish kill product on the market. I coat myself in a yeast pack once a week and keep it on for twice the instructed length of time until it cracks off. I have eaten a sugar-free half grapefruit for breakfast without wincing since leaving school, and unfailingly have a dose of Andrews Liver Salts on Sundays to clear out my system of impurities.

Last Sunday I was in a dream when I got up. Absentmindedly, I found myself putting a spoonful of tea-leaves into a glass of water instead of salts, which had I swigged down wouldn't, I am positive, have done a satisfactory job.

I crush up an Oxo cube in the greens water separate from Mum's Bisto gravy, because it is supposed to nourish the skin. All these things and more I relentlessly try in the quest for a solution to my break-out problem.

There is a multitude of the pests at the moment. More spots than pores on my dial I reckon. I've got a pimple nestling in my eyebrow, which is most painful to colour, but at least the bugger doesn't show. Admittedly, spots were ten times worse in my innocent years, so I mustn't grumble too profusely, but I would like to know how much longer I shall be lumbered with erupting volcanic craters. I remember years ago wailing about a huge pimple on my face and Rish kindly stating "But Pange that pimple is your face", which remark deserved a biff and a bop. Rish's have never been as bad as mine, not unless she had a spotty boyfriend or pinched my flannel. More than likely I pinched hers, so I deserve to be the blotchy individual. Having said that, I'm not at all sure spots are catching. Mum's mirrors were always speckled, as I'd stand in front of them squeezing away at festering pimps.

I've bought a small square of old-fashioned rouge. Maybe I'll dust a couple of fluffs on my chalky cheeks to see what it looks like. Marvellous investment! I now have quite a pleasing bloom. Clownlike, Dave and Al would say.

Perhaps I should analyse my figure as well as my face, because both could have had something to do with Ben giving me the brush-off.

My skeleton has acquired a gross amount of blubber these past couple of months. I know it, because I've been having trouble with buttons and zips. Even my feet are fat. My main comfort of late has been eating. Only once in my life have I lost a lot of weight and then few remarked at seeing less of me, except the family that is. Dave rechristened me SB, which stood for skin and bone. He said there was more meat on a chicken leg running around. But now I look like a squat jelly baby. I'm ashamed of my physique. Ten and a half stone, 35", 27" but I can get into a skirt with a 26" waistband, 38" to 40" are as accurate dimensions as I care to give.

Come off it Lucifer. That's a downright fib. Since when have you had bosoms Pange? Top deck isn't referred to as a bust in our family. That was Ally's doing. He renamed women's chest, doubles or dubs and they went into spoons not bras. I am, if I'm truthful, a fraction less than 35. I might be 34 if I project myself and I do indeed have a very wide back. To go back a couple of weeks, I bought a new bra, not that I ever need one. Still, I shall never be accused of having a droop. Barbie was with me and together we studied the assortment on the counter. I decided a 34 medium was too blasted big and I came away with a 34 small, padded one, which fits almost to perfection. I don't know why I waste my money. 'Our boys' dared to chuckle when they heard me moaning to Mum that I was lacking.

As if being scanty up top isn't enough, my pair I swear are also out of proportion. They differ in size, plus the fact the smaller one is a trifle lower down than the bigger one. This is frustrating when I am dancing, because if I place my arms round a man's neck in a smooch, lo and behold my bra rises upwards causing one dub to fall out, which means an immediate exit to the loo to insert it into its spoon again. What I have done before now is stuff the spoon holding the smaller double with cotton wool, as this helps to prevent the little one flopping about and working its way out. It is a trial at times. However flat I may be, I will not resort to falsies. Mum says she likes to see rounders on females, bouncy rounders, not poke-outs. I agree. Nothing looks worse than points on a woman. Oh, there is one thing. After dancing close to a fellah, upon moving away a girl has one pointing outwards and one chiselled inwards, or even two conical vaults staring people in the face. It has happened to me. The first I knew about it was when a male, trying to be funny, asked if a pneumatic drill had been boring holes in me. Instead of going red, I should have told him no, but he was boring me. That situation was enough to make any female burn her bra, especially if it was a stiffened one.

Once I was saying to Mum I'd get a flat and Dave butted in "What for Pange, you've got two already", meaning my poor, shrunken dubs again. They don't let up for one minute. Al did enquire how they were yesterday. He greeted me at breakfast with "How's your plums Pange?" I was going to land one on him, because I didn't like the sizable comparison (I was glad he didn't say prunes. They are shrivelled and wrinkly) when Dave remarked to Al, "Don't you mean her currants?" It was no good fuming. I spluttered that it was quality not quantity that counted. Something Rish once sympathetically told me.

Rish hasn't altogether been spared. Her spoons used to be ill-fitting, and she had a habit of grasping them through her jumper and pulling them down over her dubs when they rode up. Dave and Al copied her actions and facial expressions too.

Aptly, I suppose, they define my upper regions as two pebbles balanced on Mt. Everest. I do try to ignore their rude remarks, but they do goad me into retaliation at times. Yesterday was one of those trying days. I was washing my hair at the kitchen sink and Dave in the living room said to Al, in a voice meant to be heard, "Have you heard the joke about the girl with no dubs? Her name was Pange." Then he called out "Mind you don't get 'em wet Pange. We don't want them to shrink any more, do we?" As I climbed the stairs five minutes later in my towel turban, leaving the rabble downstairs, two male voices were singing exuberantly "Pange is busting out all over", that song from the film 'Seven Brides for Seven Brothers'. I did then open my mouth in protest, but don't know why I bothered. I was asked, "Who rattled your cage?" The thing that gets me is they haven't got anything to brag about. If I put my brothers together and counted the hairs on their chest I would have fingers left over. Being a bit untruthful there. I will be fair. Al did say the other day he had six-a-side.

There are days when I could weep at my deficient endowment, because most of my girlfriends are buxom wenches. But heck, I wasn't always this way. There are those who can confirm I was 38 plus, the envy of my class, when I left school. I suppose it was puppy fat, and not meat and gristle, as chest has simply disintegrated, or come adrift, time and place unknown. It seemed one day it was there, next day it had vanished, fallen off and lost for evermore. Barbie is an obliging friend and says she has plenty to spare. She is nearer 40 than 38, the same as I was in my lost youth. Dave has offered to take a pair of pincers to my dubs. It would be nice to have whackers again.

Downwards I go. Waistline? It's there somewhere. Sat in the bath I can't ignore the fact that I have a concertina connecting the molehills to my undercarriage. It's a horrible sight, those ruffles of fat. They crease up into three huge coils, like a boa constrictor wrapped around my middle. Disgraceful. I could get an all-in-one corset thing, but the indignity. Broad across the beam with a wobble not a wiggle to my hippo hips, but the school matron did tell me I had good childbearing hips. I'm like Mum. She eats my Nimble slimming bread eight slices at a time, because she says it's nothing more than a puff of wind. Our tiny Nan eats a piece at a time, because she likes it. It's soft. Therefore no need to put her teeth in. Nan is too honest. She says I've got great limbs. She doesn't say it unkindly, just that I was meant to be big about. That is no front, all behind. I do roll on the floor nightly in the hope that I'll bash and whittle away the hips. It doesn't, truth be told, do the slightest bit of good. I doubt whether I'll ever see bones jutting out. Big Bloss and little Nan think it's hilarious to see me rocking sideways on the carpet, but they declined my invitation to join me in a roll the last time Nan was staying with us. It was in a skylarking moment too, the time it took Dave to push and Al to pull, with a combination of grunts and coarse language such as "You lumbering great ox", "You floundering whale", to haul me to my feet.

My legs. What a hairy Nelly I would be if I didn't shave them twice a week, sometimes three depending on the rate of stubble growth. Weird, I always manage to leave quite a few hairs above each knee. Mine, during the growing years, became a painful case, to my own mental state that is. It wasn't so much thick hairs, but long ones I could brush into kiss curls. So I had to defuzz myself, just had to. I really did think, in my troubled mind, that they were going to grow and grow until I had ape legs. I often wonder if I shall be doing them in the bath when I'm eighty, a wizened old lady. I expect so, because I wouldn't like to think I had porcupine spines growing horizontal out of my legs through neglect. I like seeing them shiny and smooth after they have been scalped, and think back to how they looked in my teenage years.

I won't ever forget the first time I used a razor; Rish's it was, for underarms. Coming home from school a group of boys made a cutting remark, as I walked in front of them down the road. Immediately I made up my mind, when the awful lump jumped into my throat, it would be action stations that night. While the family was sat watching telly, I went nonchalantly up to the bathroom. After I had locked the door it was an effort to stop my hands from shaking, as I took hold of the razor, knowing Rish would kill me if she knew, her property and all that, and with a scrape here and a scrape there I walked the blade tentatively, not ran it, up and down my legs. Practice makes perfect. At my first attempt I knew not how to wield a razor and cut myself to ribbons down at the ankle bones. I stood in a blood bath crying, because I would be bound to die. The blood was never going to cease pouring. Oh the shame I endured. I had to summon Mum. My secret was out. What made it worse, Rish was courting Bob then, not married to him, and he was with her downstairs. I gave them such a fright. They thought I had been trying to top myself. Rish also thought I would get rust poisoning, due to the fact that the blade was at least a year old. As plasters make my skin go bubbly, I had to be swathed in bandages. Next day I went to school and told friends I had cut myself on glass whilst gardening, although it was the middle of winter. It was a long time before I touched a razor again. All my pocket money went on Immac depilatory cream. Smelly give-away stuff, but it was worth it.

Dopey Alan sometimes pretends he is skiing, and my hairless legs are the icy slopes. He places a foot on my leg when I'm stretched out on the pouffe, and makes believe he is sliding out of control down my slippery legs. Mum gets me depressed though. She says pity my poor husband when (and if) I nab one. He'll think he has got skewers sticking in him, should our legs entwine in bed, when the tiny molecules, no follicles I mean, start to puncture their way through the skin, as happens every few days. Bloss says too, what if I ever have to go into hospital, I couldn't shave my legs then. It would be a tough job with eyebrow tweezers. It would be a scream though if I broke a bone in my leg and it had to be mummified. Imagine when the plaster cast had to be sawn off! I would have one leg like a coconut and the other beautifully gleaming and satin smooth to the touch. It could be though hair doesn't grow in the dark. They do look like they have a glossy sheen when they have been plucked, except for a bit of a rash round my pubes, which soon disappears.

My legs actually aren't too bad a shape once I'm parted from the hair. Complimentary Al said the other day that I had a nice leg on me, and Dave quipped "Which one?"

I wouldn't advise anyone to begin removing leg hairs unless they feel it is absolutely necessary. It is a binding chore, as my bath-times extend to almost an hour stood in lukewarm water lopping hairs off gooseflesh and my God, the state of the bath afterwards! I have been known to leave the cleaning of it to Dad which, I grant you, is most unfair on my part. It bugs the boys that I spend so long in the bathroom. They always take it into their skulls that they want to do a Jimmy Riddle when I'm in there. They can't bear going to the outside John because it's dark, they say, spidery too, and they might miss, and they don't want to catch 'monia. It's at such times when they are furious with me that I say nobody loves me and I'll leave home and get a flat with my own personal shower. Dave quick as a flash offers to help me pack.

That's quite enough on the topic of my stilts. Magnificent hind legs I have every other day. The day in-between they are like men's chins at 5 o'clock. I can remember the time I was almost asleep in my bed and both Dave and Al entered like killer dogs in the darkness, bearing an advert they thought I might like to see. It was for an electric man's shaver.

My arms too are bushy with long hairs. I mean to say, I couldn't possibly razor them. I couldn't hide them in tights when needle heads began to pop up on surface skin. No, I think my arms must keep their warm coat. Years ago I had a phobia and sweltered during the summer months, because I would not strip off cardigans. I would make out I was 'just right' or cold, yet I would be hot as a furnace to tell the truth, with droplets trickling down my forehead making my eyebrows run. Nowadays I do my best to get the sun on them as much as possible, because when the arms turn brown the hairs go fair. Then I toss off cardigans and refuse further to look at my mat-like arms. I don't feel so bad about being hairy now as it happens, because Barbie said she read in a magazine the more body hair you have acquired the more sexy you are. It probably referred to men, but nice to think I might be a sexpot as well as a gorilla.

My shoulders are a bit on a slant like Dave's, but luckily my hair disguises the fact from him that I'm a seesaw. I wish I had a giraffe neck without the jigsaw pieces, but I'm stuck with my short thick stubby one, because you can't slim that down with slaps and pinches like you can buttocks. Knees are corn free, little toes aren't. I cuss flashes when they take it in turns to nibble.

The ugliest part of me has to be my feet, real QE2s. Toes protrude N S E and W. One doesn't even have a nail to speak of, just a covering of soap scum. It decayed on me, and fell off. The others are split and fungus-sy. I don't ever cut them myself. That's Mum's job, but never on Fridays, because she says that is bad luck. Fancy, 23 and I don't cut my own toe-nails! Any prospective husband might take off when he knows what marriage to me entails. The ruination of my feet began with the introduction of winkle-pickers and stiletto heels. Duffer Pange crippled herself by squashing her size 7 and a half, occasionally 8 – my patchwork ones are 9s, but nobody believes me when I say they are continentals – into fairy twinkle-toe shoes. I hate people saying "Well your feet don't look big", because that means, having cast a crafty glance all over, they detect they are in proportion with the rest of me. I do get uppity at the ludicrous size of my hooves. It isn't right for a female to have such big ones, even if there is more to balance on. Not only my feet. Mum says I've got the biggest tonsils she has ever seen. (I hope she doesn't go around asking any Tom, Dick or Harry to "Open Wide".) Rish's feet are big too and revolting Bob says. She was always using the pummy stone on them when she lived at home. I wonder if she still gets blue legs in Canada. Awful circulation she had. Dave and Al would rub them, one each.

It isn't any wonder I'm not pleased with my carcass, having assessed myself from 'napper' to 'tozzles'. I'll never be able to wear a bickini as Mum calls them. No doubt we're all similar lumps in some ways. I have just the one real mark of beauty that satisfies my vanity, my beauty spot, which is practically central, that is a fraction to the right of my belly button. I had trouble with that thing for a long time after birth, because I wasn't knotted right, or whatever it is they do to you. It poked out and I had to be bound. Mum should have sued the midwife and I might have been rich now. It has sunk though into a large dark hole over the years. I hate them. They remind me of snails. When it comes to cleaning it out with cotton wool and Vaseline, it's like touching the underside of a slimy slug. I come over all queer. I'll cease complaining further about my abnormalities and be thankful I'm intact and able to function.

Now I'll go and make Mum yell, because she is summoning me to roller her hair up. Nine times out of ten she regrets asking me, as she says I get my hair off and am cruel to her. I'll be back. There is a slushy, romantic film on the telly tonight and if I watch it the melancholy will come flooding back. Somehow it's the Sundays spent with Ben I miss the most. I must toddle before Mum raises the roof with her hollering. Besides, I know there is a cup of tea waiting down below, because I heard the clink of teaspoons meeting china a minute ago. One thing I do possess is a good eardrum.

BLOSS AND POP AND THE HORRORS, DAVE AND AL

'Lo, I'm in bed. It's ridiculously early and I feel evil with myself. I thought I had better slip away from the family below, because I felt a dreary mood coming on, and when Pange has the miseries it is best she be left alone. I flew at Dave in a rage earlier on because, when I poured him a cuppa, he said I left gubbins floating on the top. What a fuss-pot he is. He thinks to swallow a tea-leaf is fatal. He called me miso – his word for a misery moo – and a niggly babe, and a Giant Crab, altered to Crabess in the next breath. It only wanted Al to pass comment and say I had given him the wrong cup, without his possession mark on it, and I would have knocked their heads together, or had a darn good try.

Brothers, who'd have 'em! When they plague the living daylights out of me I could commit murder twice over. Then I think to myself why isn't Rish here to even things up, like in the olden days. Ten years ago we could have had a real set-to with them and won. It's two onto one since Rish has been gone. Trouble is, if I do have a go at one, t'other comes to his aid and I'm floored in a strangulation hold begging for mercy, which is never forthcoming. I only have to scream once "I've had enough. I'm leaving home" and Dave again offers to help me pack, and requests permission to start moving his stuff from the boys' room into my room.

Huh, he has filled up my wardrobe already with his running prizes. Any girl who has the misfortune to be hooked by Divid won't need to collect a bottom drawer. He has one fully stocked with goodies galore. His girl will deserve it, because she will have to spit on and polish his innumerable medals, cups and trophies. His prize this week in a race was a medal and a couple of pounds of bloody steak. We enjoyed it tea-time with some leftover Christmas wine. (Christmas was 10 months ago.) Dad said it was most agreeable to the palate and Dave said, "Hark at old paintbrush". Ally laughed and for that Dad made them both cringe and grovel at his feet. They whined their pitiful pleas for pardon and Pop relented. He let them stand up saying they were mice not men. Dad told them to get out of his sight, which they did. As they went Dave turned to Al and said "I never strike a man who is wearing glasses". "Nor me" said Al. Later, when Dad went to put his work boots on he found the laces tied.

I get similar treatment from them. I went off to work one day last week with my Granny Smith's apple substituted for a non-appetising red wax one. Al thought of the blushing Granny Smith trick, but persuaded Dave to actually do it. Furthermore they keep putting socks in my bag, often whiffy ones. The other day, whilst standing in a bus queue, I put my hands in coat pockets searching for gloves. The one in my right-hand pocket fitted like a glove, the one in my left-hand pocket fitted like a sock. They do show me up.

Mum isn't spared either. Yesterday I found her in the kitchen with a 2p price tag on her shoulder lipoma. They owned up. "Going cheap at the price" Dave said. "Shoddy goods" Al nodded. They had sent Dad off to work with a 70p tag stuck between his shoulder blades, because he is worth more than Goono the boys remarked. Better that than a "Made in Hong Kong" one I suppose. I remember when they sent Mum up the road shopping with one of those petrol Tiger in your Tank tails pinned on her mac in the appropriate place. She was none the wiser. What we have to put up with from the brothers. Yesterday Mum wasn't sensible in speech and Ally said to her "You chewing a brick?" Then she shouted at Dave for something he had or hadn't done and he said "Right mudder, you've made your point, now sit on it". When she's rabbiting on at the sink, thinking we're listening, the boys take one end of a towel each, stalk their prey and gag her unexpectedly. Her pinny too will suddenly fall to the floor when one of her sons has slunk up behind her. She was lamenting about carrying heavy bags of shopping yesterday, so along came Dave with a ruler, measured her arms and pronounced them stretched indeed. Mind you, she is a bit of a wayward lass herself. Complaining Friday night she was of Pop's baggy trousers. On impulse she pulled out the excess material round the bottom area and pegged it tight. He was wearing them at the time. What a fine sight that was to greet me on my arrival home from work. Dave often comes home from work and hails Dad "I see you've got your hipsters on again Pop the Dop". The exact opposite really, because Dad wears such high waisted trousers, chest level to be perfectly honest. His braces keep them firmly in place.

This morning I awakened with them carol singing outside my bedroom door. Christmas is two months away! I don't like to tell them to buzz off. I made that mistake once and they went and did just that. We had a couple of noisy bees in the room for what seemed like an hour.

But this evening I know why I have got the grizzles, and it wasn't due to anything the big guys, Dave and Al, or the good guys, Bloss and Pops, said or did. My rain clouds descended as I sat listening to 'Sing Something Simple' on the wireless. Ben and I usually ate our tea during that programme, or maybe we would be on our way home (his flat was home in a sense) after an afternoon's drive. I loved those half hours, humming, lull lulling, do-dee-dooing, as the old songs were sung. But that is a pleasant memory, which I mustn't spoil by getting grouchy.

Anyways, I feel most comfortable now tucked up in bed with three pillows propped behind me. To ease my spinal column, once the days pressures and toil are over, I've still got the door under my mattress (stays Nan says is the real answer for back ache twinges), but I'm thinking of chopping it, or David, up for the fire, because David keeps making me seasick. He creeps in when I'm half asleep, goes to the foot of my bed, grabs hold of the edge of the door sticking out, and rocks me up and down violently. He did drop the door down on his knuckles the last time, but I got a flip for saying "Serves you right". That boy does disturb my sleep, not just at night but mornings too. He goes for an early morning run at 6am and, upon rising, he comes into my bedroom to turn the immersion heater on for his bath. He has a habit of coming up to the bed and peering closely at my face. Instinct tells me he is there, because I immediately wake up to hear him say, "I was only seeing if you were awake". The toad is crackers. I caught him idling before tea when I dapped into the kitchen. I must give him his due. Certainly, it was intricate work he was engaged in, writing, "Dop is a twit" in the butter dish, with a knife I might add not a fingernail. It took him ages to perfect his comical italic scrawl. A nice peaceful quarter of an hour the rest of us had. If I had been Dad (Dop) I would have rubbed Dave's nose in it. All he got from Dad was "I'll knock your block off."

Blow, I've forgotten my hot water bottle, but I shouldn't need it. I've got a cardigan on over dressing gown, with flannelette toe-touching nightie under that. Sufficient body warmers seeing I am in bed. The bedsocks Nan knitted for me I wouldn't be without neither, or is it either? It has turned woolly weather now.

I'm not ready for sleep yet. I can tell. Besides, I don't want indigestion (because then I get a bright red conk, same as when I drink hot, strong tea and coffee). I've recently eaten our usual Sunday supper of cold joint sandwiches – it's the one night in the week the family eats supper and then only if Pop is here and not at work. He makes the sandwiches perfect, as he puts the right amount of salt on the meat and he doesn't give us fat and gristle like Mum would. I could even have had a couple of pickled onions if I had thought, because it no longer matters about having sweet-smelling breath. We had chicken today. Dad put skin in my sandwiches, because he knows I like it. As usual we pulled the wishbone and, as more often than not, I won because Pop constantly tries his best to let me. My silent rendering is prayer-like with closed eyes and ends with a stupid amen. I fought Al for the gizzard. We ended up having half each.

I suppose I'm a fully-fledged woman, but once in a while it does no harm to turn the clock back to days gone by when I was so dependent on Mum and Dad. Not that I recall being a tiny baby, that is I was never tiny. I was born a huge monstrosity with 'chubby chops'. Out of the four of us I've been told I was the horrible infant, a fat, slobbering screamer, forever grumpy and being sick. Mum said for years she crushed me up a sea-leg to swallow before bus rides, but it made no difference. I'd bring my boots up, usually all over her. Most likely I was a baby bitch, because I was jealous of David appearing on the scene exactly a year and a month after me. What a liberty he took coming so soon, intent on diverting the parental love I was receiving onto himself. The scrap couldn't wait neither, or is it either, for mass attention, because he had the cheek to be premature (temperature

Mum said he was the other day) and a sickly weakling. Aunty Gwen, when she first saw him, said to Mum "What you got there, Dora, a skinned rabbit?" He had to be swaddled and mollycoddled, but he never cried. I did for the both of us. Knowing what a bundle of nothing he was when born, it's hard to believe he was Somerset cross-country champion until a month ago, and then he only lost his title due to the fact he ran out of one shoe on the course and had to go back for it. (His story and he's sticking to it.) He flourished though, same as we all did, on milk, cod-liver oil, free orange juice, Vick on our chests if we were raspy, gripe water if we had a windy pain, soap up our bums if we were constipated. I think I'm imagining that last remedy, as I recall the four of us developed a love for syrup of figs, which Mum doled out on a weekly basis to keep us regular. Later on, if we were sick, Mum's housekeeping stretched to Lucozade and Ribena. They were real treats.

And so our sprouting up began. I suppose for a year or two Mum had Dave and me in nappies at the same time. Then, when Al came hotfooting along soon after, she had three toddlers clamouring umpteen times a day "Numbers, numbers!" Nan, love her, when reminiscing the other day defined me as "a babby squalling murders all the time, forever in a paddy", but I stopped my wailing when Terri joined me in my pram, or when I was put in hers. That is where dear Terence (Teresa is her real name) Cod (Codlington is too lengthy to keep saying) and I met nearly twenty-three years ago, and we've remained bosom pals ever since. Our coos and gurgles were tuned in on the same wavelength, but we may have fought when rattles met skulls.

Thinking about it, we four monsters must have been a handful for Mum and Dad. Mum had a four-year gap between Rish and me, but Dave followed hot on my heels, and Ally a mere two years later. Mum didn't really want Al. She tried to get rid of him by dosing herself with, I think it was, castor oil and liquid paraffin, but these days thinks of him still as her baby, although he's twenty and 6'4" towering above us all. Of course, Rish being the oldest got blamed for nearly everything. Mum says that now. I suppose when we were tots we often would have swapped Mum and Dad after smacks and tellings-off. They had a lot to put up with though. There was always mischief-making going on in the prefab. I remember a time when the four of us were extremely naughty and Mum went to call us bloody buggers, but her temper was so frayed it came out as bluggers (even now we get called bluggers from time to time). She was definitely going to leave us once and for all. She put on her coat and walked out the back door leaving behind a deathly hush. By the time she had skirted the prefab and entered the front door, tears were splashing down four pairs of cheeks. We honestly thought she had gone and we would be sent away to a 'special' school for delinquents, the place we used to get threatened with.

We found it impossible to control ourselves at the meal table. The more we tried the worse our giggles got, and that was something Pop would not tolerate. Mind you, he would never strike us girls, and only rarely the boys. Threaten with his belt, yes. Striking was a job Mum was good at. But we knew when we had gone too far and had tried Dad's patience to the limit, because he would begin to sigh loudly and rattle the crocks, bang things down, poke the fire vigorously, and slam doors. We knew then we had to call a halt to our devilment or woe betide us. He still does these things occasionally, but we're usually not to blame. Mum is. It happens when Mum gets in a funny mood and sulks, and won't speak to him for no apparent reason. I tell Mum straight, when these moments occur, that it's a terrible, strained atmosphere to bring children up in, but she smiles her wicked smile and keeps right on being mum with Pops until, suddenly, they are talking again and all is well, until the next time. I'm positive Pops could easily have divorced Bloss a hundred times over for cruelty and won custody of us kids. That is why presumably he hasn't done so. Mum says Pops makes her mad at times, because he's too perfect. Is it any wonder we take Pop's side in an argument, never Blossom's. Dave, Al and I tell her she is always in the wrong and she doesn't deserve our Dad. Then he goes and says, "What would I do without Blossom". But I've warned Mum, she should make the most of her time spent with Dad, because they won't be together in the next universe. Certain sure she will be bound for Hell, whereas Pop will zoom up to Heaven as God's right hand man, not that he's churchy, he's simply too good for this world.

Mum has told us heaps of stories relating to her madcap youth. She was a bit of a one. I reckon her brown eyes have it. She could melt hearts by casting looks. One day when she was out walking her high heel snapped off. A workman sang, "Ain't she sweet walking down the street" as Blossom went on her up and down way.

When Mum was in service she became infatuated with the butler. Parties were often held below stairs in the big house. Dad came to one with his pal Johnny Brown and that was how they met. Nan likes Johnny Brown and refers to him as a jolly trump. Dad doesn't see much of Johnny Brown now, except when he brings a train down from Paddington to Bristol Temple Meads where Dad's an engine driver. He'll then shout across the tracks, "Where's young Tommy Burborough then?" For every date Mum had a box of chocolates from Dad. She didn't want him at first, said he was too quiet, and was never upset at his going back to London after weekend visits. But one day she didn't want him to go and that was it. The woman of the big house loved Dad. When he visited Mum weekends she gave him the master's bed if he was away.

Men and women love Dad. Great Aunty Flossie says Dad puts her in mind of a Member of Parliament. She loves Dad and wants to kiss him whenever she sees him. She says to Uncle Les "Isn't Tom lovely". I don't know what Uncle Les is supposed to reply, seeing Dad is his brother-in-law and Aunty Flossie is his mother. Mostly Blossom and Poppers are like a couple of lovebirds billing and cooing. Mum is at the door when he comes home from work calling out "Is that my sweetie-pie?" We kids label her a false hussy, because other times she doesn't speak to the lover for days, and when we demand to know the reason why, she shrugs her shoulders and gives us a naughty, innocent look. The words she calls him when they are friends are a scream. Soppy words like darling, precious or presh, chin-chin, chickerpick, beauty cockling, sweetheart jam-tart. I do feel for him though. By golly, his knees creak when Bloss sits on them. She does tend to flatten him, and one of these days he'll break if she isn't careful. She worries too, because he hasn't got any bot to speak of. She says it must be hard and uncomfortable for him to sit down. There isn't much of him to be honest. They go out on the doorstep and pull the door half shut when Dad is about to set off for work. We're too young – they say – to witness the lovey-dovey sessions. We do hear kiss kiss kiss before Mum's usual utterance "Mind the roads". Then Pop goes walking on his way to the station.

Last week he had to go to the hospital to become a guinea pig due to his spastic colon defect, and as he left home Mum said "Don't let them hurt you Dad." (We tell her time and time again, he isn't her Dad.) "If they do I'll kill them dead". However, the hospital tested him and pronounced him a very fit man for his age. Trust the boys to say, "No Pop, you misheard. They said you were a very thick man for your age". On his diet sheet, besides fruit and potato skins, one of the edibles listed is "Bran, available from any pet shop", confirmation he was a guinea pig. And he had a letter yesterday from the hospital requesting him to pick up his pellets. One tea-time he sat and ate a plateful of uncooked white cabbage. He flexed his muscles after, thought he was Popeye and said he could take on all-comers. Dave said, "Come on my son" – Dave calls Dad and Alan his sons – clenched his fists and told Pop to stick his dukes up. Dutifully Pop put his paws in the air and they pranced round and round the kitchen sparring. When Dad landed one on him Dave didn't play fair. He twanged Dad's braces and they jerked back on Bloss and made her drop a basin of dried peas over the kitchen floor. Fun and games were over then. The brothers time Pops how long it takes him to eat his high-fibre meals. He chomps and chomps his diced carrot and cabbage, but it's as hard to get rid of as All Bran is. The boys poke fun when Dad's mealtimes extend over the hour, but much more of it and Dad has said he'll part their fibres for them.

Dave calls Mum, besides other things, Tubby Gooner, because she is getting huge. She excuses herself by saying she must have something growing in her. I doubt that she's expecting, but if it is a baby it will mean Blossom is a goner. She vowed she would jump off Clifton Suspension Bridge if that happened. It's no wonder though Goon is like a barrel – she won't go near, what she calls the weighers in the bathroom. It's gallons, not pints, of tea she daily pumps into herself. We swear her stomach must be stained and lined with teapot fur. We can often hear it gurgling and slopping around in there. Working part-time at Schweppes is disheartening, because Bloss and her mate Aggie (Aggie calls Mum Eva not Dora. Mum prefers Eva, but Dad doesn't.) are allowed to drink as many fizzy drinks as they want. Pops hasn't a hope of getting fat, not with the walking he does to and from Temple Meads Railway Station. He would rather walk than wait for a bus and who can blame him, seeing that Bristol has the worst bus service in the country. Ooh, the times ever I've fumed livid fumes over a bus that hasn't turned up, more than I would over a date. It's obvious to Dave, Ally and me that both the parents have shrunk in height as they have got older.

Going back to mealtimes when we were youngsters, we were terrors certainly and such mucky pups, especially the boys. Even before meals, we wouldn't give Mum a minute's peace. That was my fault, because I instigated bobbing. I started the craze in my pram and the boys learnt it from me and followed suit. Rish didn't copy us though. I can picture us when we were little (and not so little) on a Sunday morning. Our bobbing must have driven Mum up the wall. Roughly an hour before dinner we would start. Fold arms, bang our heads angrily and rhythmically on the backs of our chairs, chanting together in unison, "I want my dinner, I want my dinner" – sharp, quick emphasis on the word dinner. On and on and on we would go, getting madder and madder by the minute. I went to sleep in the same way. Lying on my tum, with hands under pillow, I would bang my head up and down on the pillow until I dropped off. No pleasure for Rish trying to go to sleep in the normal way beside me. But it didn't take me long to fall asleep. Rish had trouble though. When we moved to Ford Crescent I can remember her going to the top of the stairs night after night and calling down to Mum "I can't go to sleep, why can't I go to sleep, when will I go to sleep, can I have a drink of water?" Questions, questions, Mum had to find answers to. Dafty Blossom. To Rish's "I can't go to sleep" she would say "Well shut your eyes then". I nearly put her to sleep for good when she woke me up merely to inform me she was having difficulty in going. The boys have given up bobbing altogether now, but I still occasionally find myself doing it when I'm listening to music and humming. Mine is a gentler way these days, no head banging, just rocking forwards and backwards against a cushion. A pretty sight I'll warrant.

Oh yes, where was I. The kitchen table wasn't big enough for six, so we kids ate first and Mum and Dad would follow after we had stepped down. How the boys would mash their boiled spudiators (not roasters because they were boulders) and build dams to prevent gravy from drowning the peas (men) on the other side of the plate. They would jump up and down in their seats with excitement if a trickle got through, and armed with knife and fork implements would try and swish back the onrushing tide cursing, "Back you dog". Funny little whatsits they were. Should any peas get dislodged from their plates that would be the cue for further hysterical mirth and choking. It seemed the more we were sternly told to behave at table, and we did try, the harder it was to control ourselves. The silence and effort we made, trying not to look at one another, would start us off again. It has been known for dinner to eject from someone's mouth with a snort and popped cheeks, when a giggle could not be suppressed. Should that happen Mum would fly into the room, reach up and grasp the cane lying on top of the highest kitchen cupboard, and stand with her rod hovering over us saying "Right, who's first?" before dishing out four whacks. We couldn't reach that sweet pea cane no matter how hard we tried what with stretching on toes, jumping, and sitting on Dave's shoulders, which nearly doubled him up for life when I climbed aboard.

We would dunk bread in gravy and slosh it round and round until the plate was wiped clean. There was a lot of slurping and licking, stained chins and jumpers before the last traces had been mopped up. 'Afters' wasn't a thing in our house, no room for it. M & D refused us permission to leave the table unless we had emptied our plates. We used to trade if we didn't particularly like a thing. Rish was allowed all my liver for a spoonful of cabbage. Even cabbage was preferable to liver, which I swore curdled my blood. If no-one was in a trading mood, I would slyly transfer a potato onto a brother's plate before he sat up to the table – probably only to find half a dozen extra on my plate when the four of us assembled to begin devouring, usually with relish. I think Rish and I were less trouble to Mum than the boys who were finicky. We were a couple of dustbins and accepted anything more or less. Mum though was a great believer in filling us with greens. Often the four of us would sit, as if under water, holding noses and swallowing disguised cabbage in a few forced gulps, with pain and torture written over our faces. It was either that or sit there for half an hour and then suffer cold greens. Sometimes Mum would give in with a backhander and we would have bubble and squeak on Mondays. That was all right. Stew was even better if it contained lots of suety dumplings with no turnips, no parsnips and no swede. Times have changed. Nowadays I don't like stew unless it has got simply every veg one can think of bunged in.

Talking of stew, I do declare I've had a blockage since Tuesday. I've got a dump stuck in my gullet. It seems to be lodged there. It will shift in its own good time. I refuse to resort to brute strength and give Dave the pleasure of wringing my neck. What it is really is chronic indigestion through golloping my food. Not that Mum's dumplings were lead balls. Indeed no, they were light and fluffy.

Then again, years ago crackpot Pange wouldn't touch anything laden with currants or sultanas and yet now I think a steaming slab of bread pudding, spotted dick or lardy cake is nothing short of ecstasy. I like all the wrong things. No fads have I any longer, except liver still makes me heave. I begin a diet in earnest, but let me catch sight of curly, crispy bacon rind – impossible to ignore! Yes, I'm well aware I'm a selfish glutton and the birds are more needy than I.

Bloss without fail does a fry-up Saturday lunchtimes, exactly as she did when we were small. How we did conglomerate round Mum the minute she gonged "Come and get it", each one of us pushing and shoving, holding out a plate beseeching "Mostly juice, mostly juice". Tomato juice it was. Not one of us would say "When".

Though Mum persevered, we weren't great lovers of bread and jam for tea. Why, we wanted to know, couldn't we have clotted cream sandwiches like we did over Aunty Vi's? Strawberry jam was, I suppose, the best although pippy. Baby brother Ally was a peculiar kid. He would ask Mum for "some strawberry jam click click". Not once did he request strawberry jam without adding click click on the end. No one knows where he got it from.

A favourite tea of ours was dripping on toast. Arguments, nothing but arguments, should one have more than his fair share of the dark brown jelly sediment that settled at the bottom of the basin. We would start off boring neat holes to the base. When we had finished, the pan of dripping, once smooth, would be carved and chopped into a hundred pieces in the race to be first to the jelly. The things kids will fight over. We fought over whose turn it was to finger scrape the bowl of cake mixture Mum had finished with. If I didn't win I would sneak back into the kitchen later and help myself to a spoonful of syrup or desiccated coconut. Mum was forever running out of things and saying "I could have sworn I had enough". How I loved condensed milk. Still do. Sundays we always had the same tea, tinned fruit and ideal milk. Come to think of it, that's what we have most Sundays even now.

After tea I doubt whether we were allowed out to play, but we nevertheless managed to sneak out for an hour, until we got the yawns and perhaps the grumps, then we would saunter home. Some kids would have to get back in the same way they got out. Those nippers sent to bed early by disagreeable parents would rise again after five minutes, quietly dress and climb through the window to come and play until the sun went down. Living in prefabs this wasn't a problem. The hateful wash awaited us on our arrival home. Rish and I could be relied on to undress ourselves, but from the moment the boys' yellow and brown knitted Balaclava helmets were dragged over resisting nuts, it was a caper to take braces down and get Dad's cut-down grey serge baggy trousers off their little legs. It was an enjoyable sight, watching Mum chase the boys round the kitchen. The bathroom wasn't used for washing except on Sundays. At random we were lifted onto the kitchen draining board and made to sit with legs dangling in the sink with contemptuous "I hate Mum" looks plastered on four infantile mugs. Blossom nearly snapped our heads and rubbed our lugholes off with the towel after, and too bad if the moaning started that the water was scalding, or sniffling began over a grazed knee, because we shouldn't have been larking about to get it in the first place. God, when the iodine was splashed liberally over wounds we shrieked enough to raise the roof. What a din! But it didn't half sting.

On a fine Sunday afternoon we would go for a walk with Mum and Dad. Pop never has had the wish for a car, and we used to love those family walks, but we must have been a constant worry, reluctant to hold Mum and Dad's hands for long and forever stepping off the pavement. Puddle jumping was a must, with muddy water getting up backs of legs and coats. "Pick your feet up" was Mum's favourite saying on those walks. (Why is it we all know instantly when we have trod in dog's muck? It must be a texture thing. Squidgyness I suppose I mean.)

Bath night was on Sundays. In out, in out, and so on until we were all done and dusted. It wasn't a case of first come first serve, it was whom Mum could grab by the shirt-tails or ear first. True, Rish and I turned our noses up on bath nights, but we would still kick up a fuss and get in a right lather if Mum scrubbed the boys before us, because they were far dirtier and we hated having to sit down in brown water. It was a long drawn out performance of splashing water over Mum and everything in sight, except our own faces, necks and ears if we could get away with it. We never could though. Mum was too muscular and hardly ever let us retreat with a lick and a promise. She needed to supervise a wash, otherwise the soap and towels got dirty. Once the grime was lifted, we lined up for Pops to inspect his brood. Possibly finger and toe-nails had to be cut and maybe if we swore to be good for the next hundred days we would be allowed to listen to a programme on the wireless. What were our favourite progs? There was Paul Temple, Journey into Space and The Flying Doctor. We weren't a family to have television until late in our lives. Well that is, it was when we reached the pop-age and we felt denied because all our friends were watching 'Top of the Pops'. Eventually Bloss and Pop relented to shut us up. They still watch 'Top of the Pops', as well as us, and are bang up to date with what's in the charts. They know the words and tunes of the Top Ten better than I do.

The only time Mum didn't know she had us was when four devils, masked with angelic faces, curled up beneath the blankets. Matchsticks wouldn't have propped our eyes open when bedtime came, except we created one last ruction, hissing indignantly that we wanted to stay up for a bit longer to comb and brush Dad's hair. The crime rate went down in the neighbourhood after 8pm.

Sleeping, when we lived in the prefab, didn't present difficulties. We were infants then, and it was natural for kids in a family to sleep together. Being small fry, Dave slept down the bottom of Rish's and my double bed. He only came halfway up the bed so his feet didn't kick us in the teeth. They were everywhere else though, and if we were annoyed, because he had got away without washing them and they smelt cheesy, I would sit on him and Rish would tickle his pongy toes and forget to wash her hands after. Then the stupid nit grew and a new bed had to be installed somehow or other into our room for him, and his feet never bothered us a great deal after that. Ally slept in a cot in Mum and Dad's room until he was five or six, but his growth certainly hasn't been stunted because of it. Although six kids in Terri's family, they managed to sleep in nooks and crannies of the two-bedroomed prefab. David Johnny, if I remember rightly, slept in the passage under the rail of coats pegged up.

I can picture us on Christmas Eve, that is in the early hours of Christmas morning, when we crept along the passage to Mum and Dad's room. Dave and I peeped round the door and made Rish tiptoe in. We had told Alan before we went to bed not to go to sleep, only to pretend, but Rish invariably had to wake him. Being the biggest and the oldest, and the one who told us Father Christmas didn't exist, Rish found it easier to lift him out of the cot and carry him in with us. We had to make her, under protest, go back again to M/D's room to unhitch Alan's stocking off the cot and bring his presents back. Then we would open the lot. Usually delight got the better of us and we woke Mum and Dad. We heard them coming, but we were rarely quick enough to stuff Alan, wrapping paper and presents down the bottom of the bed, with us at the top. Even if we managed it, and remembered to close our eyes, our smiles and the light being on would be proof of our wickedness. They forgave us and then, amidst the babbling, someone would remember a suffocating Ally boy and retrieve him from under the sheets. We wouldn't settle down to sleep until Mum and Dad let us empty our stockings over the bed. We loved our stockings. We had a selection box, a sketch-pad and crayons, an apple and an orange each, and if Ally had one more nut than the rest of us, it was favouritism on Mum's part and grossly unjust.

There was one Christmas the boys were playing catch, and scrabbling round the front room in hot pursuit of each other. It ended with Dave knocking over the Christmas tree and breaking half a dozen pretty baubles. He had pine needles up his backside and the fairy clonked him as she fell. Mum didn't think it was at all funny. That happened when they were well into their teens.

Mum always saves a Christmas pudding for Easter. We don't have a turkey at Christmas. It's always a Capon, which is tastier Mum assures us. My job is to make the sausage balls.

Easter I don't remember that well, except for painting faces on hard-boiled eggs at breakfast time. Then it was off with their heads, succeeded by a moan because they were cold. Chocolate eggs filled with buttons are a thing of the past, but Dave and Al continue to get stroppy every year, maintaining Pops should still buy them one like he did when they were sprogs, blumming cheeky blighters. Mum tickles me. She says she loves Hot Cross Buns and wishes the baker would bring them all year round, yet she will sit for ages with one picking out each and every currant.

SHRIMP YEARS

I'm glad Mum had me, same as Rish, in Nan's old home. It makes me pure Somerset rather than Bristolian. Because of our countryside connections, Dave refers to Rish and me as scarecrows, having straw coming out of our ears and turnips for noses. Reared in the city I may have been, but think I'm more a creature of the wild.

I wouldn't want to change though how my creeping up began in the Block. Why on earth it was called the Block, when it was a circle of prefabs, I don't know. We were lucky kids who lived there, having a green within the Block to play on. Titchies would gather round when the old man with his squeeze-box came and sat on the green. He brought his own milking stool. It was such a nice place, but now the kids have gone away and only old folk remain. The green is empty, no dolls and balls left overnight to be recovered the next day, no tea parties are held there now with a strictly forbidden football match being carried on at the same time. Even fathers played football and disregarded the 'No ball games' signboard. Peace and tranquility have descended. The sun obviously shines there, but not in children's faces any more. When Rish was little and people asked "And who are you?" her reply was "Daddy's sunshine". Everyone knew each other of course in the twenty-two prefabs. The shy ones played with the boisterous ones, friends one and all, except for the occasional squabble when the boys would start biffing and hating so and so's guts, and girls would rally round to the aid of brothers in distress. The girls I befriended weren't exactly angels. Terri (or Tritz) looked like one, but I know one day she crowned me on my nutter with a tennis racquet when she got riled. Whether I screwed her nose round or flaked out on the ground I'm not sure. She must have whammed it down damn hard, because the gut sagged in the middle afterwards.

We did have nothing but respect for the boys belonging to the Block and outsiders were enemies to be suitably dealt with if they strayed onto our territory. With Rish being older, she hardly ever played with Dave, Al and me, and she hated it if Mum bade her to keep an eye on us. We were glad she never did, but instead went off with the older girls. Boy hunting I expect. I remember that yodelling boy who would wake up the whole Block before it was time, singing "Oh Rosemarie I love you" outside the house – that's her real name. She must have been about eleven when she was serenaded. The younger girls and boys, myself included, were far more interested in madcap games, playing with dolls, teddies, gollies, miniature soldiers, cowboys, Indians, farm animals and matchbox toys, marbles, three wheeler bikes, roller skates and dressing up as Mummies and Daddies when we would fit Tritz into the dolls' pram with no buts or she would be muzzled with Sellotape.

What would my tiny years have been without Marion and Johnny, my dolly and Teddy? Johnny I stole from Dave the minute he was given to him, but Dave didn't mind. Nothing could take the place of his beloved ancient little Teddy, which had most of his essentials missing and was so thin through loss of stuffing although Nan operated on him many times. Everywhere Dave went, that pathetic chewed old thing had to go too or tantrums resulted. Johnny and Marion I loved passionately. Johnny moreso. His nappy was changed first. He was a baby. Marion was a young lady, a woman of the world I could talk to on a par with. She could look after herself. She wore a napkin, but I had crayoned lipstick, nail varnish and eyeshadow on her personage. I've still got them of course. There they sit on the bedroom chair. Johnny dressed in flowered winceyette jamas and woolly nightcap with loose ends of black cotton coming out of his nose and mouth. Marion looking tres chic in a pale green dress, cut and sewn from a washed out flannelette sheet my feet went through many moons ago. She has a five bob Woolworth's ginger ponytail wound round her napper, which Rish discarded donkey's years ago. Marion lost her own blond curls through prolonged, rough, back-combing from me.

Rainy days were bearable if Mum let us play with the boys' fort, train set, cowboys, Indians and soldiers on the living room floor. We would then sprawl full length across the mats, making them slide all over the place on Dad's highly polished tiles. We did too scatter and heap clothes around for mountains and rocks in which to hide our men. Mum and Dad were then in for an afternoon of gunfire. Dave and Al were full of grumbles and got so irritated when I bombed a handful of their men. They kept standing their injuns back on their feet, even though I had killed them several times over. We got yelled at as well for playing marbles on the living room floor, as we never picked them all up after. Ally swallowed one once, but it came out the other end easy as pie, which we marvelled at. But Rish was a worry to Mum, pushing beads up her nose. Stem of a flower she did too. Fluff, all sorts went up her nostrils, clogging up breathing entrances. Practically everything was done outdoors though, because nobody liked being cooped up inside, incessantly round Mum's apron strings whining "What can I do Muh? Tell me what I can do. I'm bored." More often than not crayons and a colouring book served to shut us up.

Terence has been a screwball since she was a few inches high and can find things to occupy herself with even when she is ill. There was the time she had mumps. However, she was well enough to make several bus passengers think they were going round the twist. The Cods had a front garden at the prefab grassed over completely, except for a star of dirt and London Pride slap bang in the middle. Beyond the front garden's see-through fence was a bus-stop. Terence and her sister Sandie, who was mumpy also, watched from their bedroom window for the buses to come and each time one trundled to a halt, the perishers stood on their heads (their bed was pushed underneath the window) so that only their feet and legs could be seen resting on the pane. They didn't keep them rigidly straight neither, but put on magnificent feats for the busloads of viewers, with wiggly toes, scissor and pedalling movements. They would, no doubt, have taken a turn for the worse if their feet had gone through the window. Tritz did too knock a hole in the bedroom ceiling with a broom handle just to see if it could be done. She took fright when plaster fell around her ears and thought she had better own up to her mother, rather than her father, but wished she hadn't after.

What sticks in my memory about the ancient green and rusty three-wheeler bike we had is the time Uncle Les rode round the Block on it, looking like he had frog's legs. Aunty Vi disowned him and turned her back on him to laugh. Aunty Vi says females are handsome not pretty. How is it, I wonder, we call Uncle Les, Uncle Les, when his name is Donald. Everyone except we four kids calls him Donald. Uncle Les was a great sport. He dressed up as the Good Fairy one Christmas and did a ballet dance amongst us. He's lighter on his feet than I am. The day of the bike incident might well have been the same day cousin David took an apple out of the glass cabinet, without asking, and sank his teeth in it before we decided to tell him it was a wax one. Ruined Mum's bowl of artificial fruit he did.

Roller-skating again was a pleasurable pursuit. I myself preferred to use just the one. That is, take one skate and an unbending book, one of Rish's Girl Annuals, to a hilltop, place the book square on the skate, sit on it, tuck knees under chin, hold onto the book for dear life, receive a hefty push from behind and down the hill I would go doing 100 mph unquestionably. God help anyone in my path if they didn't jump aside, because swerving I was no good at. There were numerous times I fell off still clutching the book to my behind, and the skate went merrily on its way. I went into a fence once and ripped my knuckles open. I'm like Mum, I don't like seeing blood, but when I was little I can't remember fainting off at the sight of it. Mum, as a young girl, did twice that I know of. Nan sent her on an errand to the Butcher's and she dropped across the counter as soon as she saw red meat. And again in school, she fell out of her chair prostrate on the floor when she espied a spot of blood seeping through the plaster wrapped round her teacher's finger.

Then we had our den in the big garden of one of the prefabs where an old couple lived. It was secluded from the house by trees, weeds and overgrown bushes. Six kids could squash in, plus a lookout up a tree in case eagle eyes had seen us nip across the wall. There was a snooty la-di-da woman living in the posh house opposite the den, who sat in her window and kept a special watch for us lot to bolt over the wall. Out she would come and bawl at us "Trespassers will be prosecuted". We could only guess at the meaning of these long words spouting forth from her and yell back "Swallowed your dictionary Mrs?" Threaten us she did too, saying she would call the cops if we didn't vacate the premises immediately. That was our cue to leave the den and saunter off down the lane with her beady eyes watching our every move, so the boys imitated her affected walk. She infuriated us to such an extent we got a story going round the district that she undressed in front of the window. Girls could hold conferences in the den at any time other than when it was in use by the lads for pow-wows. Usually though it was a mixture of boys and girls crowded in there, with Terri either perched on a tree branch or hoisted onto somebody's shoulders, because she was a littl'un and would have stifled had she stood. We supported the boys in all matters. I didn't like the den when bobbly orange snake food began to grow there.

There was a person we did hold a grudge against and that was the old lady in the Block. She kept our ball even if it went into her garden just the once. We would try sneaking in to get it back, but she seemed to know if we were in her garden and came out running at us with her broom. We didn't dare give her any cheek. We were afraid to do so. We were certain she would have murdered us had we been saucy. To be caught in her cabbages – she had a mania for cabbage growing and unfortunately no flowers we could trample on at dead of night – meant one had to run off hell for leather in the opposite direction to the one in which she was advancing. No matter if one had to clamber over the fence and graze knees. Anything was better than having to face her. Little Robbie at one time did a spectacular jump onto her water butt. (Mum used to wash our hair in water butt water with carbolic soap). The lid was on thank goodness. From there he scrambled onto the corrugated coal shed roof and dived down the other side to safety. When he reached the majority of us, nearly a 'mile' away, we cheered him for his daring, quick-thinking escape route. Only once a little female went in to retrieve our ball from the cabbage patch, as we thought she wouldn't be harmed, but her ear was nearly pulled off, because it was flaming red and hot when we inspected it. I think the boys forbade us to enter the garden after that. They feared for our safety. We didn't believe in witches, but would have if she had had a cat. She did look rather like one in her black knitted stockings, lace up shoes and grey dresses with a knotted bun at the back of her head. I suppose as she aged she lost her patience and wound up disliking kids. I wonder if she misses us. We did keep her fit when all's said and done. Now should the ball go into Mrs. Hall's garden she would carry it indoors pretending she was going to cook it in the oven, but we knew she was joking and we would get it back sooner or later.

NAN AND GRANFER

Nan and Granfer played an immense part in our upbringing.

It was daft that Nan and Granfer's old stone cottage had its address as No.4 New Houses. It's years since anyone has been back to Bloomfield now Nan no longer lives there. The fields certainly did bloom wild flowers there and round Timsbury Village. I like to picture it as it was, surrounded by countryside, as countryside should be. Hills and valleys did stretch away into the distance. Fields of green, yellow and brown resembled Nan's bed blanket of knitted squares. From afar the green ones could be seen littered with moving dots, some dots being sheep, other dots being cows. If cows went down on their haunches that was a sure sign rain was on the way. Birdsong could be heard, as there was nothing noisy to drown them out apart from tractors ploughing. There were no bus-stops out Nan's way. We rang the bell by the dark green tin house and the bus rumbled to a standstill outside the Rising Sun. To catch the bus back to Bristol one had to stand on the main road or down in the ditch, due to there being no pavement, and trust to luck one's body and out-stretched arm would be noticed by the oncoming driver if it was dark. Country yokels with thick, cidery Somerset accents would stop and spare Nan the time of day, practically the whole of the day if Nan wasn't tactful.

A spell had been cast, because peace and quiet could be felt about Timsbury when we were tiddlers, the sun always shone, and Nan and Granfer's homespun cottage was right there in the midst. Damp throughout its ceilings and walls, but the Landlord charged rent they could afford. It was in the middle of a terrace. Although the cottages were joined together, maybe twenty in all I would say, each one differed in looks and size from its neighbours. Nan and Granfer did have a cemented back yard, which most of the others didn't have. It was a doddle to sweep clean, but for the barrage of bird droppings they had to contend with. The birds favoured Nan's yard, because of the choice pickings she put out for them. Stacked along two walls lay the brooms, dustbin, pig bin, watering can, Granfer's spade and fork, tin bath, rolled up brown mats and carpeting no longer required (it was hopeless ferreting there for lost balls) and Nan's priceless, antiquated mangle with the fattest wooden rollers ever seen. It could crush buttons to smithereens. It was almighty big and powerful, and where tiny Nan got the strength to turn the squeaking handle I'll never know, but turn it she did until every last drop was rung from washing, and water cascaded down into the tin bath like sluice gates opening.

It was true that the majority of the cottages had no yards, and, in fact, no back doors. These cottages, in particular, weren't very high. Therefore, when people who came through the iron U bend and down the back way arrived at their respective homes, they had to lift their legs up, straddle the window sill and climb in through the kitchen window. If there was water in the sink, one had to twist oneself onto the draining board. Nobody thought it a discomfort. We saw many old folk do it. It saved going right the way round the row of houses to the front doors and then, maybe, having to puzzle over where the key was if it wasn't under the usual stone. Besides, only out of the ordinary visitors came to the front door. Being family we never did. Tradesmen went down the back, except the Insurance gaffer who would tap Nan's front parlour window. He never knocked on the door; just his head came in through the window. All business was conducted through the window. Nan and Granfer's front door was so rarely opened, it took a lot of heave-ho and swearing when Granfer attempted to pull it open. Stiff and stuck fast it became in Nan's last years there, so it was left alone.

Nan admittedly had lots of furniture in her home, but by golly the number of carpets to a room must have topped at least twenty. Some had been cut up to fit into corners, others were in bits and pieces criss-crossed on top of one another, and underneath lay more bits and pieces of lino. No specks of dust whatsoever – plenty of crumbs though when we four kids were there for the day.

Occasionally Dad put Rish on the bus and she would go out to Timsbury by herself for a weekend, until I was old enough to accompany her. She admits now she was mean to Granfer. He gave up his half of the bed and slept in the spare room, because she wanted to sleep with Nan.

We loved spending a weekend with Nan and Granfer. We felt so grown up going out on the bus, leaving Bristol behind and weaving our way through the countryside. I don't suppose the distance was greater than thirty miles from home, but so different was country to town it felt like hundreds. Our imagination ran riot when we saw the new luxury houses springing up, lattice windowed cottages and the grand old farmhouses situated along the way. As they came into view we played our game of "I bags that one" or "Bags mine" if they were particularly pleasing to the eye. Night-times we sank onto a feather mattress pummelled and battered each day by Nan, and that in turn lay on the black iron bedstead with the shiny brass knobs Nan would huff on and polish. We grumbled profusely at having to use the po – we weren't used to it – but as the loo was outside next to the coal hole, and there wasn't a light in there anyway, we thought we had better make the most of a bad job, because fortunately we could see where to sit down.

Our little Nan with her wax night-lights! She couldn't go without one ever. That is, she did change over for a short spell some years back to having a small oil lamp burning throughout the night, but the smell put her off so she threw the "durn" thing into the dustbin and went back to slumbering with her cheerful night-light glow.

It was lovely to lie there toasting on a cold winter's night with a stone hot water bottle between us, a pair of Nan's bedsocks on, arms tightly wound round body in a bear hug and knees up under chin. We were sandwiched in snowy, starched sheets with a patchwork quilt and half a dozen thick winter coats piled over us. It was too nice and comfortable to go to sleep straightaway. Better to lie there watching the flickering light dance round the room, and listening for Granfer's snores to tease him about next morning. Just Rish and I bashing bottoms as we slid further down the bed, wriggling with sighs of contentment. The one thing we had against night-lights was that Nan had white wallpaper with sprigs of blue roses planted on it, and in the fluttering candlelight we imagined the roses moved and swore it was spiders creeping over the walls. Sometimes too the light attracted moths, sizeable ones, and they came swooping in during the night flapping and rustling against the walls. We mistook them for bats. If they darted towards us, we would hurtle under the bedclothes and refuse to come out until our muffled shouts brought Nan in to do battle with them.

We spent hours dressing up during weekend visits. Nan went to any number of jumble sales and bought ladies clothes for a couple of coppers, and we would then borrow them to parade in. We fancied ourselves as models in the making. Time and again Rish and I wrangled over a pair of white stiletto-heeled shoes much too big for us. We often ended up with one each, which was highly dangerous as we played on the stairs. We weren't cry-babies if we wobbled in our high heels and went splat, or tripped over our long hemlines and fell down a number of stairs. (Not like Sandie, Terri's sister, who fell down her Gran's stairs when she was little and got her head stuck in the spokes of her uncle's pushbike standing at the bottom, true as I'm sat here.) If we had cried, Nan would have stopped us playing on the stairs and in the pantry – our shop – adjoining the passage. We couldn't help blubbering though if we stumbled and knocked Nan's vase of flowers over that she kept halfway up the stairs. The sight of the mess and wondering how to tell Nan made us do so.

It was a big treat when Mum and Dad took us out to Nan and Granfer's on a Saturday, and we were allowed to play with the old record player. It was the kind of player where we had to stick a handle in a hole, give a few sharp turns and tinny Blue Danube would crackle out of the speaker. Granfer loved his band music. Dave busted the player in the end, pretending he was revving up a car, but we let him make his getaway and hide in the tallboy on the landing before we dutifully reported the breakdown to Granfer. Dave smelt of dried heather after. When Daffy at work was a slip of a girl she would put records in the oven until they softened. Then she moulded them into flowerpots.

Nan never failed to have a tennis ball for the four of us to play with. Invariably it was lost during every visit, either in a cow's fresh pancake (fresh 'uns), through next door's open scullery window or in a bed of stinging nettles, but next time, sure enough, there would be another ball to play with, although we had to badger and plead until Nan handed it over. Mind you, we knew most of her hiding places for it: the coal scuttle, in the sack of potatoes, under the tea cosy, but there again it could be in her pinny pocket where she now keeps handy what she calls her blood pills.

The love Rish, Dave, Ally and I shared was our walks to Timsbury Village. Starting point was outside Nan's yard, by the border of Marigolds Nan had planted, and which she covered in tea-leaves whenever she emptied the pot. Off we four kids would troop in single file down the footpath running at the rear of the cottages, swinging our arms and gaily singing "Hey ho, hey ho, it's off to work we go". The boys led, because they had to kick and beat down the stingers that tended to bar our way in places. Once in the process of so doing Al's shoe flew off into them, and we had to go back and tell Mum, who said she didn't want to clap eyes on us again until we had found it. But on with the walk! We raced past Oogie-Bob's cottage. He was a loony, or so we thought, who kept sixteen cats and a mad dog in awful squalour. Coming to the last cottage, and also the end of the footpath, there was a stile to hop over and we were then in a cow field. The cows didn't bother us, well as long as they didn't come too close, but before stepping boldly amongst them we scrutinised each one for udders in case a bull had been let loose. After darting across the field there was a stile to crawl under this time, followed by a short walk up the little lane, picking poppies as we went. Rish and I were adamant Nan should have them and not the boys for experimenting with to discover opium. The boys didn't like Rish and me wasting time picking cowslips, violets, primroses and bluebells, but we unfailingly caught them up. Borne dawdlers they were, stopping regularly to cram handfuls of blackberries into their mouths. We were almost into the village by then. We just had to go past the mission hall where British Legion, Bright Hour and Pension were all held on different days in the week. I've been to Pension several times with Nan and met the Parson. A stop would be made by the horse meadow to nuzzle muzzles and slap flies off rumps, then on to the shops in the village. There couldn't have been more than six, each one selling an assortment of wares. In Bart's Bazaar we loved to browse. Outside there was a large grating in the pavement through which lolly papers, sweet and toffee wrappers were deposited. Alas, Al lost another shoe through that grating mucking about.

In the village I liked the Butcher's shop best of all, especially if Nan had said to go in and get a quarter of 'chitlin' (chitterling) for tea. Rish preferred going in the fruit and veg shop. She invariably came out, even if she wasn't supposed to, with a quarter of mushrooms to boil on the fire when we got back. At tea I would do my durndest to swap a squiggle of chitlin for a chunk of cottage loaf, which Nan had pulled apart, thickly buttered and dipped in mushroom juice, but Rish wasn't having any of it.

While we shopped the boys got lost. Usually they could be found squinting through boy-made holes outside a large, high, fenced off compound. They would be barking mad and making growling, whining noises. I used to think they were good at whining. Still do. Behind the fence were six Alsatians, fierce and drooling at the mouth, padding around like caged lions with occasional snarls at each other. We ignored the 'Beware' sign. When Rish and I got fed up teasing them, we yanked on the boys' jerkins and proceeded onwards. We didn't eye the church where Mum and Dad got spliced, or the churchyard t'other side of the road where Granfer now lies and where Nan has her reservation made to lay on top of him. We passed them by. The old mine with its mountainous grey slag heaps was studied, but not ventured into. Granfer worked there for a spell before it closed down and he went elsewhere.

We didn't go back to Nan and Granfer's the same way we had come. We made a detour on purpose so that we could stop off at the Wreck, which consisted of six rusty swings in a corner of the football field. We figured it earned its name, because half the swings were broken and those remaining surely did need a squirt of oil. Every time we stayed too long on the swings and had to rush back to Nan's, but never in too much of a hurry that we couldn't squash the cats' eyes. Straight down the middle of the main road we came, jumping from eye to eye, and there we were in Bloomfield again. We had a further stop to make though, before returning to Nan's laden with busted paper bags containing things for tea, and this was at Claris's where we purchased a hollow stick of liquorice and a conical bag of sherbet crystals, yellow, orange or pink, the best anywhere. Claris's was the only shop in Bloomfield and Elsie, her sister, who lived in the back rooms of the shop, was the only person who possessed a telly in those days. Nan and Granfer would go up there from time to time, if something special was on, and once our family trooped along to watch Terri's Dad climb a mountain when he was in the Royal Marines. (Also every Cup Final Day we went over Aunty Vi's. They had the goggle box long before us. Spurs always seemed to be in the game.) From Claris's we went sucking on our way. We squeezed through the iron U for pedestrians (Mum could just about make it), because the gate next to it was kept locked except when the cows had to come through and then look out Nan's Marigolds! Then zooming like planes taking off over a treacherous stony runway we careered into Nan's, tainted with brightly coloured tongues and mouths.

Nan's toilet bewitched me. I would sit in there for an hour or more if I had my way, idling my time away by digging my finger-nails into the soft crumbly yellow walls. Small lumps and bumps in the plaster conjured up pictures enough to make one's mind boggle. I swore a man in bed stared back at me from the wall. Dave took comics in to read. Daydreams were broken by an impatient "Eh you in there, gone down the 'ole 'ave you?" – the next in line breaking his or her neck to be let in to contemplate.

The front garden at Bloomfield was strictly forbidden to us, because of the many flowers, vegetables and fruit that Granfer grew there. Everything thrived in the rich black soil. Nan and Granf had their lawn too, which was such a tiny square it couldn't have held two deckchairs. It wouldn't have been hard work for Nan to spend an afternoon on her benders cutting it with the scissors. We snook out there without the grown-ups knowing if we were ever desperately hungry, which was quite often, and go on a raid. We could take our pick of strawberries, raspberries, blackcurrants or perfect little carrots that came out of the soil clean as a whistle. Mum used to say munching on a carrot made our eyes bright. Goosegogs were fat and made the taste buds work overtime. Very moreish and we topped and tailed them quick as factory workers, but too many and we would have the belly ache to gripe about later.

Nan made her own wine and would let us sample a teaspoonful, no more than a smidgen. There was elderberry, rhubarb, parsley, potato, parsnip and dandelion. Collecting dandelions gave me fears of bed-wetting. Even when dandelion heads became balls of fluff, and kids blew them off in so many puffs to find out the time, I wouldn't dare go near them. Maybe I did it once or twice, I don't know.

Uncle Jim, two doors up from Nan, shot the duck size wood pigeons that came swooping down onto the gardens. Roast pigeon, absolutely delicious, but can it beat Nan's potato scallops or her pastry made with egg. Ecstasy her rabbit stew, but rabbit wasn't on the menu if there was an 'R' in the month. That meant they would be having babies, or was it the other way round? When at Nan's, appetites were large. The air had something to do with it I expect. The times we sat in front of Nan's roaring fire with her knitted gloves on, waving the toasting fork through the flames with a hunk of crusty bread pierced on the end, or crumpets. Crumpets taste like sausages to my mind. I love them both. I'd put up with heartburn too after tucking into a cockles and watercress sandwich. A plate of salted sprats was another meal ate with relish at Nan's. I loved the old blackened hearth in Nan and Granfer's living room with the fire and stove attached. Food tasted better when smoke encircled it.

I remember the Weeks next door to Nan and Granfer, both of them long gone now. Mr. Weeks limped with a tin leg. He was a war veteran. After Granfer died he was good enough to bring Nan a bottle of Stout from Moss's off-licence several nights in the week. Dolly Weeks was a card. Pooh, didn't she ever reek of snuff. One could somehow tell she had been on the stage. She did paint cupid red lips on her face. She would shuffle in to Nan's in her black felt shoes, her ginger hair a mass of frizz, and call our Nan "Mother" yet they were virtually the same age. One day she had me at Nan's kitchen table for hours, when I was supposed to be doing schoolwork, counting out hundreds of sixpences she had been saving in jam jars over the years. Quite a considerable sum of money and I don't remember being given one for my trouble. I wouldn't be surprised if I counted wrongly, as I was more intent on watching Nan pluck a chicken, one of Uncle Jim's, at the other end of the table. Boy those feathers flew in all directions when Nan got going. That old bleached wooden table served Nan well over the years. Nan felt safer under that in air raids and thunderstorms than she did under the stairs.

I'll never forget the day when we were at Nan's and floppy eared Judy, Uncle Jim's dog, came lolloping in and scared the living daylights out of Dave and me. When she bounded towards us, instinctively we grabbed hands and stood up on Nan's brown mock leather settee. Old Judy was still yapping at our ankles so we took a running leap off the settee, arms outstretched, and flew through the air together onto the washing line, filled up with freshly blued and starched whites, which extended from one corner of the room to the other. Having flea brains we expected to swing on the trapeze, but we dangled for a split second, kicking out at Yappy below, before falling to the floor covered in washing and screaming piteously, because Judy was gambolling excitedly round us and licking our flesh all over. We thought we were being eaten alive. Mum rescued us and really gave Dave and me something to bawl about. The state of the washing is best not described. Nan told us to "Bide still and kip quiet for the rest of the afternoon". Granfer undoubtedly loved that dirty off-white and brown Spaniel with the soulful eyes, but admit it? Not he. He cussed flashes constantly referring to her as, ooh I can't say, it's too ripe, but the scraps from his meal would go on the floor at his feet, and tasty titbits off his plate too. When Granfer died Judy didn't last long. She pined pitifully and was often to be found in churchyard sniffing the graves, hunting for Granfer I reckon.

I wish Granfer hadn't died when we were youngsters. I see him to this day, even if fourteen years have gone by since he was with us, stocky, strong as an ox, although chesty, with rock hard muscles beneath his vest and so handsome. He had tickly whiskers as well. He had a special drinking mug for people with moustaches. He wouldn't go anywhere unless his cloth cap was on his head. He was a miner through and through, going by the nickname of Butcher down the pits and throughout the vicinity. He made Dad drunk once down the White Hart and carried Poppers home slung across his shoulder to face the wrath of Nan and Mum. Granfer would go home from the Rising Sun at Bloomfield singing and swaying with his cap swivelled round the wrong way. Sometimes Nan would have to go up The Parrock and collect him from Moss's and walk him home the ten yards. He didn't like it if Nan got savage with him. He would come into the kitchen and tell Nan there and then to bury him up the garden underneath the apple tree. He called her "my old Dutch". One day Nan said he came staggering home with a sheepish Jobie in tow and turned "comical" (meaning nasty). When Nan offered him a cup of tea he would not take it and swore to Jobie that Nan had bloody well put soda in it, yet of course she hadn't. Mum would be sent to look for him at Gregory's Gate if he didn't come straight home at closing time. He was dead set in his ways. He wouldn't cut a cabbage on a Sunday. Bad luck would come to you, he reckoned, if you did. Understandably, Granf was quick-tempered and short on patience with his grandchildren. Mum is exactly like him. She made him cry one day when she was a little girl, because she refused point blank to go to Chapel. Granfer got in an all fired rage and would certainly have killed Mum had her Granny Martin not dragged her out of the house. Yes, well, we always kicked up a tantrum too regards Sunday school, but we still had to go whether we liked it or not.

Nan and Granfer habitually came to stay in the prefab with us, and I can't for the life of me fathom out how we slept. They liked cheese and Pan Yan pickle for supper with cream crackers, and we sidled up until one of us was on Granfer's knee, one sat behind him in the armchair, and two at his feet for a nibble and a bite. Then we would get the cards out for Sevensy or the Ludo board. Ally, the youngest, was overruled by Rish, Dave and me and not permitted to play Ludo. Nan could be persuaded that she didn't want to play, so that was fine, four of us on the board – me, Rish and Dave and Granfer. Nan could join in cards, and Ally was allowed to play when he got older, as long as he was a dead loss and didn't win. Cards were a favourite pastime with the six of us playing. Mum and Dad didn't play. They sat and darned socks, or cobbled elbows in holey jumpers, and cleaned the family's shoes respectively. For five minutes happiness would reign supreme, except if one of us took a long time to shuffle, which would make the others a trifle skittish and unable to sit still in chairs. We couldn't shuffle properly and Granfer's swiftness had us spellbound. Granfer would sing the same old song as he was doing it, "Be-de-be-de-bom-bom, Last Train to San Fernando". Was it Bert Weedon's? I'll check that with Mum. Rish gets trouble in swallowing now if she hears it on the radio. But then those brothers would start their dirty cheating. More often than not Alan was solely responsible, but being the baby of the family he couldn't possibly be to blame, as far as Granfer was concerned, so Dave instead was held to be the culprit. Let ten minutes go by and Granfer would get in such a livid temper he would throw the cards down, or, ahem, across the room, swear at David, vow he would never play with us again and storm off. Most games finished in this way. Rish and I would sit and not say a dicky-bird, but give thunderous, black looks and aim a kick under the table at the sulking twerp who was guilty. Ludo would finish in exactly the same way. Dave was guilty then, and Granfer would go off muttering with the dice and egg-cup. He simmered down soon enough with a mug of Oxo and one or other of us combing his hair. We could usually bring him round and talk him into another game. Our Dave is supposed to be the spitting image of Granfer in looks and ways.

He died suddenly after being ill for only a week with Asian flu and masses of coal dust clogging his lungs. He got out of bed one day to shoo a sparrow out of the window which had flown in and that weakened him. It was a bad omen. Mum was called out to Nanny's on the Friday and didn't come home that night, but we thought nothing of it. Saturday morning I went to Pictures with my brothers and Pop unexpectedly met us outside the Ritz cinema afterwards, and took the boys off to town. I was most upset and annoyed, because I was told to run along home, which I didn't do, as I thought I would take my time about it and kick stones. It was a put-up job to break the news to us, boys and girls separately, of Granfer's death. When I got home I found Mum and Rish crying and I had to be told. Mum said he was like a black man when he died, because of the coal dust coming out of him, but after he was washed and laid out in the passage (Aunt Olly did it), dressed in a white nightgown with his hair combed, he looked so beautiful. I wish I could have seen him. They preferred to have him home in the passage, rather than let him go to the Chapel of Rest. Rish and I stayed home from school while Mum and Dad went to the funeral. I didn't mind that. The last time he came to stay with us in Bristol, he said to Nan, as they set off on their return journey, how breathless he got walking, and that he wouldn't be able to do it for much longer. He didn't have to do it ever again. That last time, as he stood waiting for the country bus to take them home to Bloomfield, he spotted a hare in Top Dog factory gardens.

SPARE TIME

What did we youngsters do with our days apart from wreaking havoc? Yuck, school I'll think about later, but Saturdays and school holidays were crammed with frolics. Even slumbering in the Land of Nod dreams were plentiful and action-packed. Let me see what I can remember about school holidays. Saturdays would be similar except the mornings were spent at the old Ritz cinema, which is now a supermarket, where we would watch a Walt Disney cartoon, Tarzan serial and a Cowboy and Indian feature film, all for 9d!

Early to rise, a poke with the corners of the flannel to get sleepy dust out of eyes, followed by breakfast, a dish of cornflakes probably. (John, Lin's fifteen-year-old brother, has a huge mixing bowl of cornflakes each morning and he's skinny as a rake; he must have worms). A piece of burnt toast went with it, because Mum had been in a hurry to get on. When eats had been dispensed with we charged from the house. Outside we split up. Rish went her way, the boys went theirs, and me mine, to go and find whoever we fancied playing with that day. Terri (Terence, Trash or Tritz, she's one and the same) and I usually got lumbered with the pleasure of each other's honourable company. Always making rose petal scent we were. After calling for her we, perhaps, returned home skipping to sit down on the doorstep and munch a stick of rhubarb dipped in the sugar bowl, or half dozen cheese biscuits each. When Mum made them, a batch would be near enough a hundred. I don't expect we were allowed back inside the kitchen, because it could well have been flooded. Mum undoubtedly had the enormous old tin bath on the table-top in the middle of the kitchen doing a wash. I would have a natter to my mate to decide how the day was to be spent then, when agreement was reached, it was time for the off and "Cheerio Muh" who was lost somewhere in a sea of soap-suds.

Maybe we would go and root out a number of other friends, brothers included, for a game of hide and seek. We took the liberty of thinking everybody's garden was open to us. Terri's garden was a fabulous hiding place with heaps of high fruit bushes laden down with blackcurrants, whitecurrants and redcurrants. We could sit in them picking off clusters and have a feast. Terri's Mum knew though where her berries had disappeared, because we spat out hundreds of stalks, far more than birds could have coped with. But it helped ease the tension, to eat handfuls of currants, while waiting for the seeker to pounce. The only time the Block looked deserted, and kids were quiet as mice, was when a game of hide and seek was in progress.

Mum and Dad got uppity if we used our flower-beds for concealment. It meant a smack or two from Mum if we squatted amongst the Giant Lupins inside the front gate and bent them all ways, and if we hit the top off of one of Dad's prize bloomers, his Chrysanths, we knew we would have a lot coming to us and would put off going home until bedtime. (I remember that funny little young-un Boyce who used to come into our garden, pull up our onions and carrots, pick our flowers, and walk slowly round the Block carrying a bunch in one hand using the other to defrock them, petal by petal, leaf by leaf. Neither parents nor pastings could cure him.)

The best place to be hidden from view was to stand in the middle of runner-bean sticks. Our show of beans and foliage was worthless. Dad could not make beans grow and if he got as many as half a dozen each year they were stringy. So it was a neighbour's thicker beans we hid in. To crawl amongst the sweet pea sticks and lie flat on stomachs eating dirt was also a good hidey-hole, except for lanks whose feet poked out one end. My brainwave was to be wrapped up in an old carpet in the shed with a piece of string tied round the middle to secure me. I was heaved to my feet and my head was put in a sack. On the subject of sacks, we bundled Tritz into a sack once, fastened the opening with a cord and tried to lift it up onto a peg in the coal hole. We thought, as she was a pipsqueak and no heavier than a handful of feathers, there would be no fear of her coming through the bottom of the sack onto the coal. We couldn't quite manage to hang her though, so made a few more air holes in the sack, which needed darning, and left her propped with orders to keep completely still and quiet in the coal-bunker. We hid in our various rabbit warrens and we all got found, but she wasn't. We didn't exactly forget about her, but we just didn't bother to go back and get her out. She had probably got on our nerves that day, or we had had a tiff at some time I hadn't forgotten about. Anyway she was all right, if a little smudged, when she appeared on the scene again, hours later.

What was that horrible song we sang, "Hot snot and bogey pie". How revolting! And that ditty "one potato, two potato, three potato, four", which I think had something to do with two-balls.

And what about Cuffs, that enormous space for running wild behind the prefabs! It was a massive site of waste ground, utterly uncultivated. Being on two extensive levels made it full of interest to our inquisitive minds. The first level was like the Valley of Death, strewn with rocks and boulders, dried up sparse scrubby weeds and littered with rubble, tin cans, broken bottles, scrap iron too. We even had our own jalopy there. Down on the next level was a jungle, consisting of trees, tall ones, short ones, dead ones, bushes of varying size, clover carpets, grass up to our chins, lush weeds, blocks of concrete and a ghostly secret tunnel. Garden of Eden was Cuffs to the Block kids. By rights we had no business to be there, but the owners had kids our age so they understood kids' needs. We would take turns to sit in the car tyre knotted onto the end of a rope, which hung down from the trees. There were female Tarzans in our day. Every child must have fallen out at least once into the stinging nettle beds growing in glorious abundance, and gone home crying for soothing Calamine lotion when Dock leaves didn't deaden the umpteen stings. Really and truly one would be proud of the rash of red and white lumpy blotches, as everyone made a fuss of the injured party. The idea was not to spill out of the tyre into the nettles, but skim over them, and it's all very well being told this, after you have ended up in them, by grinning twit-faced boys who had cheered as you hurtled to your doom. The girls showed concern when the shock waves hit and the searing pain drove the mind crazy, as millions of stings emerged on the unclothed parts of one's battered body. Should one or other of us get multiple stings, a multitude of kids would run home alongside the victim, who was doubtless bawling his or her eyes out, to give moral support when facing an unsympathetic Mum. Dozy Tritz fell out the tyre regularly, because she would forget to hold onto the rope. She stood up in the tyre occasionally, which was asking for trouble, and naturally we would be blamed when she tearfully chided, "You should have saved me". I was such a fat podge I would either get stuck in it or the rope would break, as I went zooming down through the trees, and I would crash land into the stingers anyway. Even if it hurt like blazes, tears didn't last long. A handful of Dock leaves rubbed ferociously onto the stung parts worked wonders, green wonders!

There was one thing though that the female kids loathed and detested, and that was grasshoppers. Horror of horrors they were. One didn't know where they were going to land next. I think our main dread was that they were going to hop onto our legs and then jump into our knickers. Precisely how they would get through elasticated hems didn't enter our tiny minds, but when playing we wore old clothes which frequently meant perforated knicks. It was all right for the boys. Trousers, as well as pants, covered their private parts. Sandie, Terri's sister, had one of these crickety creatures put down inside her shirt one day by a toad of a boy. It drove her into a crazy fit. I was crying too when we got to her house, because she seemed to be in awful pain and I didn't know what to do. Mrs. Cod whipped her shirt-tail out from her shorts, but nothing fell out. Sandie gave a blood-curdling shriek, thinking it must have crawled up her back passage.

The tunnel down on the second level of Cuffs held the most intrigue for us. It wasn't particularly long, but was spooky and definitely haunted, we told each other in hushed whispers, by beasty wobbles, ghosty wobbles and the devil with horns himself. Horrific noises emerged from it: ear splitting screams, high pitched wails, grunts and groans, croaks, roars, squeaks, moans, slow plopping drip sounds and spine chilling laughter. You name it, our tunnel had it. This mixed bag of eerie sounds was unmistakably heard by kids who requested, "Cut my throat and hope to die if I tell a lie". Besides Dracula living down there, with his vampire bats and screeching, shuffling goblin serfs, tramps too curled up for the night there. We knew this, due to the stench and things we found in there, besides an awful lot of brown bottles. Empties all of them. Not many kids would enter alone into the interior, unless a money bet had been placed on it. Once I ran pell-mell into the tunnel and came out the other end tinged green. I had been going so fast I hadn't seen a bottle and had gone sprawling over it and landed on my chin. As I tripped I wasn't afraid of the goblins getting me, but I imagined millions of red, blood sucking beetles swarming over me, and earwigs walking down my lug passages. I scrabbled like hell out of there and the first thing I did when I reached daylight was to give a great big spit in case any beetles were in my mouth. Next I gave an earth-shattering blow of my nose in my T-shirt, in case some had walked up it, wiggled my ears and commanded Terence to have a look inside them. "The treacle factory working a treat" no doubt was her reply. After which I slapped every inch of my anatomy. Not content with this, there then followed a five-minute war dance, shaking, jumping, reeling and a rocking. I expect I went home and demanded a hair wash and bath to Mum's astonishment. I was scared stiff of those red pinchers. They could fly too.

The brothers locked me in the garden shed once with two of these in with me, and in the darkness I cried and cried to be let out, because I felt sure they were on me, drinking pints of my blood. I truly was hysterical when freed and went round scratching for hours, but not until I had bombarded two hellers with fists, and dug my nails deeply into male flesh.

I admit to this day loathing moths, earwigs, flying daddy long legs, grey grandfather beetles, flying fish in damp spots, huge black spiders that run fast, but the only thing I'll kill is an ant as they make my skin crawl. I save as many diddy spiders as I can from drowning in sinks and baths, but whopping ones I yell for Mum to come with a duster, and supervise her while she gently shakes them out the window.

Without fail, before getting into bed at night, I check under the pillow and blankets for creepy-crawlies. It's habit. Ever since the time a monstrous spider with inch long legs fell down from the bedroom ventilator onto the pillow right by my earhole. I had this horrible sensation of knowing a creature was there, and screamed my head off when I saw it.

There was another incident too when I was titchy and had been left one afternoon on my tod. (So I couldn't have been that young.) I was sat in the chair, being a lazy article as usual, and it was beginning to get dark when I perceived out the corner of my eye this black, long legged killer spider a few feet from me. Suddenly it began to run and boy oh boy my feet and legs shot up underneath my backside and I sat quivering in the chair. Total darkness had descended by the time a family member came home and found me cowering in the same chair suffering from leg and bum cramp. Not blooming likely would I move even then, until a thorough search for the carnivorous man-eater had been carried out. I don't suppose I would have minded that one being stamped on.

Guy Fawkes night at Cuffs was the most looked forward to night of the year. Preparations began at least a couple of months in advance. Each year we had to have the community bonfire bigger and better than the year before. Things that wouldn't burn were piled on to make it grow. The idea was that it had to be burning fiercely at 9, or better still 10pm. In other words, far too dangerous for grown-ups to leave it, which meant, with a bit of luck, we couldn't go home until it had burned down considerably. Clothes, wood, sackfuls of paper (the sackman needn't have called for weeks in our district, and might well have been warned to stay away for his own good), furniture, coal pinched by the handful and if possible bucketful, tyres, chopped off tree branches. These things and more were collected by the armload and heaped on the spot marked with a white paint splodge. The bonfire suffered damage beforehand, trying to get a floppy disjointed Guy to sit on top, but restoration work was carried out in readiness for the grand night. But then, any number of Guys went on the fire. As soon as one got charred and blackened a cry went up "Stand back". The reigning Guy was knocked off the summit with a hefty whack from a pole and, as it lay in a crumpled heap with greedy flames licking it all over, his successor would be thrown up into the angry blaze in the hope that he would get hooked onto a smouldering beam. Dads became younger than their offspring. They threw the boneless Guys with too much force, because many times one would soar right over the bonfire and scatter its head, arms and legs amongst spectators on the other side.

It goes without saying, the week before the great day it was "Be nice, extra nice to your Dad" so that on light-up day he would bring home a great selection of fireworks. Kids are crafty beggars. Nowadays they stand on street corners hollering "Penny for the Guy", but give them a penny and they look at you in open disgust. I've been admonished by a mite "Surely that isn't all you can afford" and have heard the tune changed to "Shilling for the Guy". I said no once and was asked for a kiss instead. They're artful as well. Last year a youngster swinging on his gate asked a friend of mine for dosh, but there was no Guy to be seen. When she queried "Where is your Guy then?" Cheek-of-the-devil replied "He's in 'ome', 'avin a warm". I've seen boys too, down on the centre, begging with a live Guy, a baby brother trussed up and plonked on a trolley with a "Guy" sign round his neck.

Come rain or shine, the 5th November never proved to be disappointing. Parents assembled nattering round our bonfire. Of course they were supposed to be the only people with matches. So many oohs and ahs poured forth from all concerned, as the wonderful display lit up the night sky. Squibs were a favourite. Mums were scared of them, so we certainly had plenty. Great fun when somebody accidentally never on purpose dropped one unseen near a group of Mums. When it fizzed and popped we watched tittering to see them squeal and scatter, and fall into the open arms of boisterous husbands, often ones they didn't belong to. Dads were in charge of rockets, Catherine Wheels, and the bigger, pricey, dangerous fireworks. The boys took charge of squibs and also let off bangers behind unsuspecting gatherings. We girls held sparklers and roasted potatoes in the ashes. Not once did Dad let off a successful Catherine Wheel.

Cuffs was unquestionably the best play area for us, but the boys, myself and other gang members had another rather special place where we spent many summer days. Rish was too old and disinterested. This place we found, no grown-ups knew of its existence. Well, that is parents are good at pumping, and they did wring it out of us that we had a secret hideaway, but nobody was soft in the head to tell them of its exact whereabouts. Had we mentioned where this hideaway was, it would have been banned, because it was down by the stream. Mothers and fathers alike forbade kids to go anywhere near running water, which was a nuisance to be overcome, as any child will agree the best play locations are where the muddy waters flow. To keep the old-uns from worrying, we made out we were going to Victory Park. We thought it best to fib otherwise they would have senselessly interfered and spoilt our pleasure. Hare-brained brats we may have been, but this place was our very own discovery, not to be disclosed. We christened it the Monkey Walk. It was altogether secluded from the aged eyes of adults. True, workers from the nearby Jam Factory came part way along the stream bank, but they turned off at an angle when the footpath ended abruptly at impenetrable undergrowth, and walked on along a gravel road. When we came to the footpath's end we had to lower ourselves into the stream and wade onwards until we came upon our find – a mud-flat extending from the bank into the stream on which we could sit and even stretch full length. We enjoyed complete privacy, as trees and bushes lining the banks kept everything else out besides us. Oh, except for the sun, because the stream was wide enough to let the ball of fire enter and burnish our young bodies. Millionaires basking in Florida couldn't have had it better. We even had a rather pleasant jammy smell wafting up our nostrils.

Whole days were spent on our jetty of packed mud. We weren't daft apeths to sit on damp mud. If it wasn't baked hard, we had big polythene bags with leg holes to wear. We pulled our 'pants' on, tucked dresses inside and could then sit without fear of getting the pip, or runs as Terri impolitely called it. Pastry cutters went missing from home, together with other bits and bobs. I myself became a gourmet cook, my speciality being worm pie, but my mud ones weren't bad. I gave them all the trimmings. Recipe of sand and clay mixed to a paste with a trickle of water and beaten with a bit of bark, coloured grit for flavour, worms left whole for the meaty filling, topped with pebble vegetables, and for decorative purposes chopped weed, catkins, sticky buds, pussywillows or old man's beard, whatever was in season. Caterpillar was a rare delicacy beyond our means, same as ladybirds. I wouldn't have buried them alive in a pie anyway. The girls and I weren't keen on making fish cakes and, if the boys caught sticklebacks or tadpoles, we simply demanded that they be returned to the water dead or alive.

We loved to paddle. The water rose to our knees at certain divisions of the stream. This wasn't a hardship for the girls, but the boys had to roll up the legs of their jeans or they'd cop it later. If we thought we might cut our tozzles on jagged stones lying on the streambed, we would wear Wellies or daps. Plimsolls I should say. Tritz drummed the correct name into me more than enough times, but I still forgot and called them daps. I can't remember the water ever claiming blood. I suppose slip-ups happened, and duckings occurred now and then, but it was a shame if they did, as although the girls and I would only have been around eightish at that time, we were most careful and behaved like law-abiding citizens. Girls may have got filthy dirty, but we were women, or so we thought, even at that tender age. Back would come the menfolk from hunting trips upstream, and there would be a meal laid out for them. Bloater paste sandwiches, apple and squash to wash it down, which mothers readily supplied for our days in the 'park'. We even ate bread and cheese leaves off bushes, because most kids could distinguish them from other non-tasty bushes. Stream water was there to cleanse sticky fingers and grubby faces if need be after banqueting.

That was our paradise down by the stream. Mud, water, tangled bushes. It added up to a contented way of life for us, until one summer we didn't return to our hidden suntrap. We had found pastures new and were on to other pursuits.

Occasionally Mum and Dad went to the pictures and Great Aunty Maud came to keep an eye on us. She was a cheery old stick. We considered it an enormous treat when she said "Coats on kids" and we trooped off to the off licence in the village. We hated being told to wait outside though while Aunty Maud went in. She purchased a bottle of Tizer and bags of crisps with a wee tipple for herself. Then it was "Home kiddoes in double quick time". Back there, a sliced loaf would be buttered for crisp sandwiches and down on the floor we would go, pestering Aunty Maud to teach us a new card game. I never did get the hang of the clock one.

We took ages to undress when it was time for bed. Not that we were being difficult, we were clad in a fantastic array of clothing. Liberty bodice, vest, flannelette full-length petticoat, navy drawers were the undergarments. With top clothes it was understandable why I earned the nickname of Fatty amongst my friends. At home I was labelled differently. Polly stuck.

The one song I knew from 'Listen with Mother' well enough to sing was 'Polly put the kettle on'. It's not hard to picture the four of us grouped round Dad's Granny's ancient wireless, saying a solemn "Yes" when the voice from within asked, "Are you sitting comfortably?" Pause, "Then I'll begin". We were quiet for quarter of an hour, reciting 'Pussy Cat Pussy Cat where have you been?' We were addicted to the Archers on the radio of course, same as every other family. At quarter to seven on the dot we would be waiting for the wireless to be switched on and ready to join in with the "do dee do dee do dee do, do dee do dee do do" opening and closing music, no doubt bobbing along with it. I'm still Polly, but with some variations, like for instance Polly Doodle, Doodle Polly, Polly Dood, Dood or plain Poll.

MOVING HOUSE

Then came the time when kids in the Block grew too big and too old to share bedrooms, and families had to move out of the prefabs. Nobody, I'm certain, moved from choice. It was necessity, the reason being want of another one or two bedrooms. I can't think of anyone who moved far away from the neighbourhood. We were one of the first families to go, and lots more followed in our wake onto the Ford Council Housing Estate being built, less than five minutes walk from the prefabs.

One thing which remains uppermost in my mind about day of removal was the countless journeys we made, shunting backwards and forwards from each house, either carrying seed boxes or pushing Ally's red wheelbarrow full of Dad's plants. Dad armed us each with a trowel, spoon, skewer or suchlike and we had to carefully dig up at least a hundred clusters of wallflowers and forget-me-nots from the prefab garden. (The most important thing, the rhubarb patch, we left behind.) Then we had to transport them to our new garden, replanting them anywhere in the dirt to be going on with. Each year Pop excelled himself at the prefab and we had a beautiful show of flowers. His pink and white Gyp, carnations and magnificent Chrysanths were unrivalled by other gardeners. We wouldn't have fancied the thought of leaving them for somebody else to claim they had grown them, while all we had was a huge barren new garden. I tell a lie there, our new garden, as a matter of fact, was abounding in a vast selection of every imaginable weed peculiar to the British Isles. One very common one was rampant in the soil. I do believe it is called Cow Parsley, but Terri said that was idiotic, because we didn't have cows in the garden, and named the stuff weed wort. Really it was like baby cauliflowers. Ooh that impossible stuff too, bindweed. Talk about sticking like glue when you got a long strip of it stuck to your personage. We had the biggest garden on the estate. Dad is a keen gardener, but that one almost killed him. Back-breaking work it was to keep tidy. Three afternoons on the trot it took him to shear the extensive hedge. People admired him for his perseverance and dedication in having a neat hedge. Pops had to lay a lengthy concrete path as well and that was painstaking work. He is such a perfectionist. Later on, when we were older, he did give us a little plot each to do with as we liked. Ally boy proved to have green fingers, but even his patch of veggie shoots soon turned weedy and was left to Dad to sort out. With all good intentions I did weed, but pulled up plants instead, which riled Dad. After a year or two he grassed most of the garden, but it continued to be a laboured task to keep it clipped as short as Dad liked in the summer. Trust the boys, they still have a habit of disappearing when help is required. How Pop did mow that lawn, until it was virtually bald and yellow looking. Overnight it would spring up again, lush and juicy green and out would have to come the mower for another once-over. Grass above an inch in height had to be threshed. Had Pops been a barber, he would have had all and sundry sporting spiky crew cuts. He's a short back and sides' man. Dave and Al make fun. They don't remember what a scalpist he was with their haircuts when they were tiddlers. He was more lenient with Rish's and mine. It was a parting on the left for the boys, one on the right for us girls.

It was marvellous when we first moved house. I know what became my favourite pastime, serving meat to customer friends in a Butcher's shop, which was actually a very large and very dead oak tree. Any size of joint, mince, rashers or sausage I could pick up off the ground. I took it into my head to climb the tree one day and Pop had to be sent for, because I couldn't get down under my own steam. Half the estate was still in the course of construction, so naturally that part became our new play area. Signboards in gardens bearing the words "Keep Out" either had "Workmen" added, were crossed out with paint and redone on the other side to read "Come In", or were uprooted and conveniently lost. New friends were made easily enough, and we were thankful they were like us. (Lin will always be my crony.) Several families came onto the estate from Monkey Town and left homes behind boarded up. We kids congregated in bands and roamed hither and thither amidst the partly built houses on our tours of inspection. We had to keep tabs on the workmen to see they were doing their job properly and not leaving important things like bricks and cement lying around to be nicked. Stocks could run low if they were careless. A tiny bit of gang warfare went on between the boys, but the girls would vamoose and be well out of the way when stones met glass and fists met bodies. It's a wonder the estate was ever completed, and the houses finished ready for occupation, with so many squirts on the rampage every night and at weekends. These had become the only times we could conduct our play, as school was now the order of the day.

As there were so many in Mrs. Cod's 'mob', they had to move into a four bedroomed house situated in the opposite direction to where we now lived. No matter. Terence wasn't much further than twenty minutes walk away, so we were within easy reach to pester each other and, of course, we sat next to one another at school – but not so in the beginning.

SCHOOL, YUCK

I began my schooldays in Wood Green Primary School. Terence went to an outlandish school where she was made to wear the dunce's hat on more than one occasion, yet she does have a very good brain on her. I loathed school for the most part from start to finish. That's a bad admission to make, but there we are.

The first few months were decidedly wet ones, if I remember rightly. Tears galore flowed daily and some mornings my foot stamping a flat refusal to leave the house meant that Pops had to carry me piggyback style to get me there. He invariably had his hair watered and should have developed permanent screws in his shoulder blades, because they were constantly damp. I swear I had not one single friend there. Rish wasn't much comfort. I hadn't a clue how to drink my bottle of school milk through a straw, and no teacher could help me out of my predicament, so break times Rish was sought to come and show me the way. I suppose she had every reason to be impatient with me, because she thought I was showing her up in front of her friends. She didn't care about choking me to death, trying to ram the straw down my windpipe. I thought I had to blow through the straw instead of suck. Disgraceful that a five year old should smell like a baby, as my pullovers were always milky stained. I expect the threat of bibs eventually taught me how to master straw sucking.

It wasn't long before my forlorn days were over. A brand new primary school opened in the vicinity and myself, plus the other tiny tots were transferred. Rish and her sort of grown-up associates stayed behind. Terri appeared beside me at Wesley School and the two of us began developing. We were given a jelly patch each, which we wore on our backs for a long time I believe. I think it was to prevent tuberculosis or something like that. Recently the two of us exploded with mirth when we discovered old photos and came across our first school one taken together. We were painting masterpieces of modern art squiggles, and my smile is shy as shy can be as well as gappy, because I only had two teef spaced apart, and Terri is plastered with a monstrous cheeky grin, because she had a mouthful of molars to show off. Our hairstyles were perfectly modern. Terri's head was enveloped in tendrils and dollopy sausage curls, and my hair being straight as a dye I sported the pudding basin symmetric cut. It was Pop's creation, as he was the barbaric barber of the household. My red check dress was too tight, due to the fact I resembled Billy Bunter. Terri's dress hung on her with room to spare, because she was a scrawny morsel, but underfed? Never in this world! We were both gluttons, but her rib cage was hardly covered in her upbringing. She has filled out more now of course. Another photo shows the infants' school bedecked in fancy dress costume, myself as big Red Riding Hood, Dave as a Christmas Cracker and Terri as a bride with Sandie her bridesmaid. (It had to be that way round Terri was adamant, because she was the oldest by a year although the smallest.) Nobody was smiling on the photo except Tritz and the identical spiky haired Boswell twins who found it impossible to stop. Those two moppets were cowboys pointing their guns towards the photographer.

At Wesley School it seemed to be a never-ending playtime. If we weren't playing in the playground, we were playing in the Wendy House, which had a habit of falling down the exact moment I walked through its door. Terri and I liked our teacher. She had quiet ways. Dave and I argued, because he said his Mrs. Pink was better. I suppose in those early days we did start learning to read, write and do sums. I don't remember finding the reading too hard, except when it had to be done aloud. I stumbled then. But I did like the stories, especially that Chicken Licken one. I wonder if I'm muddling that up with something else? The thing that flummoxes me even now, I say and I write m's for f's and f's for m's. I've been unable to conquer the habit and my schoolbooks are littered with red alterations. I mix instead of fix and I eat maggots instead of faggots. Writing I didn't find difficult, but people thought I did. I held a pen oddly. I was, however, a neat writer in my childhood. Slapdash now, granted, but aged nine I was one of several winners in a Bristol schools' handwriting competition. Mum accompanied me to collect my prize at an honorary function. It was a biro with my name engraved on it. I mislaid it almost as soon as I got it through carelessness.

Wesley School was all right, but I was put off by an unhappy experience. I was late back to school after lunch one day. The blasted clock at home had been three quarters of an hour slow instead of the usual half hour. (Mum and Dad still have a phobia about having every clock in the house slow.) Not that I could tell the time like my friends could, which was a worry to me, but I thought I could rely on Mum to give me correct time checks. I had walked into school wondering why nobody was in the playground and bumped into the headmistress of all people. She ticked me off stinking for being late and I was struck dumb, because I wasn't aware that I was. She didn't ask me to explain why (I would have been too timid to say anyway), but marched me off to my classroom. There she made me stand at the front, being stared at, while she told teacher she had found me wandering over the school. (One of her off days.) I had a lump in my throat the rest of the afternoon, which didn't go until I got home and gave Mum a piece of my mind. She said it was Dad's fault for putting the clock back too much and not telling her.

I remained at Wesley School for two years and then back I went to Wood Green (my first school), upgraded from an infant to a junior, with Terri and lots of chums alongside me. Both Dave and Al remained at Wesley School, which pleased Mum as she used to go with other mothers to dances held there by the P.T.A. She invariably came home with a big box of chocolates, either won in the draw or the prize for being the best waltzer. A teacher who partnered her once asked me where his chocolate was next day. I doubtless went scarlet, even though I was only seven or eight, and gave him the one Mum had given me. I considered him a greedy pig for taking my chocolate.

I didn't cry on my return to Wood Green. I could guzzle down a bottle of milk in seconds, therefore managing more than one each break time. My grossness accounted for! In our junior ranks Terri and I flowered. Wood Green turned out to be our favourite school. It wouldn't have scored points going by looks – red bricked outside with walls of green tiles inside and high swing windows to be opened and closed by ropes. Therefore well nigh impossible to look out of them. We preferred lessons in the prefabricated huts because, although draughty, we could see the light of day.

Ahem, the teachers christened Terri and me as the two gigglers, because we were always at it. That was why we doubly made sure of getting desks at the back of classrooms every lesson. We could then muffle giggles and also help one another over obstacles. In general knowledge I was a duffer. No gumption or ounce of common sense do I possess. I was too a dope at spelling, so Terence kindly helped me out. She was a dunderhead at drawling as we Bristol folk say, and completely scatty when it came to mental arithmetic. I wasn't much better, but we got by. Our worst subject throughout school years was anything remotely connected with numbers. We were at a loss figuring out equations, decimal points, etc and drove ourselves into a terrible tiz-woz if we knew there was a mental arithmetic test in store, especially as it was headmistress who presided over it. She was strict as a jailer doling out impossible questions. We scratched our brains, but no response came. Beyond hope we were, then and for evermore. We consoled ourselves that we were a couple of whiz kids at spelling. (I wasn't exactly, but Terri was, and so with nifty assistance, to all intents and purposes I was too.) We could get ten out of ten for a spelling test. Sometimes a crafty 'e' had to be inserted in a word to achieve this praiseworthy effort. What I didn't like was that we often had to go into the headmistress's study to read to her from a stuffy book. This was to convince her we were making suitable progress. I found it an ordeal. I was fair at my reading, but she frightened me. I mean to say she was staring directly at me from across her desk, thinking goodness knows what, and her old dog Bonzo was supposedly asleep at my feet. I didn't feel safe at all. Therefore, because I got tense, I gabbled and ran out of breath and paused for a lung intake where there were no full stops and consequently caused her to sigh and she would give me just average marks, but I was really quite good.

Thursday mornings I woke up filled with fear of the violence to come. It was incredibly wrong to feel like this. I wasn't on my own. Boys and girls alike from my class rose from their beds on Thursdays with the trembles. Normally we would have enjoyed the first half of the morning, because we gathered in the hall for Rhythm and Melody. The radio was tuned in. Song sheets were handed round and we harmonised with the man on the radio and his woman accompanist, all there with our majors and minors. Songs stir in me like 'Morning has broken like the first morning, blackbird has spoken like the first bird' and 'We plough the fields and scatter the good seed on the land' – an improvement from infant school days. Then it was 'Little bird I have heard' – my and Terri's first recorder piece – and 'Twinkle twinkle little star, how I wonder what you are'. I swear I'm tone deaf, and can't sing a right note, but I lived in hopes that I would be selected to chime in with a ding on the triangle or with a shake of the tambourine, and occasionally I was. Terri liked the finger clappers, castanets, but she could also sing. We were constantly being chastised for not giving zip to the songs, but how on earth could anyone when we were shaking in our shoes at what was going to befall us after break time.

The dread, which quivered and couldn't be quelled inside us, was the thought of our swimming lesson. It wasn't the water that frightened us, but the Tartar who pushed us into the baths, and yelled and shouted and screamed at us until we did exactly as she commanded. She was old, ugly, wore grey galoshes and just must have been merited highly in our equivalent to the Gestapo. She was a battleaxe through and through, hated every last one of us, and was a downright cruel person. Headmistress knew she was ferocious and told us to tolerate her. They couldn't get anybody else to instruct us presumably. We were wretchedly scared of this Monster, but we listened to her, watched her every move, and forced ourselves to do her bidding. It was either learn to swim or drown. She wouldn't have saved us. Her twisted, evil smile smirked across her face if we were struggling desperately in the water. If we managed to propel ourselves over to the rail at the edge of the baths, she would go berserk, come running to the side as if to kick our hands away, and bawl at us to get back in the middle of the water. It makes me shudder to think of her now. Haunt my dreams tonight she will. But I learnt to swim and quite like it, albeit not out of my depth. I'm my happiest when I have an ocean and wind before me.

No, Thursday mornings weren't looked forward to in the slightest. From the moment we boarded the coach an unhealthy silence fell upon us. We became unnatural kids. We had to drive up steep Jubilee Hill to get to the Baths, and most of us wouldn't have cared less if we had gone rolling back down, through the railings at the bottom, and onto the railway line. At times I even prayed for it to happen, and I don't expect I was alone in saying prayers on that coach.

Another horrible incident at the beginning of each swimming lesson was when we became vermin. We had to kneel down in a long line facing the wall and Ogress inspected our feet for verrucas and athletes foot. She yanked up every foot, prodded her fingers between toes and prised them apart. A hunter of foustiness she was. I made sure my feet had a wash Wednesday nights. She would cuff the boys and cuss the girls if they had anything growing on their feet, as if it was their fault! She was the nastiest piece of work I ever came across in my creeping up. I can't for the life of me fathom out how she became a Mrs., because she had no love in her.

It was an entirely different bunch of kids who returned to school after their swim with chocolate covered mouths. Tritz always bought a Penguin at the kiosk, I always bought a Wagon Wheel and we shared half and half. Buying them now they seem to have shrunk to half their original size. Happy as larks, Tritz and I were first on the coach, grabbing seats at the back in order to "smile" at motorists behind. In vain we tried to bounce up to the roof when the driver went over the humpbacked bridge leaving our stomachs behind on it. We would gather speed going down hill in the coach and we would all lean forward urging it on, fully believing we were doing at least 120mph. What gave us a bigger thrill was that our coach driver had only one arm.

There was an incident at Wood Green that will never cease to make Terri and me double up in helpless laughter whenever we muse upon it. One day the class was quite peaceful for once, waiting for teacher to arrive. Suddenly an angry voice could be heard coming from the classroom next door. Everyone recognised it as belonging to Headmistress, and we were most inquisitive to see whom she was bellowing at, as we knew a lesson wasn't being conducted in that room. Each child had the same idea. The whole class stood on the tables placed against the wall, and a long line of faces peered through the glass at the top. There was Headmistress below, purple as a beetroot, looking and sounding extremely angry, tearing a strip off Miss Mouse. It was just the two of them in the room. Miss Mouse was the younger children's teacher. She was shaped like a barrel, not by any means faint hearted, but she had a blank and deadpan countenance. The dumbo stood there unmoved, staring at Headmistress who was nearly blowing a fuse, and not a single cheep came out of her. None of us felt sorry for Miss Mouse, because she wasn't, I'm certain, taking a blind bit of notice of Headmistress.

Intently we listened to the ding-dong. There must have been thirty faces looking down upon them, and they didn't even know it. But then catastrophe struck. The scout posted at the door hissed Miss was coming, and some dozy clot panicked, rocked the table and several of us began wobbling, overbalanced and fell against the wall. Blow me! It started to cave in! (It was one of those sliding partition ones.) The sections of the wall all began to move together, like waves upon the sea. In a few seconds, no more, bodies had either flown off the tables or scuttled up from the floor, and when teacher came in and beamed "Good morning class", we were dutifully ready with our reply "Good morning Miss", although it came out through unsteady lips. She noticed the bent walls and asked someone to straighten them out, but asked no questions as to how it had become zigzag. We were petrified that Headmistress would come storming in and expel the lot of us, because she must have seen and heard the wall begin to stir. Maybe she spotted the odd head too – those who weren't quick to duck. That lesson I think teacher had the quietest, most well-behaved class of meek and mild she would ever be likely to come across.

Countless funny things happened at Wood Green that Terri and I often reminisce about. Like the time Tritz stuck her mitt in the air, wanting to answer a question and yelled "Please Dad" – Sir thought it laughable, which was just as well, because the class, beside themselves with mirth, almost fell out of their chairs.

If I were going to be buried I would have to have my potted cactus growing on me for sentimental reasons. It's getting on in years, as I've had it since I was seven. Then it was a baby ball the size of a pea, given to me by "Dad", Mr. Ashtree (Ashtray to us), our form teacher that year, for good attendance. Big as a marrow it is now with babies in abundance attached to it, all of them bigger than sprouts. I operated once, donned rubber gloves and gave Mum cactus several abortions. It was for her own good, because she couldn't carry any more. Weighed down she was. These excess babies I tugged off and sent over to Rish in Canada with some Marks and Sparks undies, but hers grew into sausage shapes, not round bobbles like mine.

One Friday morning Terri received a painful swipe across the chops from Bunhead, a ninety-year-old confederate of Headmistress who was spiteful at times, but she never hit me. I think Tritz had been saucy about the brown socks she had to knit. Water began to fall from Trash's eyeballs, which made Bun cross. But Trash was crosser, because when ordered to stop crying she said, "No, shan't, won't, I won't, I won't" and kept on all the more. In the end Bunhead hustled her out to the front of the classroom, and made her sit cross-legged under the desk at her feet for the rest of the lesson. Tritz couldn't even face the class and pull faces, but had to stare at the blackboard. She said later, Bunhead had pink pantaloons on. That silly nana Tritz came back to school following lunch with a bunch of pansies for Bunhead. I told Tritz straight out she was a clothead to ever forgive her, and she should have stuck a dollop of chewing gum on her chair. Terri said her Mum thought she was off her rocker to take flowers into school on a Friday afternoon. They must have been wilted, stinky things by Monday.

While on the subject of Bunhead, I went very strange in one of her knitting classes. A few days prior to the event, I had come belting out of school and knocked a boy off his bike. I bawled, not because of my scraped knee, but because I thought I had buckled his mudguards and he would find out where I lived, and make Dad pay a vast sum of money we couldn't afford to have them straightened. He didn't though, so he must have been of an agreeable disposition. Come to think of it his name was Jolly. He works with Dave now. Anyways, my knee seemed okay apart from bloody crinkles, the imprint caused by the lumpy tar road. I had a hundred foot long bandage wrapped roughly a hundred times round my knee. With my knee stiffened and bound too tightly, so that I wouldn't forget to limp, I was quite pleased with myself until knitting afternoon. There I was clickety clacking (probably the red and yellow tea cosy I took years to make), when suddenly I felt an oozy trickle run down my leg. My bladder was intact so for a moment I couldn't figure out what the sticky, yellow, syrupy gunge was running into my shoe – quite a stream of it. Then it dawned on me. This was knee poison. I was festered. I lay down my needles on the desk and flexing my shoulders began to quietly cry. Bunhead thought I was sickly until I pointed to my gone-off, leaking knee. Tritz merely went "Ugh". I expect I lapped up the attention paid me that afternoon. I'm the type.

I didn't stay home from school. I had to show I could bravely carry on, regardless of agonising pain (doubtful). It didn't hurt except when Mum bathed it each night. Then I had justification for screaming blue murder, as the lint stuck fast to the icky stuff, and Mum had to coax the bandage and wound apart. How I did scream for compassion when she came near me with the Iodine bottle, but Mum ignored my "no, no, no" screams, same as she did Rish's when she had a verruca. Rish still had to get in the bath. Mum would remark in later years how cruel she was to make her do it. I sat in the kitchen in vest, pants and liberty bodice, wailing real tears for the length of time it took to bathe my patella. I do have good healing skin and scuds soon form, so my knee healed quickly, but no doubt I swanked around with it swathed in bandages for a long time after skin had reformed.

Now you would think a nasty knee like that would have left permanent markings, but no. Terri had black scars like a noughts and crosses board across her knee which she could boast about, and she only fell on a lump of coal and suffered not half the fearful pain I went through. It wasn't fair. It served her right when she got bombed that lunchtime as we were walking back to school. She had on her brand new camel coat, the first week she had worn it, and a rook or crow nesting in one of the trees on Thornies Hill must have said to himself "Bombs away" and let her have it. Droppings splattered down her coat. She got upset, but I comforted her by saying the bird's toilet could have sploshed into her eye and that would have stung like blazes, because it would have fallen from a great height, and also it was lime and lime burns and her eyes might have been burnt out. I might even have gloated a teeny bit, because I did fancy her camel coat before it got soiled and spoiled. It's funny, we walked four times daily under those rooks/crows brooding on Thornies Hill, but although we had several near misses, we never copped their doings until poor Terence wore her new camel coat and collected a basinful. The blighter that did it made a terrific cawing, as if he was killing himself laughing, and that made Terence fume even more. We called it Thornies Hill, because Mr. Thorn had a butcher's shop on top the hill. He had nothing to do with it really. He has been dead for many years, but our family, and doubtless others, to this day refer to it as Thornies Hill. Bris Hill is its proper title. Brislington I should say.

Other than each other, Terence and I had two dear friends at Wood Green, Id and Wid. We sat in the desk at the back of the class. They sat in the one in front of us.

Roy Rogers, who sat at the back with Tritz and me, tickled us. His name I mean. He's the pink paraffin man for the Bris area now. Trigger is the van he makes his deliveries in. He's got a white balloon tied on his aerial. He no longer knows me from Adam.

Tritz and I, Id and Wid gossiped about one another behind backs, but usually got on well. I have to say usually and not always, because one day we had a row, all four of us. Actually it went on for days, might even have been for as long as a week. Goodness knows what the row was about, but it was the parting of the ways. I ditched Terri and she ditched me. My one and only best friend became Id and she had Wid. I refused to speak or associate with her ever again, and she swore to do likewise with me. Mind you, we still sat together in our combined desks, but we truly did ignore one another. When an arm went round an exercise book, it really did act as a screen.

Our snubs went on for some time, then one day the four of us were sent outside to transfer the playground onto paper, reduced in size of course. Absurd nonsense, as all we had was 12" rulers and a tape measure, and our playground certainly was large. Off Id and I marched to the bottom end of the yard, and left That Terence and Wid up the top end, as we found their presence offensive. We had a morning in which to do our workings-out. It wasn't fun. We were pretty dense. Inches weren't a problem, but confusion ran riot in our brain boxes when they had to be converted into square ones and feet and yards. It was apparent, as the morning wore on, that Terence and Wid, Id and I were drawing closer together. When we realised we were going to meet in the middle of the yard, Id and I crossed over to the other side. As we did this, those two jackasses opposite started whispering loudly and laughing, at us we concluded, so we whispered snide comments too, shouted in fact, and laughed a hell of a lot louder than them, and this developed into a haggling din, two one side of the yard competing against two on the other side. Then trouble hit Id and me. We drew a line wrongly, and we knew too it was incurably wrong, which didn't help matters. You see what made us boil over was that That Terence had my rubber. I wasn't going to stand for it so, encouraged from the side by Id, I impudently stormed to the middle of the playground and in an enraged tone demanded, "Oih you, give us me rubber". And what did she do, that mutt, my best friend up to a few days previous? She said, I can hear it now, "Comin up Ern" (Ernie was, and is, her name for me) and standing there she threw it with all her blumming might right slap bang onto the end of my nose. Her aim had been perfect. Good job it was a soft bouncy one. For a mo I was hopping mad. I could have twisted her scraggy neck round a couple of times, and then the squealer started her peals of laughter. On and on her giggles go when she gets started. I'm not half as bad. Id and Wid, rotten devils, joined in from the sidelines with raucous bellows, and then my pretty tinkly laugh surged up from within and drowned out the lot of them. Friends again and handshakes all round.

What made the morning more hilarious was when Id and I compared our drawing with theirs. How on earth they could have differed so acutely in size and looks is beyond comprehension. We persuaded Terence and Wid to tear up their efforts and copy Id's and mine, after which we went back into school, Terence and I arm in arm and Id and Wid in like manner. We had 3 or was it 4 out of 10 for effort, which was, I think, rather stingy, as Miss Sexpot couldn't possibly have known the exact measurements. I mean to say, she couldn't have gone out before us and worked it out accurately with a 12" ruler. The four of us nearly had another bust-up, due to the fact that Terence and Wid got riled with Id and me, because they said we would have had at least five out of ten had we copied their first drawing instead of insisting ours was right.

So many rough and tumbles, skirmishes and antics were carried on in that concrete playground. The toilets were situated in one corner, dark and dank, stench filled ones, but when you gotta go, you gotta go. One could hold one's nose to prevent the pong – "Pooh what a pong" was the catchphrase when entering – from filtering up there if it was a knockout, like in the summer.

For P.E. Lessons the class congregated in the yard. The girls tucked whatever was flapping inside knickers. Most rude when you think about it, but we didn't, because we were too young to care about exposing a lot of leg. We had no school uniform, but regulation navy blue bloomers were a must for each little girl. Daphne, our temp at work, said she wore brown ones, which had a pocket in them for her hanky. Imagine having to lift your skirt every time you wanted to blow your nose. We loved our yard. It was freedom from encroaching walls. Sheer delight our beanbag games. I can picture the kids racing to win a game – a squashy rattling beanbag going through one pair of legs, the person behind whipping it up and over head to outstretched arms, then down through the next knee opening and so on. The bag of dried up beans went whizzing on its way. It meant disqualification if it was dropped and butterfingers were frowned on. Mr. (Nuts and) May nearly swallowed his whistle several times, because although he peeped wildly when rules were broken and collisions occurred, the game was carried out to its conclusion oblivious of him. Netballs we liked to play with, but Miss Toby Jug was nervy and wouldn't let us play with them regularly. Sacks and hoops I disliked. I fell over in sacks and hoops I couldn't control. They failed to pivot on my hips, because I was too shy to practise the hula hula in front of boys. What was the use in pretending, I knew I didn't look like a Hawaiian Miss with my bulging bloomers stuffed with clothes. Skipping ropes I could dance with. Now let me think. That skipping song we used to sing, how did it go? "Jelly on the plate, jelly on the plate, wibble wobble, wibble, wobble, jelly on the plate". I wibble wobbled all right.

Playtimes in the yard were most uninhibited. We had a fabulous selection of bars to swing from. Apparatus we called it. It looked like scaffolding. During our ten-minute breaks morning and afternoon, Terri and I often hung upside down hand in hand contemplating the world. Hair swept the ground, collecting dust piles, or rested in the dirt and maybe rain pools if we remained still. The scent Tritz and I wore was Rust. It clung to hands and legs after a wet day's session on the bars. A boy could be a monkey along with us, but he didn't bat an eyelid at skirts billowing round our heads, and we gave him no thought. Old Mr. Boggins, the caretaker, disregarded us on our washing line. Terence and I were experienced in the art of, well perhaps gymnastics isn't the right word for it. We could hook one leg onto the bar and swing giddily over the North and South Poles like a crazed clock hand, until spinning tops replaced heads. But we only tackled dangerous feats if we felt extra daring – trying to outdo one another – and authority was nowhere to be seen. Obviously, we could have killed ourselves had we slipped off the bars during our acrobatics, but I can't remember Tritz nor I splitting our membranes. We had the usual games of Touch, chasing hell for leather round and round the crowded playground, avoiding or trying to catch whatshisname, thingumajig or droopy drawers. The idea was to dart directly into a group of infants and disrupt their game. We did outgrow our loathsomeness at a fairly early age. Terence and I took marbles and conkers into school. My game was marbles. Terence was a crackshot at busting a conker to smithereens. With studied concentration she gave of her all and many a swipe resulted in Blackman's pinches.

Sometimes I mumbled to Mum that Tritz and I would, for a change, be staying in to school dinner, but this was an untruth. We bought a bag of chips each, propped up the Chippy's exterior walls and ate them while they were sizzling hot. Tritz's bag usually split, spilling chips over the pavement. She adored vinegar that was the trouble. And then it would be "Got any to spare Ern?" and I would give her any bad, black potato ones I had in my bag. We lounged around outside the school gates until our time was well and truly up, and we had to return to lessons with less than a second to spare.

Without fail though, before school resumed, we would wind up at Vic's, the off-licence. Often, for a giggle, we would send Sarah in alone. The counter was quite high in the shop and Sarah stood way below it. Sarah was a midget. When old Vic heard the doorbell chime, heralding a customer's arrival, he would come bustling into the shop from the back room, only to find, so he thought at first, an empty shop. Then a voice would pipe up, "Let's 'ave some black jacks and refreshers Vic me old darlin" and he would wonder where the hell it was coming from. We would be peeping through the shop window and, when we decided to go into the shop, he blamed us for playing jokes and Sarah got off scot-free, often with a free quarter of fruit salad sweets thrown in with her other purchases. If we were in there for any length of time, like for instance to sup cider, Sarah would get a chair to stand on, then jump up onto the counter to sit. (Outside her house I would stand to one side while she jumped up at the back door a few times, before succeeding in turning the knob to let us in.) I wouldn't like to guess the number of times we returned to Junior School burping and slightly sozzled with scrumpy paunches. No kid developed a big red conk with veins standing out I'm glad to say. We didn't have to sway far. Vic was good to the kids. Our bus fare home went on imps, gobstoppers, chewing or bubble gum, pineapple rock, toffee, aniseed balls, lemon sherbet sweets, gob size pickled eggs or half pint of cider, whatever we fancied. It could well be my mind is playing tricks, and it was a small glass of cider. We wouldn't have caught the bus anyway. We found it impossible to go at a fast pace anywhere.

Terence and I did for a time toy with the idea of taking up careers as professional racing drivers. We would watch drivers of any kind of vehicle and imitate their actions. (Neither of our Dads drove.) We thought if we practised imaginary driving it would be useful in future years. So that is what we did. When we got on an almost empty bus, we would sit in the front seat upstairs and pretend to be in charge. We would dip and roll with the bus, change gears with or without crashing them, twist the wheel, look in the mirror, flag on tail huggers, and nothing would distract our attention unless kids we knew were walking on the pavement. Under those circumstances accidents would be narrowly avoided, as we screeched to a halt and played wiggly ears at them. Naturally, we criticised each other's driving. Terence used the accelerator too frequently. She would brake sharply, and practically throw herself through the windscreen at every bus stop. I liked to cruise along steadily in second gear, barely moving the wheel, in complete, relaxed control of every situation – a cow in the road, I would carefully manoeuvre my bus round the beast without her tail even twitching. Terence being a speed ace would have left her lying in a pool of milk, or sent her jumping over a hedge in a moon leap. Being drivers sitting beside one another, we did crack nuts when I thought the bus was going right and dolt Terence thought it was going left. I doubt that we learnt to drive the correct way. We have never put our efforts into practice. That is, Terence had an attempt. Rob got ratty with her. She threatened to brain him. And so for the sake of their month old marriage she gave it up as a bad job.

Terence though would rather have been a bus conductress than a driver. As a little girl, that had been her one ambition. She was devoted to bell ringing, much to Mrs. Cod's embarrassment. Tritz would be lifted up in her Mum's arms to disembark from a bus, and she wouldn't give one short ding on the bus bell. Oh no, not her. Her finger would stay on the bell and hell, fire and damnation would not budge it, but a sweet might. She could play one finger tunes on it. Not long ago a conductor laughed at me and said "Well I'm blessed, I've not seen it done that way before", but I ring the bell with my knuckle, as it saves bending a nail. On boring bus journeys Tritz and I changed our identity. Russians were held in awe, so we became Russians. We jibber jabbered to our heart's content, spouting forth made-up words, convinced people would think we were in the KGB. We must have sounded more like a couple of honking pigs. Keeping a straight face was the main aim of the game. A bemused or startled look from other bus passengers was our goal.

One lunchtime we were returning to school and came upon the scene of a tragic accident. Two little brothers from a different County were killed on Bris Hill, grotesquely and agonisingly inside engine machinery carried on the lorry they were travelling in. They, or what was left of them, had been removed when we were shepherded by, but we saw their blood staining the tarmac. The lorry driver was a big rugged man, but he wasn't strong then. He was sat on a stool outside the paper shop, saying "Their screams, their screams" and shaking his head in disbelief. He couldn't drink tea offered him. Those two kids should have been at school, but they had persuaded him to take them on his rounds. To miss one day's schooling wouldn't matter, and they had died. I suppose every child in that unspeaking bunch, stood watching on the hill, remembers. I recall too Ally's friend knocking on the door one tea-time, but Ally couldn't go out to play because he was still eating. That youngster went off by himself, crossed the road without looking, and was run over and killed by his own Grandad. Squished, just like that. Some sad things can't be erased from the memory.

On to happier days, there was the one afternoon in the week when the school, lock stock and barrel, trooped down to Victory Park for games. An army divided into regiments. Striding at our head was the Head, with Bunhead, her batman, running along beside her, and tripping over Bonzo the dog in her haste to keep abreast. And so they led us, but we weren't allowed to sing 'Onward Christian Soldiers'. Nevertheless, Bonzo's howl was our bugle call and pounding feet was our drum roll and so into Victory. On arrival we had to get down to the business of sporting activities. Girls slogged rounders bats and balls and practically tore arms from sockets in their enthusiasm. But once four o'clock came it was down tools – teachers' pets took whatever back to school – dispense with politeness, because teachers had departed, and with a biff here and a bash there, it was first come first serve for goes on the swings, maypole and roundabout. I liked soaring and dipping on the maypole, but I kept getting into tangles and thudding into others. Before leaving for home, Terence and I climbed up the hill in the park to our sloe tree. We called the fruit damsons. They were very bitter and often we regretted eating them when they began to work in our tums, but a quick dart to the public lavs in the village en route to abodes eased discomfort.

Every summer there was a day set aside when the school travelled in coachloads to Clevedon. On arrival we were tipped out to do the marathon walk along the cliff path to Portishead. Such a happy armed force, we stood at the ready waiting for the off. We were armed with heavy rucksacks, satchels and duffle bags, each one overfilled with plenty of grub for the day's outing. With not a grumble amongst us, we marched along in single file chitchatting as we went. We stopped at Lady Bay for lunch. Friends did a sandwich swap. After eats we walked in the water, tempting the waves to come and get us, which they invariably did. Sarah would go off searching for fossils, while the rest of us 'gills' collected pretty pebbles and shells, and watched in disgust as the boys chucked others skimming out to sea. Then it was time to gather up our rubbish, find Sarah and off we would go again on our merry way. It was an idyllic walk. I don't remember ever having a rainy, dull day for it. Although tired when our destiny was reached during late afternoon, we didn't want to board the coaches for home straightaway. We were given a free period and Terence, Sarah and myself headed immediately for the lake. Well it was a large pond really. We hired one of the leaking boats, handed Sarah the oars, and she would row us round in circles. I know we were huge and had a lot more muscle compared to diddy Sarah, but she was the tomboy of the three of us, and she enjoyed contorting with the oars, which were twice as big as she was. She coped admirably, even though we chided her that we weren't going fast enough. Let's face it, had Terence or I been the oarsman, we would have capsized within an eye blink.

When we were older Tritz, Sarah and I used to go back to the coves of Lady Bay and spend the day sunbathing.

The school kids lined the streets of Brislington one morning to see the Queen Mother go by. We had our hankies to wave. I dropped mine, stooped to pick it up the second she sailed by in her limo. I was upset that I had missed her and the others said she had a lovely face. No matter, Mum did take us out to Crossways, where the Man with Two Heads signals to drivers to be careful, and we sat on the wall with our Union Jacks and saw the Queen cruise by on her way to Bath. She's flawless.

We had the annual flower show to prepare for too. Kids were supplied with bulbs from school. I didn't do well with my bulb and corm growing, but my miniature garden one year earned me a photo in the Evening Post, alongside the Ragdoll girl and boy called Daisy. Beforehand I had spent many days tracking down bits and pieces, and had real green fingers from moss hunting expeditions, but I enjoyed that kind of arty-crafty work. Similarly, I was in my element with balls of clay.

There is one disastrous day lodged in my memory from the years I spent at Wood Green. It was the day that followed an evening to the 'theatre'. A coach party of pupils and commanders had gone to another school to see a play performed, and on the way home the coach dropped Stella and me off at a convenient spot along the main West Road. (Stelly was a good friend, although behind her back Tritz, Sarah and I called her Smelly Stelly, yet she smelt the same as the rest of us.) We walked to the rear, held hands and proceeded to cross behind the stationary coach. How many times had we been warned of the dangers? Dozens and dozens! By all accounts, we should have been mashed into the road, or tossed into the air. A car was racing straight at us. One moment Stelly and I were an inch from car headlights, the next we had moved like greased lightning and were flattened and unbreathing against the coach. How Stelly accomplished it I don't know, because she was a roly-poly pudding and a slow waddler, but gunpowder was in her that split second. Not a soul got off the coach, but what seemed like a hundred ugly mugs with hideous flat noses were pressed to the window ogling us. We surely did realise we had done wrong. Two red tomatoes said "Phew" and walked away in perspiring heat with blasphemous words injecting our lugholes. These came from inside the car we had nearly walked into. Nobody got out from the vehicle, thank goodness, as we thought he would have marmalised us. We would rather have been squashed to a pulp on the bumper than die at the hands of a nerve-racked driver. Stelly and I did more or less die walking to our homes. We felt sick and clammy with the shakes, because we knew we had come within a hair's breadth of becoming hospital or mortuary cases. One would think we had had punishment enough, but no, far worse was to come.

Next morning, after assembly, Stelly and I were ordered to stand up in the midst of the whole school to be made an example of. They were all sat cross-legged on the floor, but not the teachers. Headmistress pointed her bony finger at us, and pointed out to them our gross stupidity, negligence in road safety, and utter thoughtlessness and carelessness, etc etc in our conduct the night before. Long words poured out of her in a turbulent jet. Such humiliation and degradation to be subjected to! I felt more ill than I had done on the yester-eve, but this time I was the colour of blood not green. We were harshly told to look at Headmistress when she was talking to us, and not at the floor. We couldn't gain any comfort from lowering our scared, hounded eyes, when a sea of grinning, upturned faces was staring at us. Talk about "don't spray it, say it!" Her stinging lecture drowned us in spittle. Front row was used to it, but we weren't, and I didn't appreciate it making my hair curl. The thing was, Stelly and I admitted later, we had expected a private word-whipping dressing down and had both spent a sleepless night, but why oh why did Headmistress have to go and lash at us so openly. We had actually said prayers and meant them that morning in service. We weren't naughty girls and there she had insulted our intelligence in front of the whole school and grown-ups too, because we had made an unfortunate mistake. Stelly said she was going to get her Dad onto her. We had felt no bigger than ants, and twice as stupid as asses. We never forgave the Head. She sank low in our esteem, but it was her own fault.

When the time came, Terence and I took the eleven plus exam. Immediately after the final papers were handed in to the teacher and we were dismissed, we came to the joint conclusion we had both failed. We thought no more about it until the morning of reckoning dawned, when notification of pass or failure was to be received. I pretended not to care one way or the other, but my thumping heart prevented good digestion of breakfast. Nonetheless, I was stood waiting in anticipation behind the front door for postie to shoot the important news through the letter-box. As I scythed the letter open, panic gripped me and sped to my blood cells and pulse points. Hard to believe, but I passed. I didn't feel chuffed though until I heard how Terence had done. God 'elp us if she failed, because it would mean splitting up, and maybe going to different schools! It was the first time ever, but I hurried to school that morning. Tritz unfailingly waited for me by the zebra crossing in the village. When I spied her that particular morning, I must have been quarter of a mile away, too far to give my lungs an airing, but I began nodding my head up and down like a clockwork clown as I drew near, and I was highly delighted when she did likewise, up and down instead of from side to side.

Trouble was things didn't work out how we intended.

APPROACHING MY TEENS

Our new school was Bris Comp, where Rish was already ensconced in her fourth year. On our first day of attendance, with a mob of other young first-years, we had to sit lots of tests, which caught us unawares. Faced with these gruelling works, I went to pieces and couldn't function. My brain crawled at a snail's pace and consequently, on the second day at the new school, Terence and I parted company. It was a sad day. She was posted to the top class, and I was in the one below her. We drifted apart. Even out of school we only occasionally saw one another. I made friends with Cake and Fowl at school. Terence chose other companions. A year went by. End of term exams were taken and when the results were made known, lo and behold, I was flung out of my class and jumped up into Tritz's. Inseparables again. Ooh, but I could have brained her. My first unnerving morning in the top form, she had to go to the dentist and couldn't look after me. However, reunited it didn't take long to catch up on all the affairs of the year in which we had been separated. Tritz and I shared every confidence.

I loved my weekends spent at Terri's. These took place after she left the prefab. Six kids there may have been in the Cod family, but they always made room for any extras. What usually happened was, Terence and I snaffled the bunk beds in the box room and left the five others to sleep whatever way they could. Not that we ever slept much. It was chuckles and chatter for a large part of the night. Every single night I've spent there, even when we were sixteen year olds, Mrs. Cod has had to shout up the stairs to us "Get to sleep" again and again, using a firmer, sterner tone of voice each time. Her "wrap up" meant in fact "put a sock in it". Only when footsteps could be heard on the stairs, would we heed the warning sign and shut our cakeholes, but it was useless trying to drop off to sleep. Terence had top bunk and I got claustrophobia underneath. She bounced about to such an extent above me, she made the mattress sag in the middle so that it almost touched my nose. In the morning I fully expected to wake with my nose caught in a spring. Also, pasted above me, stuck over the sagging bulge that was Terri's bottom, was an enormous picture of Paul Newman. How could I concentrate on sleeping with his gorgeous blue eyes so close to mine? I could see the whites in the dark. I approved wholeheartedly of the Cod girls' taste in idols. Terence kept falling out of bed. She would practise at being a bat. I would just be dropping off to sleep when an upside down face would suddenly appear over the side of the upper bunk, giving me one of her screwed up, wizened old lady looks. She lowered herself until she hung by her feet or thereabouts.

Terence would insist on cooking me breakfast before the rest of the household stirred. My goodness, her fried eggs! Nobody can ruin an egg quite like Trash. She would crack them deftly into the pan, but she wasn't content to cook them on one side like a normal person would do. Oh no, Tritz would flip them over to do both sides equally. "Only natural" she said, "You do with everything else". And she'd toss them like pancakes and frequently miss the pan on their descent. I was spoilt when I visited. Mrs. Cod knew my yummy favourites. She alternated between chocolate and seedy cake for tea on my stays.

Terri's house was a nuisance though, being sited on top of a treacherously sloping grassy bank. True, there was a pathway leading up to it, but we didn't bother with that and battled with the bank for quickness. One very windy, slushy underfoot day I was on my way there with Jimmy-jams, pair of clean drawers and toothbrush in a carrier bag on my arm. Tritz and I had started up the bank, but the grass was wet and slippery and Terence herself was forced to retreat to the pathway. Not I, Pange the Conqueror. I pulled myself upwards, by catching hold of handfuls of grass and digging my nails into the ground. (Later I probably flicked mud out of them at Charles, the boy next door to Tritz whom we disliked. He went spare when Tritz called him Charley and I called him Charrels.) Terence was cheering, "At a boy, come on Ern" from the rear. She was having a further go at the Alp. Then it happened.

Rain-soaked grass, which I grabbed, came out of the earth. I shot backwards, then forwards, before slithering down to the pavement on my middle, still clutching my bunch of blades. My navy school mackintosh had thick streaks of mud running down it, and my chin was caked somewhat when I reached the bottom in a heap. I sat on the pavement and laughed until I cried. Terence had let go of the grass too in alarmed dismay when I went shooting by her on my downward path, and had followed me in rapid succession. She was in a worse state, because she said her stopper was working loose, and she was near to relieving herself. What added to our amusement, but we were too weak to do anything about it for a few minutes, was that my bag had opened up, spilling its contents, and one pair of mud splattered knickers (it had to be white ones) and brown spotted jamas were strewn across the bank. We did move pretty sharpish when the wind took them, and boy didn't we have to chase my coms. Toothbrush I expect went down the drain and a hanky sufficed. Mrs. Cod was good as gold and cleaned my Mac for me best way she could. I owned up to Mum later, because I didn't want her thinking the dollops of mud on my clothing were something else. We must have been around thirteen at the time of our doomed mountaineering escapade, certainly old enough to know better than tackle the Alp in such atrocious conditions. On a dark evening we would definitely have a bash together even now. Terence keeps me young, although she is four months older than me. She breeds merriment.

Terence also had the golfcourse at the rear of her house. That is why she wouldn't snooze in the garden for fear she would cop a stray golf ball. She spent hours out there though hunting for misguided golf balls to sell back to the golfers. The golfcourse was prohibited to all but members of the Golf Club. This didn't deter us. We children formed our own private club thereon, in a clump of bushes on the green. From Terence's garden we watched and listened then, when the coast was clear, zipped across the open spaces to our den-ery. Many golfers passed by, unaware there was a cluster of trespassers within a few yards of them. They should have watched their language. We called the golfcourse Germany. Terence and I withdrew our club membership after being discovered. We got caught mid field zooming across the course by a huge blackman golfer. He sent us back the way we had come. During the snowy season kids ignored the No Trespassing signboard and the golfcourse teemed with toboggans and sleds, having changed its name to Switzerland. In such weather the members knew that kids outnumbered them and banishment was impossible.

It was commonplace for shoes to be lost in drifts, and nothing unusual to find odd ones littering the course when the snow had melted. One of my Wellington boots disappeared one year, but then my feet grew accustomed to being removed from nice, warm shoes and ending up in cold, wet places. I had a habit in childhood of falling into the stream, which ran alongside the golfcourse. Goodness knows how many times it happened, and my feet should positively have shrunk to a size 7. It was always mine that took the plunge, never Terence's. I've forgotten the number of occasions I've squelched into Mrs. Cod's kitchen, emptied a shoeful of water down the sink, wrung out my socks and asked her could she please please dry them under the grill for me before I went home, because Mum and Dad would blow their top notes and it wouldn't be a reputable duet. A pair of my brown leather sandals was left sodden with stream water one day and they went white and mouldy. Somehow or other Rish's brown Mac, which I had 'borrowed', received a ducking in the stream as well. I ran to Mrs. Cod and she patiently held up the saturated garment in front of an electric fire with a bowl underneath to catch the drips. I was very late home, as it took hours, but at least I was relatively dry if extremely crumpled – there wasn't a sweet smell enveloping me neither. I can remember plainly going "Eek!" early one evening, as I made my way to Terri's. I disturbed a water rat as I vaulted the stream and it nearly ran over my feet. That caused me to side step into the stream.

Once freed from school's shackles at 4pm, I mingled with a group of all-sorts, girls roughly the same age as me. We met on the new housing estate when we were eleven and grew into teenagers together, passing through the normal fads and crazes. We grew out of gargantuan flared skirts, worn with four or five net or stiffened petticoats rustling underneath, into skin-tight skirts, usually black. God, we must have walked daft, being able to take only weeny steps and certainly no strides.

We deluded ourselves into thinking we were bright, as we rounded up as many wee sprites as we could lay our hands on to form our own school. We netted them in Jill's garden shed. You never know, the girls and I may have tutored a brainy bonce.

Why do I remember Jill? She wasn't any more of a close friend than the rest of the bunch. In a happy frame of mind she possessed an infectious, throaty laugh, but the other girls and I have witnessed several slanging matches, and a couple of brawls, in which she participated with another screaming wench with no holds barred. After lunch one day I was powdering my nose, before leaving for the fortress that was school, when Jill pounded on our front door crying in a fit of hysteria. Apparently, while cleaning out her mice (she had two white ones) she had picked up the dirty newspaper lying on the cage floor, saw a dozen half inch long, pink skinned creatures writhing about in the muck and sawdust, and dropped the paper in fright into the two foot high couch-grass. Such an untidy garden it was out back, but the front was neat with gigantic sunflowers growing. Back we ran up the road and while Jill supervised I had to pick up those pink baby rodents one by one, each no bigger than a squirt of toothpaste. They reminded me of pygmy rhinos. Evidently most of them were dead, but Jill cried and cried so there was nothing for it but to pick each and every one up and put them back in the cage. It made me feel queer, plus I was scared silly of that mother and father mouse. My hand went gingerly into the cage, and quickly dropped the babies on the floor with a 'thud', instead of placing them down gently and lovingly. I had an idea the parents were carnivorous and would eat their young, and they might have mistaken my fingers for babies and tore them to shreds.

I went with Jill on a Saturday visit to her grandad's. He was a burly, snow-haired old man living on his own. Strangely enough, I can picture him in his grubby white, collarless shirt, with a tie round his middle acting as a belt, shyly making us tea. Extraordinarily, I can recall precisely what we had, bread and marge and a dish of sliced tomatoes in a highly spiced vinegar. Jill and I cleared the dish, which pleased him, but we did have blow-offs afterwards. Years later Jill came to tell me he had died. She cried, as I had cried when we lost our Granf.

AUNT OLLY AND NAN

Aunt Olly went to live with Nan after Granfer's death. Olice we called her behind her back, giving her half of Alice, Nan's name. They bickered, as sisters will. Chalk and cheese they were but when all is said and done, they depended on each other for company. It was better to take no notice when they both let off steam. Darling Nan, normally so placid, yet I've heard her in anger say "I could shake her guts out" and "She can go and frizzle". Every time I stayed with them I was told tales whilst the other was out of the room. Both Nan and Aunt Olly took me into their confidence about the other's annoying little habits and idiosyncrasies, which drove the other batty. Aunt Olly wasn't so bad. I didn't like her 'suety dumps'. She called them suety, but in fact they were made solely with flour and water, nothing else. Her Yorkshire Pud was perfect though, exactly like Madeira cake. If she was windy, Aunt Olly said "Manners". Everyone else we knew said "Pardon". When Aunt Olly went to live with Nan she brought a telly with her and, because of this, we loved more than ever to visit Nan's on a Saturday, although it wasn't the same without Granfer being there. The boys and I loved The Lone Ranger and Tonto, but we saw Slim and Jess in Laramie the one time and thereafter much preferred that prog.

Aunt Olly didn't like Timsbury. She wanted to be a mile and a quarter away at Farmborough, near her daughter Coral and grandchildren. A year or so went by and Aunt Olly did get an old people's flat there. She urged Nan to put her name down on the list for one too, but Nan could no longer manage stairs easily, and consequently had to wait a long time before she got her bungalow opposite Aunt Olly's upstairs flat. Nan was so alone when Aunt Olly left her. She had loneliness unimaginable. She went for days not seeing a soul apart from the paper-boy, and going in Claris's for her few groceries. Oh, there was the black man with the turban who tapped on her door with his case of pegs, tea towels, toothbrushes, etc once a fortnight. Nan wasn't dubious about inviting him into her kitchen late at night. He was her friend and someone to talk to. She often remarked she felt full of misery and had a job to stick it, but she had then, and has now, mammoth courage beyond belief and without it she wouldn't be here today. She's blind in one eye with a cataract over it, and countless years ago she had a life or death operation for gastric stomach ulcers, which left a sore and tender scar right the way down her body. Whatever she eats gives her gip and goes through her like froth. Even a spoonful of cornflakes works her belly she says. There isn't a day goes by when she isn't racked with pain. She knows what suffering is. Her distasteful peppermint medicine has no real healing power. I wouldn't be surprised if the start of her stomach trouble began after one of her babies was born. For a time following the birth Nan stunk to high heaven and had pains, but nobody could think why. Then all in a rush her afterbirth, which must have been rotting inside, came away. I consider it gross negligence on the part of the midwife. When Nan had her babies she had to hang on to a towel tied to the bed rail. When her milk went lumpy she put butter on her chest to ease the pain. Nan had milk galore and fed all her babies until they were two or three. Mum was a toddler by the time she was weaned. Although Nan was so tiny and flat chested, the milk ran in streams from her and she wore nappies round her chest to help soak it up.

But now, when Nan gets one of her bad "rummy" days and her tum is "nig-nagging", or she "hasn't been up the market" (which means she doesn't feel that spesh), she then potters round, does a bit, sits down, up and does a tad more. That way everything gets done near enough: the cooking, cleaning, etc. She won't have a home help nor will she have meals on wheels. And at the close of each day she says "Once more once less", climbs into bed, has a swig of brandy, and prays to the Good Lord to give her strength to get through another day, thanks him for everything he has done for her, and hopes he will let her see Rish again. I know all this. Many times I have lain beside Nan and listened to her pray. Coming up for eighty, she's Dave's light of his life. It is a comical sight to see Al leaning on her shoulder. She comes up to his armpit and is less than half his weight. She is six and a half stone with all her clothes on. And what clothes! It takes Nan goodness knows how long to dress in the morning. She wears two pairs of thick stockings with suspenders and garters to keep them up. She has got to wear soft wadding and a vest next to her skin on account of her scar. She handed me the scissors and requested that I cut the ribs out of her stays the other day, because they were digging into her flesh, so I went round her and snipped out the bones. Her Long Johns insulate her as well. She wears a couple of petticoats, and tells me off, because it isn't very often I wear one. A jumper goes on before her dress. After her dress a cardigan goes on top, followed by a nylon overall, and then an extra cardigan in case she gets the shivers. She likes her clothing loose though and most of her dresses are outsize. If she feels the least bit penned in, she gets hold of the scissors and cuts clothes while she is wearing them until she can say "Ah, that's better". She likes room to manoeuvre. She is our little matchstick lady underneath. Nan is like Dad. He is thin, but cuddlesome. So is Nan. She says she is nothing but skin and shrivel.

When Nan came to stay after Granfer died, it meant three of us in the double bed and it was I, naturally, who was pig in the middle. Rish was quite a demon to me. I dared not turn over, because she would get stroppy. She didn't care tuppence about my sinuses seizing up, and I would panic thinking I was suffocating in the pillow, but she was anything but sympathetic. Nan made room for me, but Rish didn't like me within an inch of her, and if I had shoved over as many times as I was told to, Nan would have been on the floor and me on top of her. I suppose I still bobbed myself to sleep. It's fine now when Nan comes to stay, as it's just the two of us in the double bed.

Nan was with us four years ago the day Uncle Jim came in and dropped a key in her lap. She had got an old people's bungalow in Farmborough at long last and she did cry. I went out to Timsbury that weekend to help her begin packing. We had a terrible night. The beds weren't aired. Nan slept on the settee and I slept in two chairs. We talked throughout the night, as we couldn't sleep. Nan was poorly after. Aunt Olly was thrilled to bits about Nan going to Farmborough. Nan was too, because she knew so many people there, practically everyone being a distant relation. Nan had been dying a slow, horrible death by herself at Timsbury, but when she had settled into her new bungalow she became revitalised. Each evening Nan and Aunt Olly met in either one's home to watch telly and have supper and hot chocolate. Eliza regularly joined them. She's dead now. At ten o'clock they swapped a shilling love story, not smammy ones Nan would say, and parted. They got ready for bed and last thing, before dousing the light, they would wave to one another across the street.

But that has come to an end, as Aunt Olly died a while back. Nan misses her dreadfully. For quite a long time Aunt Olly could only eat bread and milk and then all she could get down was Bovril. She dwindled away to nothing, yet she had been a big woman making two of Nan. Nan used to say Aunt Olly was fat as mud. The last night Aunt Olly spent in her home, before going down Coral's to die, Nan stayed with her because she felt very ill. The nightlight blew itself out near to midnight and Nan went round on all fours searching for the po. She did find it. Then she lost the campbed. Eventually this came to hand, but her pillows were missing. Nan had climbed into bed the wrong end. What a carry-on, but it did make Aunt Olly laugh. Aunt Olly knew every time I went to stay with Nan for a weekend I would be in possession of three things: a grapefruit for breakfast, Andrews Liver Salts for before Sunday's breakfast and ladders in my tights. When Aunt Olly went down Coral's, Nan sat with her every day. They talked about everything, even what it felt like to be dying. Coral overheard this quiet voiced, intimate topic of conversation. Aunt Olly hoped Nan wouldn't be long in coming after her. She would let Nan wash her, but not Coral her own daughter. On the doctor's final visit he gave Aunt Olly ten days, no more. Obstinate to the end she lasted eleven. She got through Christmas, but didn't see the New Year in.

To get over it, Nan has been staying with Uncle Jim and Aunty Gwen. She needs to have company. Trigger, their dog, idolises her and stands guard if they go out. His tail hurts Nan when it wags and slaps her legs. But Nelson misses her. Dear Nelson next door to Nan. Nan goes home to her bungalow for an hour during the week to tidy the grate, because soot comes down the chimney in gusty weather, and Nelson pops in to enquire "When bis comin ome Alice, make thee mind up and come on ome". It was Mrs. Bridges when Nan went there in the beginning to live, but it's first names now. Nan will do as he says soon I would think. She loves her little home and can't leave it for a long stretch. Nan often sighs and says to Nelson that they'll both keep rubbing along. Creaking doors last the longest.

I can't imagine life without Nan. She has got so many funnies. She thinks I should carry a hat-pin or scissors in my handbag. Her intention is that I must threaten a man's private if he dares to venture further than he should. Nan has never taken a proper bath in her life and never will. It would petrify her. Even in hospital she wouldn't get right down into the water, but would wait until the nurses had gone, and then stand in to wash. Nan loves to stand with her back to the fire, and lift her skirt up to warm her derriere. She puts her foot on the fire whenever she thinks the coals might fall out, and stamps them securely into position behind the fender. She also carries on talking whilst picking up red hot coals in her hands, as though they were cough drops, before pushing them to the back of the fire. Fire doesn't appear to want to harm Nan. I don't believe Nan has ever said "Ouch" in her life.

She has got her own lingo certainly. I love to hear her speak of getting nubs of coal off the nubby man and chumps of wood off the chummy man. It is her emergency heater, not immersion. Soup is sup. It is sustificate not certificate. She fills up cartoons with blackberries and it was Typhoon tea not Typhoo. She says some females are brazen hussies and some men are sexicle. She says a thing costs ten and oddsies and our new pence decimal money she calls brown money. She says a cardigan gets nibby when it's worn. The time Mum was sickening she looked white and maggoty. If Nan is unwell she doesn't feel genuine. She bumped up her sideboard for firewood. She says dark people have got bushy heads. When I went out in the rain without a hood she said I would get sopping and my head would be streaming. And my goodness, what she said to Dad one Boxing Day! (She isn't allowed to go anywhere except in with our family for Christmas.) Pops was trimming up the front room (we're certainly slowcoaches) and Nan said "That's right Tom, hang the streamers from one pelvis (pelmet she meant) to the other". No wonder Dad nearly came a cropper and fell off the chair he was stood on. I think that was the year Mum wrote on Dad's Christmas card on the 2nd Jan, their anniversary. Nan and Aunt Olly were both as bad as one another when it came to Alka-Seltzers. Nan calls them Helter Skelters. Aunt Olly called them Scooters. The chemist knew precisely what they were after.

Nan to this day washes her hair in Daz and washes up with Daz and it is too late in the day to convert her. A few months back, what was it she did, put porridge oats in her boiler instead of washing powder, and added clothes before she realized her mistake? Then there was the time she put clothes in, switched on, smelt burning and pulled out scorched and smouldering garments. Forgot to put the water in, hadn't she. For a Sunday dinner she sprinkled mixed spice over her chicken wing instead of pepper. Her latest escapade was to knock a pint of milk over the kitchen floor, and as she got down on her knees to mop up, she hit the sugar bowl off the table into the milk puddle. "Soak me John," she said "I only needed the tea caddy to go over as well and I'd have had my tea on the floor". Once, by mistake, Nan emptied the teapot into the dustbin instead of over the garden dirt. She followed this up by filling a jug with water to take to the kettle, and poured the contents over it, and down onto the floor, instead of into it. She had forgotten to take the lid off. That happened after a snowball drink. Nan is naughty. In her canteen of cutlery there are dated knives, forks and spoons marked Woolworths Cafeteria. How she came by them, she isn't saying. She can peel a potato in one peeling. I marvel at that. She can recite poetry too. She knows the days of the week in French, and how many poles there are in a furlong, which is more than I do.

The last holiday Nan had, I accompanied her. I was, I think, 13 at the time. Not that we went far. It was just to Weston-Super-Mare or super-mud as we were apt to call it, when we sank in it, swam in it and brought it home in our nails and hair as kids. Nan, Aunt Olly, Mar (Aunt Olly's grand-daughter who was four years younger than me) and I had a caravan for a week in Green Tiles Holiday Camp. What a marvellous time we had, although the weather was diabolical. One day I was the only person bathing in the sea – it was raining at the time – and Nan rubbed my skin off, making sure I was perfectly dry when I came out from the deep. And she goffered my hair. I couldn't believe my lucky stars when three fellahs became interested in me. I wrote to girlfriends on the backs of rude postcards, which Nan helped to choose, that they were boyfriends, but they weren't proper beaux in the true sense. Nan, Aunt Olly and Mar were tickled to death, and I was ecstatic if extremely shy and embarrassed. No.1 was a ginger haired Tom holidaying with his family at the camp. I can't remember who went the deeper shade of pink if our eyes chanced to meet, him or me. I knew he fancied me, because his brother told Mar. We ourselves didn't speak a single word to each other. Mar and his brother got on great guns together. No.2 was the Postman. I was at the post box when he came along. He asked me out, but he was a great deal older than me, at least twenty. He must have mistaken me to be older than I was, because those were the days when I was a 'big' girl. I ran for my life back to Nan after I stammered a "No thank you". No.3 was Dennis the Menace, the camp owner's son, a mischievous, lighthearted youth who adored Nan and Aunt Olly, and they returned his affection. They tittered helplessly when he locked the door of the outhouse with both of us inside. I found it awfully hard to look him in the face after, and he knew it. A terrible tease he was, although really I enjoyed driving to the town centre in the camp bus sat on his knee. To be perfectly honest he preferred lightweight Nan to me. She received the compliments, I didn't.

That time, years ago, when Nan was staying with us and our chimney caught fire! It was an awful fire that Pops couldn't control. In a blind panic I attempted to run to the phone box to call the fire brigade. (I was home from school with gastroenteritis.) I had on my feet rubber flip-flops. I was near to tears because I felt sure the house was going to burn down. Luckily, I snaffled Lin's oldest brother in the street to telephone for me and I ran back home carrying my blasted flip-flops. Poor Mum and Dad were beside themselves. The fire was raging furiously in the grate and the whole street had gathered outside, gazing skywards at the belching black smoke, flames, ash and soot. Dad was pacing from room to room inspecting the walls, fearing the house would cave in around us, as huge wide cracks were appearing. He ordered us out into the garden, but we wouldn't go because he wouldn't. Nan calmly went upstairs. First she put her teeth in, and then she made the beds, because she said, "What will the firemen think". Commotion in the road heralded the arrival of two fire engines and any amount of firemen swooped on the place and busied themselves about their work. All the while, as this was going on, Nan was sat at the kitchen table writing a letter to Aunt Olly, recounting everything as it was actually happening.

LEISURE

Let me go back to my days on the Ford Estate.

I had that fight with Billy, if one can call it such. Our quarrel happened because of me and my big mouth. A group of girls and boys had gathered outside our house when my friends and I appeared on the scene, and there was Billy socking away at this little chap. I was angered at the injustice and yelled that he was a big bully. Why he picked on me heaven knows. Others were calling him names too. Someone his own size I suppose. He pounced. He didn't thump me, but grabbed my thumb and cricked it back and back to my wrist. A deathly hush fell on the mob and I certainly wasn't going to be a coward in public and resort to crying, so I bit my lip hard. Billy was smiling with quite an evil leer and I tried to match it with a similar look through gritted teeth. Relief came only when one of my darling brothers dapped in home for Pop, who came running and threatened my adversary. Billy instantly let go without a murmur. My thumb was released from its murderous attacker. I walked slowly, head held high, into the house and then burst into shrieking wails, swearing I needed hospital treatment as my thumb was broken in ever so many places. Not so, of course.

Until this year I think Billy remembered the thumb encounter. I'm glad I showed him some spunk. If ever I saw him he smiled and said "Hello" and he did the same to Dad, addressing him as Mr. B. It was a pleasant, open smile not ugly like he may have given to other folk. He didn't change his boyish ways. He was a bad lot most people said, a no-good, yet he came from a lovely family. He had a twin sister, who was in our gang. Over the years he grew into a hoodlum. A big and beefy hippy he became with unkempt hair except if he was in borstal. He looked that smart when he came home after a stretch inside, but it didn't last long. I don't suppose he ever did an honest day's work in his life. He's no longer with us. The police found him dead in September in a ramshackle hut on the outskirts of Bristol. He had suffocated in his own vomit. He did himself and his family the greatest harm.

There was though a bully on the estate I could not take to, and I loathe the sight of him even now. This one was older than me. Billy was a year younger. Scuddy boy we called him. He was a tall and gangly beanpole with shocking bright ginger hair and mean looking with a permanent twisted conceited smile.

The other day I went to the Doc's. (I went all of a doo-dah in the surgery and asked him for spot pimples instead of pimple pills.) On my way home a little red pop-pop pulled up alongside me and this ginger geezer – hideous colour scheme, what with his hair and the moped – asked me if I wanted a lift on his pillion. Did I heck. The bugger is married too.

The boys and I got the better of that mealy-mouthed punk years ago. I would have been thirteenish at the time. I had accompanied the brothers on a mission up Stock Lane to gather hay for our rabbits' hutch. We were returning with a sackful, managing to tow it and shoulder it. We rounded a corner by Bluebell Wood and there was Scuddy Boy and another twerp straddling the field gate, eyeing us menacingly. They lurched at my little brothers and started pushing and cuffing them for no good reason. I became incensed and kicked at Scuddy's shins. He then elbowed me which made me hellish mad, but I got him when he turned his back on me. I lifted the sack of hay and dumped it over his head. He was caught completely by surprise. I had him well and truly beaten. I grappled with him and tugged the sack down past his shoulders. In his tomb I could hear him coughing and spluttering, but I held onto the sack resolutely. Okay, I'm not saying the hay didn't all fall out. Ally held on for dear life to Scuddy's pal's pullover with him still in it. Dave gave Scuddy a punch in the belly and with that attended to it was time to scarper. The three of us took to our heels and belted up the lane. We stopped for a last look over our shoulders, and there was Scuddy reeling about with the sack over his head very near the edge of a ditch (we told friends he had fallen in), flailing his arms thinking, maybe, his helpful friend was us. Bloody scarecrow! It was worth losing the hay, but our poor rabbits had to make do with just sawdust for a while.

We surely did love our rabbits. I remember the day I brought them home in a cardboard box, knowing full well Sooty was male and Bobtail was female, because I had been shown, but I informed Mum and Dad they were two of a kind. I told them later anyone could make a mistake. They said Rish looked like a boy when she was a baby, and Alan was too pretty to be a boy. We were naughty though, as we left it to Pops to clean out their hutch of currants. (Guinea pigs did sultanas Ally said.) Sooty was a grumpy old so and so. If we picked him up he would punch and butt us, and do the dog paddle for all he was worth whilst we held him in our arms. Bobtail, on the other hand, was docile and she would snooze as we cradled her. Dad was a gem and built them a big wire pen on the lawn. They were happy in there and got so frisky they sometimes jumped clean over the top and went bounding across the garden on the nibble. Pops had to fit a mesh canopy to the framework to keep them in.

Bobtail had one lot of babies before she died and we kept one, our Thumper. What a charmer she was, and it was no wonder Sooty fell for her and gave her babies upon babies. Out of the dozens born to her there was one runt we loved best. The poor little scallywag was cruelly deformed with no back legs, but the colour of its coat was beautiful silver grey, whilst the others in the tribe were salt and pepper. This tiny dot had the courage of a lion and tried and tried to hop like its brothers and sisters, but couldn't. Thumper had no time for it. Sooty totally ignored all his offspring. Only we cared, but Dad had to take Silver to the Dogs Home to be put to sleep even though we begged him not to. By careful elimination we chose good homes for the remaining babies.

Thumper was still young when she died. It was horrible to see the life going out of her. I had left for school that morning knowing she was on her last legs. I was home again within the hour, because when I got there I pretended I felt ill, went to see Nurse and was sent home. For a while I sat watching her panting, as she lay on her soft duster, but I got upset so left her alone in the shed and kept going out every five minutes to check on her, until I looked in once and found she wasn't breathing. I made myself ill that day and would have been better off at school.

Sooty we had for many years after Thumper died. He didn't want the likes of us to bother him, and was content to sit and doze day in day out. His eyes got weepy, but when Dad undertook to bathe them he got clawed. Sooty died of old age peacefully one night. I do have a conscience. Towards the end of his days he lived in wretched squalour. We should have emptied the refuse far more often than we did. Dad reprimanded us, but he may as well have talked to a brick wall. The wood of Sooty's hutch was rotting with damp from his toilet, which must have upset him, but he never went hungry – a poor consolation. We missed him most and we buried him fittingly. The other two we had wrapped in sacking before they went to their graves. Sooty had a cotton wool bed in a shoe box. Stones we put round each grave and mounted crosses. I hope the graves have been well cared for by those who came after us. We also laid a sparrow to rest next to our rabbits. A cat had started to paw and play with it after gashing its throat. We couldn't revive it with water and brandy. Dead rats found at the bottom of the garden we didn't trouble to dig graves for. They weren't pretty. Dad got rid of them, because he put poison down as the pest man advised. Mole tumps came up in the lawn, but lucky for them they didn't stay long before burrowing elsewhere. Lucky for Pops too, he's such a softie he couldn't have killed them.

How we four kids did love our weekly trip to the cinema with Mum, if the film being shown permitted us to view. Telly wasn't thought of then in our house. We would rush home from school, gobble tea, and make Mum's legs go faster than they could carry her on our way to the picture house. Once she wished she hadn't been such a pleasing Mum when she had four sobbers on her hands. The distress we felt during that film 'Old Yeller', as the old dog died.

I do like films. Lin and I admit to having seen 'Sound of Music' at least four times, probably eight. Christopher Plummer sends me. Day-dreaming of stardom I once said to Tritz I could just see myself as Julie Andrews, running up a mountainside, flinging my arms wide and singing 'The Hills are Alive'. Tritz threw cold water on my aspirations. "Ern" she said, "after running up a ruddy great mountain, you'd collapse in a heap and be too breathless to manage a whisper, let alone vibrate your tonsils".

But to go back to our cinema visits with Mum. Without fail, they finished up with the sulks. We weren't content to see the films through once. Always we wanted to stay for the second showing. Mum escorted three angry children out with her, but left one cross child sitting alone in the dark. Me. At first I unyieldingly sat tight, expecting Mum and the three others to come back in and sit down again, but let a few minutes go by and I would flounce out and hurry after them. Immediately I had the four in sight I slowed down and lagged behind on the way home, calling Mum all the names under the sun. Later on I did remain in the cinema on my tod to see certain films through a second time. Warnings about men didn't put me off. I was oblivious to everything but the screen, and it's doubtful I would have noticed a hand on my knee had one chanced that way. In one week I went to the Ritz three times to see 'Seven Brides for Seven Brothers', trying to decide which brother was the nicest.

I do, however, remember most the time Rish, at fifteen, took Dave, Al and me to the cinema. An A certificate was showing. We knew she was supposed to be sixteen to get us in, but we kept on badgering her to take us, and that if the lady in the paybooth queried her age she was to say sixteen. Rish said she would, but when we got there and she was asked Rish coloured up and went and said she was only fifteen and we weren't allowed in. We were furious with her and called her a chicken hearted, lily livered, yellow bellied ninny, a cowardy custard, and that she was frightened to fib and that she was just plain 'orrible. She was, I believe, near to tears, not because of our ridiculing and chastising, but because despairingly she had wanted to see the film too. Then her rotten friend Marg, who was sixteen, came along with Nid (Enid) and she went in the Ritz with them and left us three to go home by ourselves. We walked into the house crying through temper. The boys and I hated Rish for a day or two, even moreso when she said it had been a really good film, which needled us further.

I OWE GRANNY TUPPENCE
(International Order of Good Templars)

Instead of joining a youth club, Rish and her friends and me and mine joined the Band of Hope. For a couple of hours on a Thursday evening we young ones went to Temple in the church hall, which was followed by Lodge for the old people. They had taken the oath, the pledge rather, not to touch the drunkard's drink. At a certain age we girls were approached with regard to being initiated into the Lodge. Some girls did, some girls didn't. I gave a polite refusal. We did enjoy our Thursday club nights. Rish and the older girls arranged games, perhaps Bingo, a Beetle Drive, and Blind Man's Buff, Pass a Cotton Reel or Hunt the Thimble. We also had our own meetings where Rish read the Minutes from the previous week, as she was the Hon Sec. We would often stay for the Lodge sessions. We lived in hope that we would learn or overhear the whispered password, but we never did.

I won't forget in a hurry the night we performed Sleeping Beauty in front of the Lodge members. We practised to perfection for our debut. The younger girls had parts and the older ones directed and made costumes. We were an outstanding success, though I say so myself. I felt I had one of the leading roles, the witch. It was definitely me and I revelled in it. Deep down I hadn't forgotten an incident at school when I was about thirteen. In a French lesson members of the class had acted a play. I had been selected to take part and turned down by teacher, because she said I was too quiet and couldn't project my voice, nor pronounce that bloody armchair word, fauteuil. That hurt my feelings terribly.

However, my chance had come again, a bigger and better chance to act. My witch's costume consisted of a pointed hat made from newspaper painted black, and yards and yards of dark brown material we'd found in the understairs cupboard at home, which had to be wrapped round me and stitched to hold. Sacking was my shawl. Pops made me a broom and I wore his gigantic hob nailed boots. For a giggle, and egged on by my friends, I wore the boots down to the club and created quite a traffic jam shuffling across the main road, sweeping as I went. Rish and her roguish friends, Fran and Marg, went to town on my face, though they really didn't need to. It was whitened with chalk rubbings (a piece swiped from school no doubt) and joke warts and inflamed pimples were stuck on with one, of course, resting on the tip of my nose. Wrinkles were etched in deep ridges across my forehead and chin. A convincing moustache was deftly sketched on. Brows were thickened and made to meet in the middle. My eyes were encircled in black, and to finish me off, bright red lipstick was smeared well over my natural lip outline and fever spots of rouge were emblazoned elsewhere with gay abandonment. That was my face. My hair, being long, was back-combed by countless pairs of hands. When one pair began to ache another pair took over. My hat was clipped on and then strands of matted hair were pulled from under it, to lie horizontal out of my head. I was indeed knotted. The final touch was made. Paper claws were glued over my nails. Sleeping Beauty was a very pretty girl. Her make-up took five minutes.

My grand entrance nearly caused one or two pensioners to fall off their chairs. I was worried for them. I was supposed to swoop in amongst them on my broomstick. Instead I, Witch Cruella, scuffed in slowly because of Pop's outsize boots, with the broom cocked between my legs. I didn't forget to hee hee hee and cackle. Mrs. Jones distinctly blanched, which was the reaction I had hoped for. I lost my fake nails, but we didn't lose any of the old people through heart failure. We excelled ourselves and we did take an encore, because the old boys began stamping their feet and the floorboards weren't that strong. After the play my dear friend Mr. Williams was glad to see me as me with a red scrubbed face, although still outrageous hair-style.

We then gave a concert. I conducted the girls as they sang. Envious I was of their bell like voices, but as I've been blessed with a windpipe that is out of tune, I knew my place was up front of them with my pencil, conducting after a fashion. That night at Temple was Sarah's night without a doubt. She was a super star. She sang 'Wooden Heart', Elvis's old song from 'G.I. Blues'. She had a husky voice and we were all visibly moved, so much so that tears of emotion had to be wiped away from some of the old folks' eyes. She curtsied and bowed and then came running off the stage, stopping only to do her high kick in the air, clicking her heels whilst she was up there. She was always performing acrobatics for us: somersaults and such like. A midget Sarah may have been, but whomever she met took to her. Her gaiety was spontaneous. It must be eight or nine years now since she moved to Cornwall. It's sad to say we've lost touch other than Christmas cards.

One night we good Templars had an outing to the main Fire Station at Bridewell. As we were shown round the alarm went off and we jumped out of our skins. A quiet authoritative voice said, "Stand back if you please", so we did. But it just so happened I stepped back directly under the hole in the ceiling through which the 'greased' pole extended. If I hadn't been quickly hustled out of the way, I would have had a fireman sitting on my shoulders.

We became Ladies in Waiting to the Temperance Queen, travelling to functions held throughout Bristol doing our duty as her attendants. There were six of us. Mum won't part with our long white dresses, Rish's and mine, with the lilac braiding Mrs. Williams made for us. They hang lifeless in the wardrobe. I suppose they would be midi on us now. The pomp and ceremony of being on show to the public we gloried in, but I didn't particularly like walking up the aisle towards the stage behind our Temperance Queen. I'm not one to walk at a snail's pace and, if I didn't overtake the Queen, I usually made it to the stage at exactly the same time as her, and had to be reined in. Once the Queen was rooted to the spot. We wondered why and then realisation dawned. My feet were preventing her from continuing, because they were planted on her train. A chance remark I overheard later had me almost handing in my notice. The Queen was asked what fairy elephant had been tramping over her train. When seated on the dais, overlooking mere serfs who had come to pay homage, we wallowed in the attention paid to us. We ignored the wooden creaking stages in the draughty church halls, the woodworm chairs with raised nails on which we sat bolt upright, the piano thundering next to us causing lug-hole damage I'll be bound. These minor discomforts did nothing to mar the honour bestowed on us. We knew we had a sumptuous banqueting tea after the service and speeches with thanks to us for coming.

The happiest affairs though were the annual money-raising processions through the streets of Kingswood. I.O.G.T. Queens and attendants came from miles around with their lorries and, my goodness, weren't those lorries a sight to behold, bedecked in flowers, coloured crepe paper, balloons, streamers and even confetti. (But no men sat on the lorries. Kings didn't exist.) We put faces on painstakingly, dolled ourselves up in our finery and climbed aboard our lorry, after which inch by inch we crept through the town centre waving to the swarms of people, mostly Saturday afternoon shoppers and barely a dozen who had come specially to see us. The trouble was how to look composed sat on rickety old chairs balanced on an unstable lorry that had no sides to it. Whenever the driver swerved round a corner our chairs slanted perilously near the edge. Nobody did fall into the road, but it was a close call once a year. Following the regal procession, we polished off a gooey tea, changed into ordinary togs and walked to the park where the annual sports events were being held. We mingled, making sure people knew we had been attendants to a Queen that afternoon. Flirts we were too with the boys who recognised us. One we thought was super-duper, because he was good-looking. He followed behind our lorry once on his bike with a gaggle of his pals. In exchange for their winks, the girls and I gave kittenish smiles. That first year we embarked on the lorry he graciously bought me a lolly later on. I felt highly favoured and that is why the following year I got palpitations beforehand, wondering if he would be there again. Utter daftness. Of course he wasn't.

As the girls and I aged we became 'disenchanted' with the Temperance movement. The taste for liquor snapped us up one by one, but I don't believe any of my friends turned into an alcoholic. My sis certainly didn't. Angela and I were the last of the girls to wait on Queen Marg. Being two Angelas, we were referred to in an opening address as the two angels watching over Her Majesty. Load of cobblers. We begged to differ. Wings didn't sprout from our armpits. These days my first-class, framed certificates for passing the International Order of Good Templars exams (or, I Owe Granny Tuppence, as the Order was more commonly known) lie hidden in the closet. I've taken to drink as a sociable gesture.

I nearly forgot. My first boyfriend belonged to the Temperance movement. He had to hold me up the first time he kissed me, because my knees gave way. He was a bit of all right and someone to fill my dreams and waking hours other than Slim and Jess, the two cowpokes from Laramie I fancied. I can't recall how long my crush lasted, but I did get a large boxed card from him on Valentine's Day. I've still got it, a big red heart with an arrow piercing it.

FAMILY PURSUITS AND
LIFE THREATENING INCIDENTS

Once Rish, Frannie and Marg let me accompany them to the Humpty Dumps for a picnic. They were bracken hills near Bath, at their best when Tom Thumbs carpeted them in dazzling yellow splendour. We waved to the London trains as they chuggedy-chugged through the countryside. I didn't approve of having to spend a penny on a secluded spot of ground while Rish stood guard, but as she explained where else was there to go? We couldn't very well flag down a train for the purpose of using a British Rail loo. We walked home in the rain, and got scared coming through a turnip field when the farmer bellowed at us and shook his fist. He seemed to be coming after us at an alarming fast pace, and I had a tightness in my chest as I began steeplechasing over ploughed furrows immediately behind the others. We got away.

I only ever went to one Bristol City v. Bristol Rovers football match with my brothers. I suppose I was thirteen or fourteen. The once was enough. A party of us went. I reckon there were half dozen or so of the lads whom Dave and Al grew up with. What I was doing, the only female tagging along, I have no idea. I expect I was at a loose end that afternoon, and the boys allowed me to go on condition I dressed and acted like one of them. By golly, the whole bunch of supporters turned from Jekyll into Hyde creatures and frightened me out of my wits. I didn't watch the game, as I couldn't take my eyes off the boys, of whom I was one, or supposed to be. Thunderstruck

I was. They were in a frenzy, shrieking, swearing, yelling their heads off, stretching lungs to the utmost, banging on the crash barriers, stomping their feet, flinging their arms wide and all the while alternating between booing and hissing with hoorays and cheer whistling. "Penalty", "Foul" and "Off" whether it meant off side, send him off or f off, were the most common words used apart from the other unmentionables. At times it was an en masse love-in with practically men only taking part, a clutch of them being real slobber chops with their delighted hugs and rapturous faces aglow when a goal was scored. If the opposition scored it was a different matter altogether. An elbow went in the ribs of the nearest rival team supporter, as long as he was pint-sized. He was so elated he was immune to pain or anger at that moment.

Only Big-Eddie-Girl would take on absolutely anyone from the other side. Edwin is the first blue and white striped man in his knitted bobble hat and ankle length scarf to charge onto the pitch at the end of a match to congratulate his team, win or lose. Woe betide anyone in his path, especially if they're adorned in opposing colours. He was up before a magistrate not so long ago for unruly conduct on the pitch – clouting the ref with his rattle. He's harmless really. I believe he's married now to his Brendal.

To go back to that match, glad I was when it was over, to have Dave, Al and their mates revert back to some semblance of normality. I can remember to this day running for all I was worth in and out of the teeming crowds, bumping into several grumblers as the ground emptied, in a vain effort to keep up with the boys' legs. We had to get to the special bus before the rest of the mob to grab seats. I couldn't hurtle along as fast as the boys and slowed up to take a breath. As I did so a dirty dog, old enough to be Dad, pinched my bum. I was astounded. How dare he! Hurt and angry I went tearing off in pursuit of the brothers. When I caught up with them, on the bus, I indignantly told them I had been got at in broad daylight and it truly wasn't the seat of my trousers that had been pinched, but my rear. Dave didn't care an h'apeth, and he merely remarked, "Did he give it back?" First thing I did when I got home was to lower my trousers and hunt for a red mark in the mirror. Mhmm, I've not been plucked at in the same way since. Shame.

I've been dropped on my head though. Rish gave me a Black Pudding. I had my legs round her neck, she had hold of my wrists, and was supposed to throw me up in the air and catch me. But something went wrong. My head met concrete and it was zzzz for Pange. I woke up hours later in the boys' bed. Mum had put clean sheets in my bed and didn't want me being sick over them. I felt terrible, but angry, as I had missed going to a matinee with the girls. Mum says she will never forget the sickening thud the moment my skull crashed to the path. I'm hard though, because my brains didn't spill out. The family say I've not been right since.

Then there was the time Dad became a Chinaman. He was stricken with severe yellow jaundice in our childhood. Rats at the bottom of the garden were to blame, or their fleas. The four of us were quite upset the day he got carted off to hospital and we couldn't laugh at his colour any more. He was gone from home for weeks, and Mum ruled the roost with an iron hand when it was called for. Lots of postcards and letters came from the Railwaymen's Convalescent Home in Kent. His homecoming was a hundred times better than any Christmas. We were jubilant and we climbed all over him and wouldn't leave him alone. Mum didn't have a look-in. We had presents and our first taste of pomegranate. He came home via London and bought one off a barrow outside Paddington Station where, as a lad, he started on the footplate.

I belong to an ulcerated family what with one and another of them. There was the time Mum went round for days, trying to carry on as normal, and didn't tell anyone her stomach ulcer had burst. We nearly lost her. She was rushed into hospital with just a few pints of blood left in her. It was a little after 4pm when the ambulance came and the stretcher-bearers took her away from us. The school children, on their way home, stopped in their tracks and stared from across the other side of the road. We didn't realise Mum was in danger, but it wasn't a pleasant feeling watching the ambulance speed away, and to hear its bell ring fainter and fainter. I hate that sound. If an ambulance does pass me in an all-fired hurry, I silently say, "Please God let them be alright". Millions of people say the same thing, of course they do. Horrid kids really we were, because with Mum in hospital Mrs. Stew next door (It was never Stewart. Mum shortened names, like Mrs. Peg was actually Mrs. Peglar) gave us tea each night and she had a telly. Best night was 'Boots and Saddles' night. Four impatient kids, with ears pricked, would be eagerly awaiting her knock on the door. Dave and Al fought as to who would peep round the curtains looking out the window for her. But they could be excused their delighted "Psst, she's coming" the minute Mrs. Stew's door opened. Very excited, we would file shyly into her house, devour delish beans on toast or poached egg, which tasted heaps better than Mum's, then watch with enormous goggle-eyes at an unbelievable box called a telly. We got in a mood when Dad came back from visiting Mum in hospital, and collected us from Mrs. Stew's. We were four whiners stepping through the two-strand wire fence separating the houses. Invariably a wire rebounded on someone's nose or leg to start a "You did that on purpose" rumpus.

I mustn't say we didn't want Mum home, that wouldn't be true, and we did gyrate like mad when she came, but sadly no more telly nights in Mrs. Stew's. Mum did say, just the other day, that she hadn't precisely wanted to come home to us when she did. She was discharged for Christmas, but would genuinely have liked to spend it in hospital, which she said would have been lovely, and there was a tree at the bottom of her bed. I told her she was an unfit mother, to be so uncaring of her winkies' plight being motherless at Christmas. Dave gave her a warning, be loving towards us or he would report her even now to the N.S.P.C.C.

I don't suppose Mum minded being rid of us for a spell. Our pranks must have driven her and Dad scatty at times. Dad had infinite patience, but once he chased naughty Alan up the stairs. It was so rare to see Dad in a raging temper. Mum was scared of what he might do, and we three kids sat downstairs sobbing, because we thought Al was going to be killed. Not Al! He locked himself in the bathroom. He said he even crouched down inside the bath, fearful that Pops was going to break the door down.

Dave got knocked off his chair too for back answering, but this is the only time I can remember Dad's hand being raised. I don't recall, but he did say I got a smack from him once, on account of me hitting a child whose mother complained. That was spiteful of me.

I made strife at times I know I did. Dad bought the boys a weekly cowboy and Indian or war picture story-book. They cost a shilling and the boys had one each. I wasn't supposed to read them until they had finished with them, or it caused rows and friction. Attempted bribery didn't always work. But then Dave often read our weekly Girl comic before we did. He recently brought up the names Miss Tantrum, Miss

Beak and Lettuce Leaf who appeared in the comic. I had forgotten about them, but not our Dave.

We used to get a shilling pocket money until we reached our teens, then Dad raised it to half a crown. Ally, last in line, said it wasn't fair that Dave and I were getting half a crown and he only a shilling, so Pop indulged him and he had a rise before he was rightly due.

I was scared of Dad's reaction to my behaviour regarding one incident. During an afternoon's play I had a barney with a girl in the Crescent. Her Mum came out and interfered, so I snapped, "For crying out loud, go and do your washing up and let us get on with it." For my cheek she declared she would be down to see Dad. I instantly got the wind up, but I didn't apologise. She had no right to back up her daughter, making it two onto one. Also she wasn't a party to what went on. However, I was upset when I told Dad he could expect a visitor, but Mrs. T never came. Leastways I don't think she did. It's best I don't remember what my punishment was. Mum was the main crime fighter. The times ever we have side-stepped her and fled with "I'll box your ears when I catch hold of you" spurring us on.

I do love Weston-Super-Mare. It's my get-away-from-it-all place, most favoured by me out of season when the wind blows, and the sea is rough, and the sands are devoid of people. My love for it grew when I was a nipper, and Mum and Dad would take us there on day trips in the summer. One such day I made us miss the train home, simply because I refused point blank to move myself off the beach until Dad had bought me a bag of winkles. I don't know what got into me for being such an obstinate toad, but though I got a telling off and a threatened pasting when we got home, I kept right on squawking for those winkles. Dad relented, muttering, "For pity's sake, give me strength". It seemed there was no other way to shut me up. I had winkles thrust at me, and a "You wait my girl when we get home" threat from Mum. Unfortunately, I couldn't get the hang of digging the perishers out of their shells with the pin supplied, and wasted most of them. Rish endeavoured to show me how it was done, and popped one into her mouth, which started me off on my convulsions again.

I wasn't the only nuisance. Who, on the pier screamed, "I feel sick" when we were perched right at the top of the Big Wheel? The operator had to bring us down specially to let Rishnald get off and be sick. Ooh she did madden me, because I had to get out of the basket too. Mum said so. She wouldn't let Dave take Rish's place, and Dave didn't particularly want to. Lin did the very same thing to me when I went on the darn thing with her years and years later, yet she had been perfectly all right on the Figure Eight. She wouldn't come on the helter-skelter with me. I enjoyed that after a false start. The mat went without me, and I had to go down umpteen steps to get another one.

Without fail we, as a family, had a daily excursion to London every summer. One of the day's highlights was at Paddington Station. Dad invariably knew the driver of our loco, and we kids got lifted up into the cab on the hot plate with him. Those were the old steam days, not diesel rubbish. There's a photo I came across the other day of Rish, Dave, Al and me in Hyde Park. We've got awful squints to prove the sun shone in those days. One year, when the family was sitting on benches in Hyde Park eating sandwiches, we heard rustling and peculiar noises coming from the bushes. Dad pulled them aside and there was a grisly sight confronting us. A ragamuffin boy, clad in tatters, was slitting the throat of a duck. He flicked his wicked penknife in Dad's direction too before running off. Dave can remember the four of us getting on an escalator in a busy London store without Mum and Dad. We reached the top in tears, thinking we were lost for evermore and that we would never see them again.

Of course, Dad is a Cockney. He was an orphan raised by Aunt Madge and Uncle Gus who were stricter than jailers. He ran away from home once. He got as far as Birmingham and spent the night on a park bench, before returning to Forest Hill and suffering the consequences.

It was the last family trip to London that made Mum jealous. I should say it was coming home from there on the train. Being a very late one, it was jam-packed solid and we had to squeeze into carriages wherever space permitted. Ally, who was about thirteen at the time, managed to bag a seat and he fell asleep with his head resting on the shoulder of a middle-aged woman sat beside him. Mum got to hear of it, peeked in to see and was quite distraught to see her baby with another woman.

A further pleasure trip we had every year was to spend a day at Weymouth. We loved the sea and sand, except when it got in our egg sandwiches and we scrunched. Railway Stations smell like egg sandwiches to my mind. There was the time Rish and her then boyfriend Bob, now her husband, took Dave, Ally-Wally and me to Weymouth for the day in Bob's little Mini. It didn't turn out too well for Pange. Firstly, on the ride down I was car-sick. Luckily Rish had a skirt with her I could change into. Later that day I went on the Wild Mouse with the boys and, unbeknown to me, I split it right down my backside. Rish, Bob and the boys brought it to my attention only when I questioned the lot of them as to what was the big joke. Rish thought it funny at the time, but not when we got home and she realised the skirt was way beyond repair. I wasn't a good sister to Rish. I wore her clothes on a regular basis without asking or telling her. Often, when I came home late, after being out with girlfriends, she was parked outside in the Mini snogging with Bob. I would dash indoors, yelling "Quick" to Mum, "unzip me", "unhook me" or "unbutton me", grapple with and unravel myself out of a piece of her clothing, throw it behind a cushion and quickly don anything close at hand, whether it be Mum's, Dad's, the boys' or my own, as long as it wasn't her's, the exact moment she turned her key in the lock. She regularly caught me at it, or would be bound to find out later when she espied busted seams. She should have been my size.

The first and last holiday we ever had as children was at Weymouth, and it's a cherished memory to this day. At dead of night one evening Mum and Dad roused us from our bunk beds in the caravan, bundled us up in warm clothes, and took us out in a gale to the highest shelf of pebbles on Chesil Beach to witness a stormy sea. It was an amazing sight, but Al over-elaborated to his school chums the following week, by saying he had been in a hurricane, a tornado and a tycoon. He had overheard us saying it was like these things. Mum and Dad hired a transistor radio from the caravan site office, so that we wouldn't miss Pick of the Pops on Sunday afternoon. Week after week Rish religiously wrote down the Top Twenty charts as they were played on that programme. She did it for years.

Mum, Dad and Al went to Weymouth for a week's holiday a few years ago in Mrs. Hugo's caravan. Twice, the plug blew out of the kettle while they were away, and I had to run up the road with it for Lin's Dad to mend. I gave Dave a chop one tea-time, which spurted blood when he pierced it with his fork.

That time when Rish went to Switzerland with the school for a two week holiday and the three of us wrote letters, along with drawings of monsters which were supposed to represent her. I know I started my letter "Dear Rosinald" and wrote, "We are missing you (don't hurry home)". Dave wrote, "Hope the weather is fine and you're getting burnt". What an unkind lot. Dave and I both told her we were collecting feathers from the beds. How weird is that! Ally, who must have been eight, copied Dave's letter word for word. Dave, Al and I finished off our letters by saying, "Don't forget my present". She cried when she received our letters with a nice one from Pop. Not because we had upset her, but because we had made her homesick.

I've still got the cave man on my dressing table which Al gave me twelve years ago. It was a present he brought back from a holiday he had when he was about eight years old with a friend's family. That flaming, red haired cave man with the hypnotic eyes is shocking, as underneath his loincloth there's a naughty little Wilfrid. I remember the postcard Al sent us during that week. He signed on the bottom "Trerio, love Alan". He hadn't come across Cheerio before to know how it was spelt. Often, as he goes through the door, we yell out in unison "Trerio Al, spelt T-R-E-R-I-O", goading A-rabs that we are. We do get threatened with a biff up the bracket.

And how can I forget Al and his "What's this?" He walked into the front room once, when we were all seated there, Blob as well – and Rish wasn't even engaged to him then – holding aloft one of her Tampax. Mum fobbed him off with an outlandish story about it being a plug for nosebleeds, which satisfied his curiosity. Mishaps do occur with Women's oogies. I shouldn't call them oogies. One day I forgot myself and asked for a packet of oogies in the chemist. A little boy Des knew walked into a family gathering wearing two sanitary towel ear-rings. Then there was the youngster playing Doctors in the street with one across his mouth, hooked onto his ears. Barbie used to take her Mum's box of towels when she was small, go out in the garden, search for straight twigs and make hammocks for her dolls.

BACK TO SCHOOL DAYS

Tritz called for me in the mornings on her way to school. Her timing was perfect. She caught me most days as I was brushing my teeth in the kitchen – we keep our toothbrushes in the kitchen – and proceeded to make me laugh while the water was swooshing round my mouth.

On one occasion I was standing over the kitchen sink washing my hair, clad in just my undies, when Mrs. Stew's young nephew let himself in the back door and asked where Al was. I couldn't get rid of him. He was at the inquisitive age, and he didn't have a sister.

I was hardly a pretty sight setting off for school. For starters, turning over the waistband several times shortened my skirt. It didn't matter that the pleats didn't hang right. I wore a man's pullover (House Mistress gave me a ticking off practically every day, because it was black and not regulation navy blue) and if this were stretched my skirt would ride up a trifle more. In the end my jumper came way down over my hindquarters, and roughly six inches of skirt could be seen. When thick red stockings were introduced at school I'm sure I was the only girl to feel jubilation. They weren't compulsory, but I had a pair. It meant no more hairy legs on show to the public, and therefore no more titters from piggish boys. That was before my defuzzing days. Berets were frowned upon. We wore them only when the Senior Mistress created a stink, as she did from time to time. Boys at school pulled out the stalks in the middle, leaving a draughty hole. Mums were none too pleased, and could hardly be expected to believe moths ran riot in school cloakrooms. Boys were a cussed nuisance. A group would sit quietly behind girls on the school bus, and when the poor unfortunate creatures got up from their seats, their heads nearly broke off. Mackintosh hoods had been tied onto the back of the seat rail. Hoods could quite easily be ripped off in this way, plus wrenched necks.

The girls in my year developed a curious fixation in their noddles about disliking showers. Me too. We tried any way we could to get out of having one. Body shy perhaps, because we were either lumpy or ribby in those days, and some of us haven't altered much over the years. Our usual weekly excuse was a period. I can't think why the Games Mistress didn't recommend we all be put on the Pill to regulate us, as her marking book was a riot of Ps and very few ticks – the ticks meant we had been under the taps. She cottoned on, of course, and told us we would have been dead through chronic anaemia long ago if her marking book spoke the truth, so into the showers we were ordered. That is, our big toes went under the taps. Towels remained knotted securely around beefcake and fleshless bones. Hands were cupped together, and water collected therein could be thrown into faces, giving the impression we had walked through the Falls. There was an oddball girl in school we nicknamed Jez, short for Jezebel. She would parade through the changerooms showing off her tattooed chest. One couldn't help but look.

I knocked the Games Mistress down due to a mishap. Tritz thought it extremely comical. It was a freezing cold afternoon with snow on the ground, and we had been led on a brisk walk to Victory Park. The hill in the park is awfully steep. It had iced over and I slid on my feet from top to bottom without stopping. I was beginning to think I was going to go on and on, right out of the park, until Miss, realising I had no brakes, valiantly stood blocking my path and whoosh, off balance she went, sent flying by Speedo. We ended up two collapsed heaps with plaited legs on the wet ground together.

How could I forget the music room incident in school? Thinking back, it was a wet afternoon and we weren't permitted on the courts to play netball, which was a good thing Terence said. Ern, moi, wouldn't be able to fall down. (True, I was useful in netball, because I was tall and could jump to a great height, but I couldn't land properly. My bottom made it to the ground before my feet.) So on this particular day we were shepherded into the school hall to execute ludicrous physical jerks. We also had to become Trolls and dance and express ourselves to the music of Peer Gynt. We thought it was soppy and stupid, and it embarrassed us to act so ridiculous. Terence wasn't having any of this, and excused herself by saying she had a music lesson, which was acceptable. I thought "Blow this for a lark" so stealthily I slunk away too, while the others got into the swing of things, and joined Terence down the music room. She said she had been expecting me. Of course, Terence was an excellent fiddler, no doubt about it, and was one of Mr. White's star pupils. The particular music room we had both made for was a practice room, roughly four feet by eight feet. Tritz had no intention of fiddling that afternoon. We were going to have a good old gossip about everything and everybody, but she thought she had better get her viola in case of prowlers. She did. We began our chin-wag. Suddenly footsteps could be heard approaching, and we could tell they were manly ones. In fact they belonged to Mr. White, the music master. We could figure that out, because he wore recognisable steel tips. Quick as a flash Tritz propelled me behind the door and told me not to breathe. She picked up her bow and fiddle and began playing furiously like a demented thing. I would have laughed, had I not been cringing. I just knew it was going to happen. The door opened and I was flattened good and proper all the way down. He was blameless. He knew instantly by Terri's face, and by the fact that the door had a wedge, which hadn't previously been there, that she was not alone. "Come out, come out, whoever you are" said he and out I sheepishly came. Aha, it's come to me, how I lost my dubs! Mr. White wasn't too displeased. Naturally he didn't believe I was Terence's music stand. She should never have said I was. I was let off lightly on condition I joined the choir. I said I would, but didn't for the sake of the choir's reputation.

Dad's one regret is that none of us inherited a desire to play an instrument. Pops had a brilliant future mapped out for himself years ago, playing the violin. He won a scholarship to Crystal Palace, but didn't go because the Railway meant a weekly pay packet, and it was needed at Gran's where he lived. He still has his accordion up in the attic, a beautiful instrument inlaid with mother of pearl. He couldn't play it now, even if he wanted to. The locks on its case have rusted and need to be broken open. Although not musical we four kids were arty besides being crafty. Like Pop we could draw reasonably well. Dad has, however, always taken a keen interest in Tritz's musical ability. With hubby Rob's backing, she is at present learning to play the organ.

My first period came during a music lesson at school. I didn't go to bed for a week like a girl we knew who thought she was dying, but I went uncharacteristically quiet the first day and wouldn't budge from the chair all evening.

Miss Min Cream came to teach in our last years at school. She looked as though she should have retired half a century before. Trash gave her the nickname of Min Cream, that toilet bowl cleaner, because she used it for her scent. This is what Trash's nose detected.

One rather bleak day my Geography class went for a trek across the Mendip Hills. That is we started off at Point A and Taffy, our teacher, gave us instructions as to how to arrive at Point B. He would meet us there at such and such a time. Full of confidence, the boys plotted a map and off we went at the double. The dopey boys went at breakneck speed. We girls had a terrible time trying to keep up with them. An hour went by and Fowl and I found it impossible to stand the pace. Our sturdy but tired pins were lagging further and further behind until, we couldn't believe our eyes, the boys and the crazy other girls had disappeared from view altogether. That finished us off. We imagined search parties, tracker dogs, the lot. They would find us by nightfall surely. On the other hand, what if they didn't? As we couldn't have dragged ourselves another inch, we sat down on a boulder for a long rest. We laughed nervously as we unlaced our bumpers for a breather. Tweaking our toes, it did cross our minds that if we used our common gump we might get out of that wilderness alive. Make for a road or farmhouse was an obvious move and, after a few circular attempts, we found both together. We began sauntering the road without a clue as to which direction we were headed in, and where it would bring us. For five minutes, no more, we tramped the road then, who should come driving along, going the opposite way to us, none other than Taffy! Now there's a gentleman for you. He thumbed us into the back seat – I won't say what he called us – and we arrived at Point B way ahead of the rest. Truth be told, Fowl and I must have been the brains of the class. I can't think why I failed Geography 'O' Level. Fowl and I sniggered when the weary band of travellers caught sight of us fresh daisies at Point B. Mouths fell disbelievingly open. Dumbfounded they were. They had left us for dead, but they were deader than us. The thing that marred Fowl's joy and mine was that they flopped down on the grass to eat and drink their refreshments. We had had ours at our earlier resting place. Next day most of the boys, and me, were off school with tender cherry blisters in need of popping. Taff didn't like it. In his next Geography lesson the shirkers (I was the only girl) were ordered to the front of the class and he gave us a flaying with words. The boys didn't blush, merely smirked, but I made up for the lot of 'em.

Sarah, Terri and I did that Mendip walk by ourselves afterwards. I can't imagine how we achieved our goal. They weren't in my Geography class and therefore hadn't been on the previous walk, so they relied on my sniffer, skills and memory. Although we may have walked twice as far, for twice as long as was really necessary, and we did have a number of sitdowns, we came upon Point B as dusk was settling, quite by chance.

One day we had a current affairs lesson from a new teacher, a man who had lived on the equator. He told us to write about Telstar. I was at a complete loss and hadn't a clue what it was even, because I hadn't listened to or read the News for weeks. Bone idleness I suppose. I felt ashamed and panic stricken, but Tritz helped me out with whispers.

I don't know where Terence got to one lesson, but she was later in arriving than she realised. We were seated at our desks and Shark, as haughty as ever, was addressing us when Terence appeared on the scene. What a grand entrance she made. You see she didn't twig the lesson had already begun, and that Shark was in the room. As she opened the classroom door, she let it be known "Here I am fans", and at the same time gave a fantastic ballet leap across the width of the room, satchel and all. She had had ballet lessons and knew her stuff did Terence. She nearly ended up in Shark's arms. He wasn't a bad sort. Much to Tritz's embarrassment, he made her go out and come in doing it again.

Friday afternoons! By golly, but they did put the fear of God into us. Our lot was one library lesson, followed by a double lesson of chemistry. Library was okay, but it was difficult to concentrate on reading a good book about a wild stallion when I, and others like me, had shredded nerves. We were that way inclined, because soon we knew we would be spending a couple of hours with the worst teacher in the school. It was generally accepted that he was a tyrant besides being a Welsh nit. Usually in the Library I wandered from bookshelf to bookshelf passing notes or word of mouth messages between the lovers – Tritz and her current beau. Then, when the bell clanged announcing end of lesson, we walked the corridors in a deathly hush to the chemistry lab. Gosh Slime did rant and rave at us. He was without doubt a sulky brute of a man. It was so obvious that he picked on his Youngers. Boys were jostled into his small chemical room if they answered a question wrongly and, with bated breath, we, in the adjoining classroom, waited to hear the whack of the slipper and the customary "Ouch". (Both my brothers he slippered.) He wasn't merciful with the girls either. Knuckles were ruler rapped, chalk stubs were thrown, or he would give a menacing glare and yackety-yak on and on about our infinite dumbness. The odd thing was I held him in such awe, I made myself a wizard at Chemistry, and it became my best subject. That is, until I gave it up in favour of Biology, which I wasn't especially good at, because the other girls in the class did too. Chemical symbols fascinated me and I was all there with my plumbums. The one thing I didn't relish, nor Terence, nor Potty Dotty, was using the Bunsen burner in group experiments. This we left to Sarah. She hardly reached the desktop, but she wielded it as she saw fit and never killed anyone. We would have killed her had she refused to work the thing, because it terrified us. But as I say, we couldn't face years of ugly scenes with Slime, so when we had the choice of carrying on with either Biology or Chemistry every single girl in the class favoured Biology. Tritz, Sarah, Dotty and I were pretty thick at the subject, but the Biological teachers we could stand. There was the Frizzy Lizzie Stork, Teddy Bear whom Terri and I adored, (We went "Ah, isn't he lovely" each time we clapped eyes on him.) and the Colonel. Tritz said the kernel came too close for comfort. He had a paunch, which rubbed against her when they stood conversing. Terence was maybe a little more dense than some at Biology. In 'O' Level she studied a fish and wrote down that it was a baby Cod. In fact it was a stickleback. Ahem, I wrote flowers had pistols. Who's to say it wasn't a slip of the pen. If the marker had looked for a dot, I'm positive he or she could have found one. Terence hated Rob (her hubby) in those Biology lessons. That was during their courting days. In tests he would emphatically not come to her aid.

Methinks I was a shy young thing with regard to having boyfriends at school. They disturbed my peace of mind, so weren't worth bothering with. I can remember liking one boy, a fact I kept entirely to myself, and mooning over him for a reasonable length of time, like four years. There were a dozen boys, well they must have been practically men, in the upper sixth form at school whom my friends and I worshipped from afar. Pointless, because they didn't know we teeny-weenies existed. I was content to be delirious over them and concoct fantastic daydreams of midnight rendezvous with the whole dozen of them. The closest I came to being observed by the dishy head boy was when I had an infected eyeball. It was black, red and yellow and made me look extremely ugly. He asked who had poked me one. I wanted to reply I had a wicked father who repeatedly beat me, so that he would feel "poor thing", but I spluttered instead that a cob of mascara had gone in my eye, and he snorted "muck". I went right off him and preferred deputy head boy for the rest of my numbered, thank goodness, days.

In my last years at school there were two boys who thought I was a bit tasty. One was satisfactory, and true I had a crush on him. A William, but I could call him Bill, and he was clever at Latin, which was of great assistance to Tritz and myself. What a bonkerhead I was. Each time he asked me for a date I was too reserved and stuttery to accept, although I wanted to. Apart from my stammered noes, I even had the audacity to invent a possessed boyfriend, which ultimately killed what could have been something nice. I could have done away with myself for being such a crackpot, and went around for weeks mumbling into my beard "Balderdash, blunderbuss, fiddle-de-dee" (swear words), because I was that mad at, and sorry for myself. I couldn't weep on Terence's shoulder. I stated my case once, and she went into stitches of laughter at my woebegone countenance. She said, "Cheer up Ern, you wouldn't fancy being married to a Box, and giving birth to a lot of little Boxes would you?" He couldn't help his surname could he. I've seen him since leaving school. I came out of a phone box on the Ford Estate wearing rollers and no make-up. He was waiting to go in, wearing a smart suit and having parked a flashy car at the kerbside. I'm glad he didn't (seem to) recognise me, as I had never looked dowdier.

The other boy who said he had affection for me, I felt sorry for. In his presence my blood pressure stayed normal. He was one of Tritz's cast-offs, whom she christened Peach. He came running to me when she threw him over for another, and I felt like his wet nurse. Not that I minded lending my compassionate ear, but Terence rebuked him for his action – he knocked on my front door one evening looking for sympathy – and he didn't ever lean on me again. Tritz knew how to handle fellers. I admired the way she worked. I reckon she had a campaign going, and I helped when I could with planning tactics. She went from one smitten soul onto the next, and in this way she ransacked the whole school, leaving a trail of sorely wounded and conquered hearts behind her, until Rob came along. He stood no nonsense in or out of school. He wouldn't let her copy his Biology homework, and wouldn't allow any more boyfriends. Now of course they're spliced and nothing short of a perfect match.

Terence did fix me up with a blind date once. She and her then boyfriend Harry, Arnie, no it was Mick from school, were to tag along too. I had only condescended to go when she said my boyfriend-to-be didn't belong to our school. I, um, chickened out at the last minute. I'm glad I did. It was intended to be a day's fishing in the middle of nowhere with these two boys. Terence and the girl who took my place went, but the boys didn't show up. They said the rain put them off. I say they forgot. We hadn't had rain for days. I can't remember if Terence forgave them. I expect Mick was dumped and soon replaced.

I almost bypassed Bobby. That would never do. I dated him during late schooldays. I took a chance, because I hadn't clapped eyes on him until we actually met. He lived in the country and saw me walk into Mum's cousin Coral's one day. I was told he was interested. He wrote me. I wrote him. He wrote again asking for a date. I replied yes please, and would he mind if I wore my hair up. What a nincompoop. Back came the letter no, he didn't mind. We met at Keynsham Church. I hadn't expected him to be so large. My heart didn't go pit-a-pat. He took me to his married sister's near the weir and we had cocoa. Then we went to the Bug Hutch and I didn't get to see the film, which annoyed me. I was also upset. I didn't want him to kiss me. He had asthma and I was scared I would catch it. I was gentle about not seeing him for a second date. I didn't mention his sloppy wet kisses. I said it was because he didn't have a car. Ooh, the relief I felt to be shot of him. Tritz sighed and said she despaired of me next day in school.

MINOR AND MAJOR MISHAPS,
(And Being a Little Weird)

Olive! She was a fuddy-duddy bossy spinster at school. Truthfully, I did at all times give of my best in her lessons, because cookery I enjoyed. But, for some reason during the school years, I never felt I pleased her, however hard I worked. Rish shared that feeling, and our two little brothers did too. Perhaps she was envious of our great long surname. She was nothing but a plain old Smith. We were tarred with the same instinct that she didn't like us. Yet we were good kids, quiet, well mannered and behaved, as Pops saw to that. He wouldn't even let us talk Bristolian, and drummed it into us we came from Bristol not Bristle. Neither he nor Mum liked sloppy talk. Olive seemed to pounce on Dave and Al at lunchtimes, and had them dutifully running round as waiters. Their dinners were cold by the time they had served her ladyship, and got the opportunity to sit down and eat. We used to tell Al to pour gravy into her lap. He succeeded with a few drips one day, because she was so fearsome and snappy his hand shook. It beats me because as housemistress she should have been proud of Dave and Al. At house meetings they had their names read aloud every week for unrivalled brilliance on the games field, and they gained many housepoints.

Due to my awkward shyness at school I grew my hair long to hide behind, against Mum's wishes. I wore face powder too, because I thought my blushes would be toned down. (I hate to be told I've gone red, as instantly I go a deeper shade.) Olive summoned me and a friend to her cookery rooms one morning and, in front of a first year class, read the riot act and made us go and wash our visages. We had to return for inspection after. Piffle! We blooming well weren't the only powdered specimens in the school. And any woman with sense knows that washing off make-up with soap and water leaves one looking like streaky bacon. Olive should have provided cream, but no, not her. To boot, she handed me a piece of string and ordered me to tie my hair back. When she left off picking holes in me, I felt hurt and unhappy throughout the rest of the day, and glared daggers behind her back. Not even her words "Now that's better, you've got an attractive face, show it off" could dispel my gloom at having my ears on show. And she had said attractive not pretty.

Another thing too, she commanded me to cut my nails off before a cookery lesson. I forced myself to titter titter with the rest of the class when she ruled that if I didn't, she would lay my fingers down on the chopping board and go at them like she did parsley. At the end of every baking session she said I had more pastry under my nails than I had rolled out. Give her her due. I did wonder where a nail had got to one day, and fortunately it was I who found it in a sausage roll and not another member of the family. Looking back, all I ever seemed to make at school were sausage rolls, lentil soup and soused herrings. Tritz was taster in chief.

One thing I look back on with a smile is the day I received a detention along with Terri, Sarah and Dotty. We were fifteen when it happened. No girl in the top classes got a detention. Not many boys did either. We were the elite, goody goodies of the school, supposed to be eggheads. Terence and I truly did take our schoolwork seriously, and usually we did have an air of quietude about our personage. (Not like Sarah. She was always prancing around the school.) But just this once we went off the rails.

Come to think of it, we were unsavoury louts. Daily the four of us each took four slices of toast and marmite to school for our mid-morning break. On the day in question, it was drizzling with rain and we couldn't be fussed to mosey over to our own houseroom, which was situated in the far wing of the school, so we nipped into the toilets pertaining to a different house. Stupid regulations decreed that one had to visit one's own house toilets. Other houserooms and their loos were out of bounds. Crapola! We locked ourselves in a loo. Glad there wasn't much of Sarah. She stood on the lavvy seat, because her head wasn't visible over the top of the loo cubicle. We proceeded to eat our toast. Crumbs went down the wrong way and we got coughs and giggles. Then tragedy struck. No, Sarah didn't go through the seat, worse than that. There was a subsidence outside. A lull in girlish speech we detected. We could hear too the approach of firmly trodden footsteps. They ceased inches away from our closed lav door. A pounding came on the door, and a thundering voice reverberated off the four walls. "Come out this instance". Even we knew it was instant. Chewing stopped and chomped toast was stored in cheek pouches, but fleeting seconds of alarm over, we began to snigger, because we thought we recognised the voice as that of another friend. Terence spat out "Beat it Jane, you old scraggyneck". Gracious me, an unholy silence met us for a split second, and then the door nearly fell down on us. It did receive a battering. The person outside sounded as though she was having a seizure. The pitch of voice was high and shaky with anger. We stared dumbly at each other and a found, tremulous voice said quietly "That isn't Jane Brazil". A statement of fact we sensed to be true. A seething spluttering came again, demanding we unlock the door. We let the unknown door basher have her say. Evidently we had boobed and it was probably a priggish prefect who had her knickers in a knot. Not to worry. All the same we were ashen when we filed out of our three-foot square cafeteria. Good God! It was enough to make a body faint off. We came face to face with Head Girl, whose name just happened to be Jayne, with a y, and her underling would you believe! Miserable squirts both of them, full of their own importance. She was still steaming, so we let her get on with it, the old windbag. We could tell she wanted to hit us. She had worked herself up into a frightful tizzy. I wanted to flap a towel in her face to simmer her down, but she wouldn't have appreciated my kind gesture. Without asking for a reasonable explanation – I'm sure we could have thought of something – she issued us there and then with detentions in front of several toothy grinning first years. Detentions for disobedience, cheek, rudeness, childish irresponsible behaviour and unspeakably unhygienic manners, plus a thousand and one other black marks against our otherwise spotless characters. We stood and took all those insults, although we would willingly have laid one on her given half a chance. Lord God Almighty didn't speak to us like that, so who the heck did she think she was, throwing her weight around.

When she at last ran out of steam and told us to get lost we did, quick, but breaktime had ended and we were late into next lesson, so that meant a further blot on our copy-books. I'm certain though if snooty pants hadn't let us go when she did, one or other of us would have reached bursting point, because sealed lips were very ticklish. We could hardly wait for the lesson to finish. Eventually it did and Tritz, Sarah, Potty Dotty and I were overcome with laughter bubbles so much so we had to rush down to the same toilets again, as the hysterics got out of hand and our bladders filled rapidly.

The teachers classed a detention as a social stigma, but nobody else thought of it as such except poncey know-all brainies. Well parents too I suppose. A disgrace it may have been, but we didn't think so. Our triumph came the day the detention was confirmed and made public. Friday morning, after school assembly, the names were read out loud and clear of those degrading pupils who had let the school down. A couple of usual weekly names belonging to youths from the bottom classes rang out. Then four unfamiliar degenerates were announced. All from the same class, the top class of the fourth year, and all girls. Ears pricked up, I distinctly saw some, and disbelief flickered over teachers' faces mounted on the platform. There could well have been disgusted mutterings escaping from one or two mouth corners, but our teacher, bless his heart, didn't bat an eyelid. He may have been forewarned. Terence and I couldn't see awfully well, because being well endowed in feet and inches we were positioned at the back of the hall in our rows. But we sensed the reaction up front and around us. Terence and I exchanged knowing smiles. We were slightly pink, but we felt like heroines as girls and boys to our left and right directed their gazes upon us. Teachers were soon walking from the hall and we were dismissed. We left in single file. When it was my turn to about turn and lead my line-up out of assembly, the piano was being hammered and I strode almost jauntily. I couldn't look at anyone though and kept eyes dead ahead, so there must have been an iota of shame in me. Lips were working too, as giggles wanted to emerge.

With one exception we had enjoyed morning service that day. Sarah alas was the outsider. Sarah had squirmed and wanted to dig a hole to crawl into. Being an inchworm and not snakes like Tritz, Dotty and me, her place in assembly was at the extreme front of the hall immediately below the platform. When her name had been curtly disclosed, the teachers' eyes had burned holes into her. Most unfair she said and if looks could kill she would have died twenty times over. There had been Terence, Spotty Dotty and myself grinning like Cheshire cats on the perimeter, whilst Sarah sorrowfully studied her feet in the front row.

What our detention entailed was worse than corporal punishment. We had to stay behind after four o'clock, for an hour and a half on a Friday night, and write at least a four-page essay on Hygiene. Chimp and Olive were our overseers. I would imagine our scribble touched on cleanliness is next to godliness and such like, but Sarah excelled. She strung words together until a ten line sentence was woven (précis wasn't one of Sarah's strong points) and, on the three and a half pages she wrote, this sentence was inserted five times. She was a bright spark. I wouldn't have had the nerve. So that was how toast and marmite disgraced Tritz, Sarah, Potty Dotty and me. We knew we had done wrong. Once the worry was over, and we knew what to expect, we held our heads high. Chuffed we were. Detentions weren't doled out willy-nilly. Dave and Al never had one. They got other things besides. Ally was lumbered with hundreds of lines one day. He was nabbed putting a chalk cross on David Johnny's navy blazer (one of Terri's brothers). It's quite funny, because the teacher who caught Al and pulled his hair lives nearby. Al now passes him every morning on his way to work and they exchange pleasantries. Al and another Bris School teacher are thick as two thieves. He calls Al, Burbs. They often go golfing with the rent collector. Parsnip, a boy in our class, got a det. He was fixing a hangman's noose above Latin teacher's chair and, who should walk in and catch him in the act, none but the Druid herself.

I was asking for a second detention when I told Miss Smith a lie, the biggest one I've ever told in my life. What possessed me I can't for the life of me fathom? I said the reason I hadn't been in her cookery class the previous day was due to the fact I had taken my German 'O' Level exam. Before I knew it, I had said it. The truth was that I had knocked off school for a period of extra revision at home to cover other, more important subjects than cookery. It was the done thing with exams looming on the horizon. Trust muggins to cop it and be questioned. The lie was a whopper, because I know not a word of German. I told Terri if she were my best friend, she would murder me before I got found out. She didn't and I wasn't.

Dad couldn't help but find out what I did during homework one evening. A couple of days after he had papered the living room at Ford, I put a dirty great big ink splodge on a 'fresh' wall. It wasn't my fault. There was a wasp in my lacquered bouffant. It was my fault when, the morning after Mum had a brand new ring fitted on the cooker, I let the milk boil over on it. Rish wasn't any help to me, as I scurried this way and that, trying to clean up the mess before Mum came downstairs. Needless to say I went to school with a flea in my ear that morning.

Naturally, confidential end of term reports, addressed to Mums and Dads, were handed to us sealed, but they appeared to have come unstuck when passed to the Big Guys. It would anger Mum, because we had opened them to read on the way home, but I mean to say, we might have had to prepare her for some shocks, mightn't we. Teachers' comments revealed hard hearts to my sensitive mind.

Terri and I failed our Maths GCE 'O' Level. I know why. We sat at the back of the classroom in our Maths lessons and did History homework, History being the next lesson. It transpired that one day Tritz showed me up shamefully during a Maths lesson. The class was peaceful, most likely a logarithm day. Terri and I had felt the strain and given up in defeat. A change of exercise books and we settled down to write historical jargon. Tritz had to be chewing gum, didn't she, which gave her wind, and boy oh boy the rude noise which quite unexpectedly ripped out of her when she turned to me and said "pasture". What she said was "Birdbrain (she was Fishface) how do you spell pasture?" "How do you spell pas" came out all right, it was the "ture" which didn't. Terence's burp was a burp to beat all burps, as it belched out of her on that "ture". It had a tremendous impact on me at first. I went rigid under her body blow. Heart failed, but revived again, and I had great difficulty in keeping my hee hee hees in check. Initial response to her outburst, when numbness departed, was to push History books off our laps onto the floor in case we were ordered to stand, but we weren't for reasons only God knows why. Chimp, the teacher, wasn't one to get discoloured. Tritz's unmusical sound he disregarded, although everybody else turned in their seats spontaneously to look our way, their broad smiles denouncing us. We had to lower our heads and bring to order mirth-riddled, shaking bodies when Sir roared "Quiet!" So it came to pass, Maths GCE appeared and disappeared, leaving in its wake two miserable failures, Tritz and I. The pass mark was 45. I got 30 and Tritz, I believe, got slightly less, but that was Terri's first attempt and my second. Dave sat the same GCE paper as Terri and I, although a year younger than us, and the rotter had to go and pass first time. He belittled me good and proper. He must have been above average.

Perhaps my Maths deficiency can be overlooked. In Maths lessons I began to get the heebie-jeebies. Really quite tense and nervy I became. I'm positive I hid these alien afflictions from everyone, but myself. The cause was due to the History lessons which pursued Maths. Tritz and I separated for these. I was politically minded and she was economic. Tritz and I referred to my History master as the Butterfly, because he fluttered his eyelashes when he spoke. He was awfully good looking as well. It made me feel funny all over. I suppose I had a crush. I achieved high marks every week for my work, as I wanted his praise and to be noticed. To think back on it now, I'm perfectly aware I was a crazy coot full of rampaging hormonal activity.

There was a time I did conk out from a spell of nervous exhaustion. One Saturday I was in a heavy breathing condition. My gasps worried the family. They thought I had pneumonia. Rish went running for the doctor. He came and slapped my face. He said I had hysteria. Breathing became normal. The doc asked me if I had a boyfriend. Cheeky beggar. I've never been so humiliated in my life. I thought damn me he's inferring something which is nonsensical. I refused point blank to pardon him. Pops didn't thrash me, so how dare he. I never went to see that particular doctor ever again.

When Terence and I reached the ripe old age of fourteen we went through a short-lived phase of skiving. I wasn't keen on school, and Terence had moments of fed-upness, but not as frequently as I did. So if we were both feeling cheesed off, we would 'go sick' for an afternoon. It was an easy task to write absenteeism notes next morning signed by Mrs. B and Mrs. C. Tritz and I had to work it out beforehand that we weren't due to attend the same lessons, otherwise it would have been noticeable what we were about, had we both failed to turn up. Nobody gave the impression they had cottoned on to our deviousness. We were thought of as model pupils.

We had two favourite ways of spending our free afternoons. One was to leave school immediately the bell rang announcing lunch, and pretend we were going home for a meal. Once through the school gates, we would stealthily circle the school and walk via the winding country lanes to Keynsham, paying no heed to the 'Don't feed the horses' sign we came across. We would go to the Stop-a-While Transport Cafe for a bite to eat, or have six-penneth of chips from the chippy opposite the Police Station. The afternoon would be spent in the park. It had swings, slider, roundabout, everything for children's and two young ladies' pleasure. It was divine ecstasy to slide down a 'mile' long slider, or to swing until we nearly went over the cross bar, or to trundle the roundabout until it gathered a nice fast speed for us to jump on and go round and round 'fifty' times. The see-saw, however, didn't give me any enjoyment. I never got off the ground if Terence was on the other end. We left the park I suppose at threeish, feeling sick and giddy and walking like drunks, because chips, Daddy's sauce and a bottle of pop did not agree with flipped tums. We had to judge our departure to coincide with school leaving time, so Mums would not jump to conclusions and think any 'funny business' was going on. We had to retrace our steps. We couldn't take the main road back to Bristol, on account of the fact that many teachers lived in Keynsham. It would have been just our luck, had we been on the main road, to be passed by one motoring home from school. We weren't daft to take unnecessary chances. No one glimpsed us in the leafy lanes. Far more satisfaction anyway in feeding curly coated baby lambs refresher sweets than getting grit in our eyes from madheads on the main road.

The other favourite way in which to spend an afternoon of liberty was to borrow Dave and Al's bikes out of the shed at home. They didn't ride them to school, as it was but five minutes walk from the house. Bike riding was a highly dangerous pursuit, because Terence and I didn't have an ounce of road sense. We hadn't, to tell the honest truth, mastered three-wheeler bikes at ten years old, and there we were at fifteen, not only taking up with two-wheeler bikes, but boys' ones at that. We could well have inflicted terrible injuries on ourselves with those dissecting bars lying from bow to stern. I can't say we rode the bikes. We wavered along. Also, I wouldn't take my hands off the handlebars to signal, as I was about to turn corners. That would have been asking for trouble. Therefore, anybody at my rear end knew nothing of my intentions.

One day in particular was calamity. Tritz and I had loaned the bikes for the afternoon. (Mum was working in the school canteen then, so she wasn't home when we came for them.) We had taken it into our pea nuts to cycle to Terri's along busy West Road. I had the biggest bike, christened Dinosaur, and Terence was seated upon the Lizard. She pedalled for all she was worth, but didn't make much headway. We were nattering, as we cycled shakily abreast down the main road. Suddenly we heard from behind a terrific roaring and beeping, which got louder and louder and, as far as we could make out, it seemed to be bearing straight down on us. I didn't look over my shoulder. That would have been fatal. Instead of closing up and tucking myself in front of Terence, who was cycling in the gutter (that was too complicated thinking for me), I thought I would give this bull of a lorry plenty of space in which to pass by. I rode across his path and on over the centre white line. I didn't exactly forget it was the wrong side of the road for me to be pedalling on. I didn't have a clue what else to do. I didn't know how to stop, so I had to career onwards. I couldn't wave to him to pass me by, so with eyes firmly fixed on the road ahead, I shouted for him to "Please do carry on". I thought it was nice and polite of me. The lorry driver did not. It certainly was a formidable lorry. As it hurtled between Terence and myself, nasty words were flung at me. I was astounded and fell off. My stars were favourable that day, because no traffic came to roller me into the tarmac. Terence tried to slow up, and come to my aid, but doziness prevailed. She swerved into the kerb, thinking it would stop her, instead of applying the brakes, although it's possible they wouldn't have worked, like mine. Tritz fell off too. We lay where we had fallen nursing instant bruises, before composing ourselves and inspecting the damage. The chain had come off Dave's bike. I was worried about that more than my knees and Terence's funny bone, as it wasn't the first time it had come adrift. I knew Dave would thump me harder this time than he had done the last, and he did.

Terence and I got to school early next day and in the cloakroom wound bandages round a knee, a wrist, an ankle and an elbow, aiding and abetting each other. We conjured up a gory tale about a road accident we had been indirectly involved in, which had prevented us from returning to school after lunch the previous day. To be perfectly honest, I don't remember how I did explain things to Blossom. I expect it's a case of some things are best forgotten. I was too old and too big for a tanning, but a warning that Pops would be informed, and a visit would be paid to the school, put paid to mine and Terence's adventures for a week or two.

There was another sorry episode of bad luck which occurred on a scrimshank afternoon, again on the bikes. We wanted them to take us to Terence's for a plate of nosh, because her Mum was out. This time we had walked the bikes along the main road, and had only proceeded to sit on the saddles when we came to the muddy lane, which was a short cut to Terence's. The lane, I would say, is two foot wide with the stream to the left of it, the golfcourse to the right. We didn't ride into the stream. We weren't that daft. In fact Terence was more than capable of controlling her Lizzie that day, but my Dino had a mood on him. I don't know how it transpired, but the bike wanted its own way and got it. I shot through a gap in the railings and there I was, cavorting across the golfcourse. It was completely out of my hands, and all I could do was try to keep my seat. Brakes didn't work of course. I did circles on the green, and rode down hills big and small, until I came to rest in a sand pit, conveniently placed for my benefit I do declare. Thankfully, the golfcourse runs into many acres, and if golfers had witnessed my capers they would have missed the target, had they aimed and fired their balls at me, as I was moving at top speed.

Not surprisingly, following my Olympic trials on the golfcourse I went home with a puncture. Dave's bike as per usual. Dave throttled me, but Al never laid a finger on Tritz. We gave up the bikes eventually. We knew our limitations and accepted that our vocation in life wasn't to be pedallers. On the boys explicit instructions we ditched the bikes, or more appropriate to say the bikes ditched us.

One year Terri and I broke friends on the last day of summer term and ploughed through six long miserable weeks' holiday without seeing one another, simply to patch up our petty quarrel the first day back at school. During the holiday (our split was over a banana of all things), Tritz told me later when we were talking to each other again, she was actually on her way to see me one day before she remembered she wasn't speaking to me, so she spun on her heel and went back home.

It was during the course of a school summer holiday that Sarah and I took six little tots for an afternoon's fishing. We were fourteenish at the time and motherly urges had overtaken us. They were nice kids. There was Sarah's stepbrother Ronald, who would have been I reckon four, and the various assortment next door to Sarah, ranging from a three to a seven year old.

I remember only too clearly that little girl next door. Far too intelligent she was. Baby-sitting one night, I sat on her bed and began to read a story. I came to the name Penelope and pronounced it, as it looked, Pennylope. "You mean Pen-nel-ope-ee don't you dear!" Mary remarked significantly. She'll go far that girl. Down under she is now with her family.

Well, on this fine day we had had an excellent afternoon's fishing with the squirts in St Anne's Woods, lots of brooks there to dabble in. Tea-time came and we thought we had better make tracks for home, so with each child clasping a large polythene bag filled with murky water, several tadpoles and sticklebacks, we set off for the bus-stop. Sarah was piled high with bits and pieces, even though she was smaller than most of the children. I was entrusted with no-good bait – the crust of a loaf with its inside torn out – and the rods – half length bean sticks with an old sieve, tea strainer or the foot of a nylon stocking tied on one end, laddered but not holey. Sarah had said that Ronald, before coming out, had taken a pair of scissors to a brand new pair of his Mum's stockings. He had cut the feet off and buried the legs in the garden, bringing a spare foot with him. The rush hour bus came along, sardine packed with the Board Mill workers. The kind conductor let us get on. He was foreign and prattled on in a queer lingo whilst we clambered aboard. We suspected really he was saying "Bus full, can't take any more", but we crushed together. We had a fairly long ride ahead of us. Numerous members of the public alighted and finally the six kids got the front seat on the lower deck of the bus, and squeezed Sarah and me in amongst them. More and more people got on, and there were, I would say, ten stood facing us down the centre aisle. All of a sudden a little voice piped up "My hands are hot". Another said "Mine too". Another, "This is heavy", and another didn't say anything, but sighed. Simultaneously, four bulging polythene bags were placed gently on the floor. They sort of simply opened up. No need to say anything further. The bus suddenly had a river flowing through it, with real live fish swimming about. We'd had a good catch. Sarah and I didn't say anything apart from "Oh Lor" until we got off the bus. We were entreated to "Go, go, go" by an extremely irate conductor. We could understand him that time, and his forty odd busload of paddlers. We needed no second telling.

One might think Sarah and I saw the funny side of the events, which had brought about our ejection from the double-decker. We laughed for

128

a minute, but then decided it wasn't going to be so amusing walking six dejected imps home, and it wasn't. They cried solidly. They were tired. They were wet, understandably. They were hungry and they wanted to go back for more tiddlers. We promised faithfully we would take them fishing again. A promise broken I'm afraid.

Sarah was crazy about animals. What with her mice, snakes, lizards and ferrets, I was never sure what I would go "ugh" at next. But Rusty, her dog, and I got on famously. Strangers he wouldn't let near Sarah, and if he thought it meant defending her with his teeth, he would do just that. I wonder if he knew she was somehow different from the rest of us, and he would not let her suffer any jibes or taunts. The fights he got into, because a dog made a pass at one of his bitches. I've witnessed a good few of his scraps and they certainly have been robust, dead angry to be exact. Buckets of water did nothing to cool Rusty's temper (nor ardour) when roused. He would make certain he had won a fight, before letting Sarah pull him away. He loved her undeniably. He would be sat at the school gates waiting for her bang on four o'clock each day. If he arrived early, he would pad in and search the school for her, and a big school it was too. They had it worked out between them, I'm positive, because it often meant Sarah was released from school early to lead Rusty off the premises.

For a spell I took to having lunch at Sarah's instead of at school when Mum worked there as a dinner lady. Occasionally I got hot under the collar when, in my presence, Sarah received a severe ticking off from Bettina, her step-mum, for having had Rusty sleep with her. But Sarah was undeterred. She would still tiptoe downstairs and bring him up with her at night. Bet would know, because of chestnut hairs in the bed. It was up to me, Sarah said, to pacify Bettina and compliment her on a superb lunch. I meant every word actually, as her cheese and potato pie was indeed praiseworthy. Old Rust was destroyed before the family moved to Cornwall. It was a sad loss not only for Sarah. People and bitches alike missed him throughout the suburbs. A fine figure of a dog he had been.

Tritz and I called for Sarah on our way to school. We greeted one another cordially. She would pose a question, "Hey you up there, weather alright?" "Not bad", I might reply, "Same down there?" "Yep Lofty" she would answer looking up at me. I hope Sarah is surviving in Falmouth. I went to visit a couple of times during school holidays. During one stay the family sent me down the results of my 'O' Levels on a postcard, which I was reluctant to read until Sarah told me it was okay, as I hadn't done too badly. I found out many things on those holidays. Sarah, I learnt, had flogged the clarinet she took with her from Bris School in a Truro pawn shop. She hadn't finished paying for it, not by a long chalk, and she'd be the first to admit she couldn't play the bally thing. We spent wet afternoons supposedly chatting in her bedroom, but in fact we were reading. The book was a thick one, the Tropic of Cancer (or is it Capricorn?). That is, we were picking out the spicy, juicy bits to read. Sarah had found it behind numerous other books on her Dad's shelf. The last I heard of Sarah she had flipped her lid and was completely gaga over her driving instructor. I'm not sure how she was making out on both counts.

Terri and I didn't know what to do one afternoon in the school holidays. I came up with a suggestion. Why didn't we go down the churchyard and search for Sarah's Mum. Sarah had been in Cornwall for quite a long time then, and I have no idea what made me think of it. I could visualise Sarah's Mum lying in a cot downstairs. She was a gentle woman and she did look tired and worn out. She died of cancer. Her Dad married Bet later on, who was ever so young we thought, and had three kids in rapid succession at the last count. Sarah had an older brother who was exceedingly tall and helped design the Severn Bridge.

Burial grounds fascinated Tritz and me, and we whiled away many a school lunchtime reading gravestones. We were most careful where we put our feet, because Nan had drummed it into me that it wasn't polite to walk on the dead. Tritz and I would separate, calling to each other to come and see should we come across a baby's grave, or a body who had passed away at a great age. Some of the inscriptions put gob-stoppers in our throats. I get them now when I read the Deaths and In Memoriam columns in the Evening Post. It upsets me to go to the cemetery with Lin, should she take flowers along to put in her Dad's vase, because she gets teary. Rish and I would go quiet if we went with Nan to cut the grass round Granfer. I would speak silently to him, say "Hello Granf, how are you?" Things like that, and stare fixedly at the dirt on him. Rish told me she said The Lord's Prayer to herself, as she stood at his graveside watching Nan pull up encroaching weeds. One day when Rish was tiny she passed a graveyard with Dad and said to him "Look at all those tables and chairs".

In my last year at school I stayed up until midnight on Saturdays. At five to twelve Mahalia Jackson came on the telly singing gospel. Five minutes well worth waiting for I thought, and if she sang 'He's got the whole world in his hands' I went to bed thinking aloud "That was bloody marvellous". I'm not so keen on all that wailing these days. If I was on my own at home I would pretend I was Brenda Lee and try and sing all gruff and throatily 'Sweet Nothin's'. It wasn't a pleasant sound coming out of me not at all at all.

The first time I donned a suspender belt was for a school Christmas party. I didn't have any idea how to put it on. It completely baffled me. Rish came to my rescue and explained what went where. I'm glad tights have replaced nylons. My suspenders kept losing their round heads and I often went out with three or four sixpences keeping my stockings up. The trouble was that sixpences kept falling out through the loops. It wasn't so bad if they fell on the floor, but difficult to know what to do if they slipped down inside a stockinged leg.

Tritz and I, of course, became great fans of the Beatles when they first emerged on the pop scene. We read in the evening paper one day that they were coming to Bristol for a concert at the Colston Hall, and hurried along to the booking office to stake our claim. Mum was paying. Mum was smashing. However, we were in for a disappointment. The lady behind the grille informed us postal bookings exclusively were to be accepted. She couldn't make any exceptions, although she had wads of tickets there in the booth with her. How mean. By the time we sent off postal orders, we were resigned to the fact that the couple of days' delay we had encountered would obviously mean the best seats in the hall would be taken when our application was received. A week went by before Tritz notified me she had acquired our tickets. We were climbing the stairs in school on our way to do monitor duty, and Tritz pulled a woebegone face and said, "They've come Ern". Her look prompted me to say "Not so good, eh Terence?" "No, see for yourself Ern" she replied. I looked at the pink squares in her hand and nearly lifted her clean off her feet, as I emitted a "whoopee". We had been given none other than the very best seats in the house, front row and centre aisle.

Come the evening we were beside ourselves in the grip of Beatlemania. Tritz pinched me black and blue, but I felt not a thing as she squirmed in her chair and bounced up and down in paroxysms of delight. Hers was an outward glee. Mine a swooning inner fire, while we saw our beloveds perform. I swear I didn't blink once, so spellbound was I. Tritz and I are in agreement to this day; we had a wink from Ringo and a smile from George. The other two didn't seem to notice us, but that's life.

BECOMING A WORKING GIRL

At fourteen I was desperately in need of money for cosmetics and nylons. A paper round suited my brothers, but not me. Girls I knew at school were working Saturdays in supermarkets, or in the big departmental stores in town, but those jobs didn't appeal to me, partly because the shop assistants seemed to wear only navy blue skirts (our school uniform) and overalls, the colour of which does nothing for me. Also I knew I would get flummoxed charging people, and het up with thousands of shoppers milling around. I did, however, come up with a fitting idea how to boost my half-crown pocket money. As I loved to muck about with friends' hair, I thought I would enjoy a Saturday job helping out in the local hairdresser's. I wrote a posh letter to 'Gladys', extending my services, and had to go and see her at the shop one night after school. All these years have passed and I've still got Glad's reply letter with a lipstick blot on it, which I put there not her. I don't remember a thing about my interview, probably because my brain had blacked out. I felt exuberant and immensely proud of myself when I was accepted as a Saturday morning new recruit and occasional Friday nighter. I hadn't told a soul, apart from the family, in case my application was scrapped, so I was delighted to spill the beans and hear envious voices wishing they had my glamorous job.

During my first Saturday morning I drowned several customers and flooded the shop and ears, but loved every minute. I loved Glad, Tess or Testicle as she was affectionately addressed, and Kitty, the staff. I loved every customer, the shop and every single task I was given to do. Over time my five bob pay packet doubled, but it wasn't the money I appreciated as much as the company. Glad's was such a friendly salon. Women with no males in attendance to subdue them were enriched with electrified personalities. Their great sense of fun was a tonic to chase any blues away. Friday nights and Saturday mornings there was never any peace in the street outside. People walking by could hear the bedlam at Glad's. Customers queuing at the fish and chip shop down the road would ask the owner what the hell was going on. They were the ones who weren't used to us. I lost a lot of shyness and replaced it with a whole heap of broadmindedness. Jokes, very rude and downright smutty, but told with frankness, were stored up by customers from week to week, to be poured out in torrents when they kept their appointments. No doubt husbands had passed on the jokes. Filthy dirty they may have been, but nobody in their right mind could raise a distasteful eyebrow and think "How crude" when a tale of tails was accompanied by bawdy actions. One can't keep in what wants to come out, laughter and tears especially. I laughed at many jokes in the early days, because everybody else was crying helplessly, but I honestly didn't have a clue as to their meaning. I tried to remember them to tell Terence, Sarah, Potty Dotty and Smelly Stelly at school on Monday mornings. When I got home from Glad's the first thing I did was to go upstairs and jot them down, so as not to forget. It's a good job Mum never saw the bits of paper I wrote on. I tore the paper into flakes and flushed them down the toilet after I had recounted the jokes to the girls. Friends and I often puzzled over a joke for hours, and even then haven't been able to get the gist of it, and I would sadly say, "Well, Glad and the customers laughed fit to bust over this one". That annoyed us intensely.

Every woman who entered Glad's shop, from the well-to-do, down to the pickled herring who came in with her thieving crafty brood, became one and the same when an obscene sex-filled joke was being vividly told down to the minutest detail. Their raucous laughs echoed throughout the shop, and I was at beck and call to hand out the tissues for eye mops. They never stopped coming. Week after week the same faces entered in a hurry and left, not wanting to, hours and hours later. I was spoiled, but in return gave them good service. Pops taught me creditably how to make a good cup of char. Brew-ups went on continuously throughout the morning, and my pots of Rosie Lee were a welcome sight. I can't say I had any favourite customers, because they were all special. Each one was different, same as their heads. I learnt how to treat them to their liking. Sib delighted in a knuckle hard rub, another woman with lumps needed a gentle touch and liked me to wash her neck with frothy lather, somebody else wanted cold water, a different bod scalding hot, although I warned her she would get scubs on her scalp. Buttercup was a gnarled old oak I tended to. The skull-cap went on her and through its colander holes I pulled strands of hair to be dyed yellow. I was free and easy with conditioner and ladled palmfuls over nuts when Glad wasn't looking. I believed in giving them a thorough bath. I wasn't one to stint on shampoo, but slapped it on and swilled heads til they squeaked. If anyone came out of the basin with eyebrows remaining, they hadn't been done properly, and were promptly plonked under the taps again with no buts. We had a session one morning of tinting fair eyebrows dark brown. It was a scream to see customers sat under the driers with inch thick brows meeting in the middle. We cleaned them up afterwards with ammonia.

Young cops were frequent visitors to the shop, but not for hair-dos. They came in from the beat for a cuppa and a chat, and to swap jokes. They never came through the door without hitting their helmets off, because they were all so tall. Once one got nabbed, or almost. The sergeant came in when this particular constable was supping tea. He had had a tip-off I expect. Clever PC Fuzz told the Sarge that Glad had asked him in for advice regarding locks and safety devices. He got away with it too. Glad took a long time to recover. She needed the brandy bottle not tea. She was a dead loss at fibbing. She managed plenty of stutters and splutters and oh, ah, ums. Glad looked as innocent as Shifty Sam and Fingers Fred put together when she said to the sergeant "Oh yes, I asked him in to look at me bolts". Guilt was written all over her face. She always told a joke backwards too. Testicle was the one to get away with murder. She could have won over Hitler himself. Every time the phone rang in the shop, she would be ready with her singsong voice and "Good Morning, Glad's Poodle Parlour".

Joss, Tess's daughter, would join me on Saturdays, and we became like two peas in a pod. We occasionally did things wrong. One Saturday morning, before the first shampoo and set got under way, Glad sent us off to the launderette with a polythene bag as big as me full of damp, used towels from the previous day. We took it in turns to heave it onto each other's shoulders going down the road. Joss, being a weeny dot, had to keep stopping to sit on it for a rest. She would sag a trifle more each time the load was placed on her back, and she was folded nearly in two halves when we got to the launderette.

I hadn't been to a self-service laundry before. Mum didn't have a washing machine then, nor now, so I didn't know what the procedure was, but Joss said she did. We put the towels into a machine with a box of soap powder, found the slot for the money, read the instructions on the inside of the lid, switched on and sat down to wait for results. There was an awful lot of noise and clotheads that we were kept opening the lid and peering inside to see what was going on. I was jittery, thinking my face might be blown apart, but a soaking was what I got and Joss did too. The floor was in a worse state though by the time we had finished. After a short while we heard the whirring begin to slow down, followed by the sound of rushing water (going down a plughole?). We thought, "Right, time's up". The light went out so we figured we had accomplished what we set out to do. For the umpteenth time up went the lid. There was no water left in the tub, but we couldn't understand why the towels were still dripping wet and full of soap, as they must have had a rinse and a spin before the machine switched itself off. We couldn't fathom out why Glad had sent us first thing in the morning, because the towels would now be far too wet to use, whereas they had been merely damp in the first place. We had masses of sixpences left over, but were clueless as to why.

We picked each detergent sodden towel out of the machine, wringing as we went. We thought the dopey spinner couldn't have been working properly, and concluded that they hadn't been rinsed due to our interference with the lid. They would dry hard and rough, but we couldn't be blamed. We quarterised the towels into neat, soaking piles, flung them into the bag and then tried to lift it. We couldn't. We had thought the bag heavy coming, but now going we had sopping towels and the Atlantic in it. Joss did the splits leaving the launderette. She slipped in one of the pools we left behind on the floor.

On our return journey to the shop we dragged the bag. We couldn't lug it on our shoulders. I'm afraid when we got back we were called feeble minded dunderheads, nincompoops, numbskulls and things I won't repeat by Gladys and Testicle. The towels hadn't been spun. Well we knew that. What we weren't to know was there had been separate tumblers to use after the washers, hence the coins stashed in our pockets. Fiddle-faddle. Back we had to go. There were the notices plain as day with arrows pointing to the tumble driers opposite the washing machines. Eyes in the back of our heads wouldn't have made any difference I bet.

We spent a further mouldy hour watching towels circulate. I couldn't call them interesting. We inserted all the sixpences into the tumble drier save two. We bought two bars of chocolate upon leaving the launderette, because we thought we deserved them. We didn't mention to Glad that a hole had appeared in the bag, quite a large one, which might or might not get bigger. We were out of favour as it was without rubbing salt in our wounds.

After knowing Joss and Tess for many months, I had an invitation to join them for Sunday tea. I caught the Clevedon bus from Bristol bus-station. I should have alighted at Tickenham, but I lost my bearings and stayed in my seat for the return journey to Bristol. This time I got off at Tickenham. A frozen Joss was sat on a field gate still expecting me to come, although nearly an hour late, but certainly not on the Clevedon to Bristol bus. She said it was just a minute's walk to home and unlatched the field gate. In we went. There weren't cows on the grass, but caravans. I was quite puzzled. Joss walked up to one and said, "Here we are". "Jeepers creepers, you never told me you lived in a caravan" was what I said. "Course I did" was what she said. I had been too busy at the shop washing out other people's ears, whilst my own needed doing more than theirs. Tess and Joss's Dad were at that time building a house in Clevedon. I knew Joss was a hindrance not a help, because we were told to scram as soon as I had looked over the foundations on the plot.

After a year the house was up and habitable. I went there to stay for a weekend. The family and I climbed a ladder to the bedrooms, as the stairs were yet to be affixed to the banister rail. On the Saturday evening Joss and I went to a sailing club dance with Tess and her Dad. Joss introduced me to Jeremy, who looked like George Beatle with the same moppish hairstyle and thick knitted eyebrows. During the evening we chin-wagged and in conversation he said he was a Ladies hairdresser, and that's how he could get his wigs cheaper. "Huh?" I said. He looked quizzical. Hadn't Joss told me he was bald as a coot underneath he asked? No, she had not, and what's more I didn't believe a word he was saying and told him so. After all, he was only about seventeen. How could he, at such a tender age, have had king-size worries enough to make him lose every hair on his noddle? He offered to take me outside and show me, but I declined the invitation. Well I ask you! Joss said he was telling the truth, and it was confirmed when I inspected his hair-line. False. I had an immense urge to swivel the wig round back to front, but curbed it. I did feel quite despondent. He wasn't bad looking wearing a wig, but he wouldn't have made a second Yul Brynner in my rating.

I got more wiggings than I bargained for when I bought my long false piece in Lewis's. Mum said I was foolish and it must have cost the earth, that I was silly to waste my money, that I could have spent it on a decent pair of shoes instead, and don't come to her if I ran short of dosh. I let her run dry. The last sentence I remember her saying was "I suppose it's a fiver up your shirt" and I mumbled "More or less". I never did summon up the courage to tell her how much more. Fifteen pounds it cost me! Gladys gabbled on more than Mum what a stupe I had been. I couldn't fool her over the price. She knew it was real hair. I had bought it in a moment of weakness, without consulting Gladys who could have got me one a great deal cheaper with her being in the hair trade.

February Lin and I had a night out to look forward to. Glad arranged and paid for an evening's entertainment for her 'worst' fun loving customers. A coach filled with a cargo of women, and oh what women – hand-picked – descended on the local pub at Pucklechurch, a sleepy little village three hundred and sixty four nights of the year. The proprietor was ready for the onslaught. Of course Glad's customers knew Lin as well as they knew me, because they went in Lobb's, her station of work, for their newspapers, sweets, ciggies, toys, games, comics, etc.

The ladies, Lin and I assembled in the back room of the pub set aside for our use. We had a barmaid and a woman pianist as merry as ourselves. We gorged ourselves with eats, sang the old songs, danced every dance (fitting our own steps to those we didn't know), and sat back to watch the show, centred round Testicle and four or five game customers.

Mabel appeared as a bikini (home-made) clad beach belle and then in a tutu to perform the Sugar Plum Fairy. She couldn't ballet on her toes, because she had football boots on her feet. To see Mabel one would know why we ruptured ourselves. She was over sixty, hardly higher than four feet, about fifty inch bust, forty inch waist and sixty inch hips. Her sultry mystic dance of the seven veils was exquisite until she got caught up in them, but the exotic belly dance overshadowed everything else. Every part of her anatomy quivered and shook frantically and her chest went wild. She had been waiting for years to be claimed by the Sheik of Arabi she said.

The others participated in sketches like Birth of a Baby and First Night of the Honeymoon, which creased us up until it was too painful to carry on laughing. Fashion shows through the ages were far more stunning than Dior could have dreamt up. Mabel looked ravishing in her hubby's long johns and a rugby jersey. I pity the poor devil that wore it after. He must have had two enormous empty compartments in front of him. We did have one or two wonderful singers in our midst. Mrs. Peg (Peglar) could sing 'The Last Waltz' and make my throat swell.

The last dance we had would be a conga and we would gyrate through the public bar into the lounge, giving plenty of oomph to our pliable hips. Lin and I exaggeratively so if any dashing young men were at the bar having a pint. I suppose we two looked a little out of place, but we never felt it. The men propping up the bar joined us in the conga line and followed us back to our room. Throughout the evening they had been craning to have a peek at our goings-on whenever the bar hatch had opened. By their stunned incredulous faces, one would have thought the Martians had landed inside the snuggery. Their eyes goggled and their minds boggled.

We didn't allow any to pass through our door, save for one Mabel took a shine to. He was a doddery old boy of ninety plus, friendly, lovable, deaf as a post, and he did the conga with his walking stick. Mabel thought he had money, and she told him to come visit her on certain evenings in the week when her husband would be on night shift. She divulged in his ear that she had a rambling country mansion, beside a river teeming with trout and swans. Rather elaborated upon, because she lived in a dilapidated terrace house, the front door of which opened out onto the pavement, and stagnant Bris stream trickled past her back garden. Her pet swans must have been water rats in disguise. The old chap said he would take up her offer, and I've often wondered whether he ever did hobble up to her front door. Nights to remember, our annual shindigs were.

I think it apt to say I matured when I went to work at Glad's.

My occupation of washing hair and making tea expanded. I became a saleswoman. Ada had a shop near Glad's and on a Saturday morning she brought along cases of clothes to show the women under the driers. If any of the goods caught their eye they could pay for them in weekly instalments. My job was to mark up the credit cards in the shop. Also, before closing time on a Saturday, I was entrusted to carry tins of money from Glad's to Ada's. I had to be on my guard for vagrants. I could have been coshed going up poky Fry's Alley. Odd bods lived there. Wooky Dap was one strange old inhabitant. As children we knocked on his door and ran away. I never did get waylaid.

So it came to pass Ada made Lin and me agents. Our age was overlooked. We brought cases of clothes home and went hawking our wares round Ford Estate. Not until we had tried on most of the pretty dresses though. One time I tried on four and pleaded with Dad to take my photo in each one. Lin and I had lots of customers and no real bad ones. We let the odd one off with paying a shilling instead of five bob. The cups of tea I got through on a Friday night collecting payments! Lin was a squash girl. Hilda and Leo were our favourite customers, because they supplied cake too. We avoided calling on a couple of women on the estate, the one who dances round the Christmas tree in her front garden all through the year, and the other one who scrubs the telegraph pole outside her house. Thanks to our rounds, Lin and I made commission that went towards paying for the clothes we ourselves purchased from Ada on the weekly.

Buying on the never-never though can cause nothing but worry. I bought on credit a mac out of Terri's club book. (Her Mum's really.) I wasn't seeing her one week to pay my remittance, so I sent it. I wrapped a pound note in newspaper, sealed it in an envelope bearing a Green Shield stamp, a pink one and a threepenny one and addressed it to the Hon. Terence Cod. I went through this rigmarole, because I had been short with her on the telephone when she rang and caught me at a busy flustered mome. After I had popped it in the letterbox, Dad told me I shouldn't have defaced the

Queen's Mail. It was a serious crime, he said, and I could be prosecuted and brought to law and order in court. For three days I worried myself sick, and repented every sin I had ever committed. Then Tritz phoned to say the unopened envelope had been safely delivered and I could wipe the sweat from my brow.

THE PICTURES AND MY
FIRST GROWN UP DANCE

It was the wage Glad paid me that I squandered on enjoyment. My pay covered not one visit, but usually two to different cinemas in Bristol every week. I was very avid. Lin too. Going to the pictures was definitely our favourite pastime. Only a few times we didn't enjoy being in the Ritz. Once was when we were watching the X-rated 'Whatever happened to Baby Jane' – we probably weren't sixteen. We had just seen a dead budgie dished up for a meal on the screen, when suddenly a scream of "There's a mouse" rang throughout the picture house. A multitude of panicky cries of "Where, where, where?" plus shuffling of feet, and flashing torches pursued the cry, but the mouse wasn't found. Lin and I spent an uncomfortable hour seeing the remainder of the film with knees clasped under our chins. The other time we went to see a double feature of 'The Girls of St Trinian's', and came out of the cinema before the end choking back sad tears. The Manager had walked onto the stage to inform us President Kennedy had been assassinated. It was a horrible sickening moment, which numbed the entire audience. As it sunk in, people rose in ones, twos and groups and left the cinema to hurry home and watch the telly for more news.

I can remember one other disturbing event down the Ritz. I had gone with girl friends to a Saturday matinee performance. We sported beehive hairstyles with kiss-curls. We had covered our eyelids in black liner with vivid green under the brow for me, and sky blue for Lin on account of our eye colour. And we had either put safety pins in our straight skirts, to make them murderously skin tight, or tacked them with three-inch stitches. We must have looked tarty. We were on the lookout for the opposite sex. To attract the boys it was the done thing to smoke like a chimney, because this gave us a sophisticated air, especially if smoke came out of our nostrils. So there we were, taking up the whole back row in the cinema, much to the annoyance of courting couples who made a beeline there. What they got from us was a sly grin. Our laps were free, but frosty-faced females pulled their beaux away. With watering eyes I puffed away, not very merrily, when I espied through the thick haze, a couple of rows down the aisle, members of the opposite sex I didn't want to see, Uncle Les and cousin David. I ducked my head under the seat. Lin's head appeared alongside, wondering what I had lost. I grimaced "I gotta get out of here". I stayed where I was though for most of the film, and the entire interval – head below seat level. I thought sure as ninepence I would be spotted and they would go home and tell Mum I had turned into a dragon. (Mum and Dad say smoking is a filthy habit.) She never said Uncle Les split on me though. It didn't take long for me to give up ciggies. I rarely was able to get through a whole one. A half made me feel sick.

Lin, Josie and I went once to the pictures to meet our dates. Inside they had said, so inside it was, the tight-fisted merchants. Josie's hair fell down. I had unsuccessfully put it up in a bun for her. I fondled her napper, taking out the hundred clips, and told her I would attend to it in the interval. Come the break we trotted off to the Ladies and I coiled and pinned her back up. When we returned to our seats, her boyfriend had disappeared, never to be seen again, which was most upsetting for Josie and I felt somewhat responsible. I can't remember if she stayed there with us or went home. I know going home we lost Lin and her attentive lover-dover same place as usual, out of sight round Ashbin Drive, sat on or in an ashbin I don't doubt.

Lin and I went to the Ritz cinema one evening and thought we would have a fling and go in the best seats upstairs for the first time. During the interval Pange wanted the toilet, so leaving Lin I went scouting for the Ladies. I walked to the rear of the cinema, went through a door, and by golly fresh air hit me. I was outside. I had mistakenly come out the side exit. I got quite panicky and thought I couldn't possibly face going round to the main entrance and explain my mishap to the doorman and ask to be let in again. So I struggled with the door and, by inserting my nails in a paper fine slit, Bob's your uncle, I managed to ease it open and get back into welcome darkness. I was perspiring when I got back to Lin. She said, "What happened to you, get locked in the loo?" I enlightened her and she has never let me live it down.

I don't know why it was, but Lin and I were quite unfair to Josie at times. We could be so mean. One Sunday afternoon I was accompanying Lin to her Gran's. As we neared the bus-stop we saw Josie standing there. Lin had told Josie she was going to her Gran's alone. Therefore, we couldn't very well be hurtful and appear together at the bus-stop. Lin and I squat down behind a car and waited until Josie had climbed aboard her bus (and our bus) and gone out of sight. Then we had a long wait for the next bus. Our sin caught up with us though, and we laughed the other side of our faces. When we got off the bus at Barrow Road, Josie was at the same stop waiting for a further bus to take her on to her Grandmother's. I left Lin to make feeble excuses and peacemaker Pange went in the pie shop for three hot sausage rolls – impossible to walk along Barrow Road without buying a hot pasty or something. It was guaranteed the shop would be open morning, noon and night, any day of the week, until a crane came along and swung a metal ball at its rafters.

Terence and I went to our first dance together. It was a New Year's Eve 'do', to be held in the Victoria Rooms near the University. Because of this, we thought it was bound to be a big attraction, and we would be able to look over lots of thrilling bodies. For weeks prior to the occasion, we practised our come-hither gazes, even attempted hypnosis in case it should be required.

The day arrived and we were on tenterhooks, sure as sure we were going to be whisked off our feet by Princes Charming. We left home with the shivers – growing excitement at the prospect of what lay in store. Two bashful fifteen year olds made a wash-out of an entrance. We slipped in, trailing a crowd of ladies and gents, and hid behind a marble pillar to survey the scene. We couldn't believe our eyes. Everybody at first seemed to be over fifty and dressed in penguin suits, chiffon, satin or Lurex long evening gowns. Some flashy sparklers glittered around the room too and mink and fox nuzzled arms. I clutched my neck feeling for my rolled gold necklace with the two-inch square 'emerald', and Terence's ear-rings were slipped off her lobes before you could say Jack Robinson. They were paste. We felt quite drab in our new cotton frocks. The band started up. We gave each other a dismal look. It was a waltz. Terence and I had never been able to master the waltz at school. We had managed by slowing down a polka. Well, we couldn't peep from behind pillars all night, so we bought ourselves drinks. Juices, because we thought we would have been booted out if we had asked for spirits. We should have though. Liquor might have made us into instant adults, which we desperately wanted to be that night. We found seats, but they weren't loungers, and watched the proceedings intently. We perceived a handful of girls about our age. Their faces told us this; their dresses made them look fifty-year-old frumps. We even enjoyed ourselves, making fun of everyone in the room. Nobody escaped our scrutiny. We could tell if bosoms were real or falsies had been added. We giggled at hair creations, for the men as well as the women. There were an awful lot of comb-overs. We figured out three-quarters of the women wore wigs and half the men wore a toupee, or topaz as Mum calls it, and we forgot ourselves by rudely pointing at those whom we thought did. The remaining men were sporting hairless domes, which shone with spit and polish. Talk about ballroom dancing! I thought waltzes were supposed to spark off love affairs. Rubbish! It's true, the old 'uns that night kept in perfect time and sequence, but nobody held their partner close. There wasn't a cheek to cheek to be seen. Terence and I were the only females wearing short dresses without tinsel. I wish Minis had been in fashion then. We would have raised a few brows. As it was, our dresses came to our kneecaps and felt everydayish, which they were.

Eventually we stopped feeling dowdy and sorry for ourselves. The fruit juice went to our heads and when the band struck a rousing chord, and broke into a lively polka, we thought hells bells we'll show them what two gypsies could do. We twirled and swirled and caused the odd smile here and there, and when a Gay Gordons took over we stayed on the floor. That was my downfall. We got encumbered with two dinner-jacketed half-wits who butted into our midst. The pair lasted a dance. My fault. Terence was well away, looking ever so femme fatale with Don Juan. I wasn't getting on that brilliantly with my fop. At school in dancing lessons it was customary for me to take the man's part, because I towered an inch or two above

Terence, not because of a masculine build. So I mean to say, it came natural to me in the Gay Gordons to raise my arm in the air and start pivoting this young whippersnapper. He was no bigger than Oliver Twist. But I suppose his manhood was slighted. We were dancing in a large circle and I consistently appeared on the men's side and he on the women's. I thought I was charming, as I kept chuckling "Sorry", but he wasn't gallant, because he gradually went cerise. My scarlet geranium muttered thanks and something else and, what a swiz, went off and left me in the lurch after a miserly one dance. Discourteous pretty boy I thought. Terence, bless her, returned to my side, because she didn't like her toff neither and her feet were killing her.

We went out into the gallery to unstifle ourselves and take several inhalations of cooler, smokeless air. We were both lamenting about cramped tozzles and, unthinkingly, I pulled my stilettos off and hopped from one leg to the other, massaging scrumped up piglets. Lo and behold Terence and I had our first encounter with a couple of Sugar Daddies. They approached from out of the Blue Room. One was very portly, very drunk and very old. He had beady eyes and dribbled. He couldn't even hold his glass and kept saying "Whoops" when drink flipped out. He began chatting us up in between hiccups and rude belches. Patter went something like "Shall I rub your tootsies for you oh beautiful one?" "Sir, I am quite capable of rubbing my own toes". He loved it. Terence and I felt awkward and teenage, not because of him, but because of the man with him. Well, perhaps I should say I did. He was quite dazzling. Suave, sophisticated, forty to fiftyish, tall and slim with not an ounce of middle-aged spread. He might have had one of those sash cummerbund things holding him in I suppose, but his suit was immaculate. He was most handsome and I wondered whether he would catch me if I swooned. He didn't say a word, but his face talked for him with a sort of laughing expression, so tantalisingly sexy. The eyes had it and it searingly was powerful stuff. I was awestruck and zings zithered down my backbone. The old geezer with him said I looked like Dusty Springfield – ladles of blacking on my eyes I suspect – but I glowed because being a fifteen-year-old fledgling I felt suddenly womanish at the comparison. Romeo smiled a disarming smile and nodded his head. It has just come to me. What if he was dumb, because he spoke not a word? An unreal smile came from my quivering lips. I can't say if they quivered with nervous tension or alluring anticipation. Terence clicked her fingers behind her back and it was like a crescendo of crashing cymbals, jarring me out of my trance. We put our shoes on. Terence mumbled that we should rejoin the gay waltzers, as the boozy gent was breathing fumes over her. Feeling coquettish I had a go at rippling my derriere, as I sallied in Tritz's footprints back towards the dance floor. I did have a sly glance over my shoulder, which was met with a half smile, I think. I watched for him amongst the dancers, but he didn't return. He had to take Tiddly home I suppose.

Terence and I had had enough by elevenish. The strain of sounding all our h's had become an irritant. We collected our wraps, macs that is, went outside, called "Here my good man" to a taxi driver, bundled ourselves into his cab and said "Home James and don't spare the horses". We were home by midnight and had a lovely time banging dustbin lids, picking a chicken, raiding the pickled onion jar and having a couple of glasses of the hard stuff. No doubt I went to bed and contrived a romantic notion involving 'Cary Grant' whom I had met that evening. I was at the dreamy age when any idolised pop star, film star or bus conductor could be fitted into a cowboy outfit and I was a stunning squaw and we made mad passionate love all over the prairie. Vivid imagination ran amok in my dreams.

It has to be said, at sixteen Tritz and I became daredevils and started going out for a drink once in a while, just a little boozing. We were in a pub one evening and our youth showed through, because we left giggling when a man started a strip-tease. If we had been eighteen we would have stayed to see the finale and egged him on.

LEAVING SCHOOL,
THANK GOD

My loathing of school overruled my better judgment and convinced me I wanted to leave at sixteen. Terence implored me to stay on, as she was doing, until I was eighteen, but it was out of the question.

The years had rolled by and shall I say I flowered, as it sounds nice. In my sixteenth year I packed my duffle bag with bits and bobs and left school never more to return. I heaved a sigh of relief the day I passed through the gates for the final time. I can't remember if I cut my tie off. It's only now I can recall a number of favourable days spent in the prison that was school.

As my last school term drew to a close, I applied for a job in an accountants' office. Madness must have interfered with my brain cells. The joy I felt to be turned down. I thought I would be though, because the day I went for my interview the bus I was travelling on was struck by lightning. You try telling that to four or five executive bods you had kept waiting for half an hour. There they sat round the boardroom table puffing on cigars, not the least bit interested in my far-fetched excuse, which believe it or not was the truth. The cards were stacked against me right from the word go, but I do remember putting my foot in it when asked about hobbies and suchlike. I said I didn't belong to a youth club, but I did belong to the Band of Hope. Naturally I mentioned the pledge, "Never to touch the drunkard's drink". Those pompous men were the exact opposite of being impressed. Humbugs and alcoholics all of them I came away thinking. I was never more pleased in my life to be struck off their short list. They had wet lettuce handshakes anyway.

The Smelting Works at Avonmouth had no qualms about employing me as a junior trainee shorthand typist, together with June. Debbie and Barbie were already part of the fixtures and fittings, having joined the company a year earlier. June and I hated the first six months of our working life. We were paid, I know, but we didn't appreciate being sent away to college to learn shorthand and typing with Debbie. We do appreciate it now, as it's our living. But seven years ago I looked upon college as pure misery. Far worse than school I classed it. June and I kept ourselves to ourselves. We didn't fit the bill as run of the mill students. Debbie was in a different class and we only saw her lunchtimes over sausage and chips in a Filton cafe.

The first day at college will live in my memory as hateful from start to finish. I didn't understand what the deuce any of the teachers were blabbing about. Shorthand was hateful, typing was hateful, and I went home and bawled. I hated everything and everybody and I never wanted to set foot inside the college again. Aeons later I learnt that June and Debbie had gone home the first evening and cried the same as I did. We got by though. Typing and shorthand we had to do well at, for Work's sake, but we also chugged through English, Commerce, and Accounting lessons as well. We did have a funny occity for an English lecturer. He had a limp and wore pumps. I did an essay once about life on the ocean floor. I had to chop it apart, make insertions and deletions, and redraft it half a dozen times until it was what he wanted, and not me at all. There was an English lesson that did absorb me. We looked at a book of paintings done by schizophrenics, and I found them quite mind riveting. Each week the English lecturer would tell us what was on at the Scala cinema. We knew full well what kind of film was being shown there! Dubious sex fuelled ones. He thought we ought to go and be indoctrinated. I didn't like the Commerce teacher. He made a petty remark about June and me talking in class the one time, but June stood up for us and he sat down quelled. Besides he was cruel to his kids. They were allowed to eat plain yoghurt, but not ice cream.

June, Debbie and I had to send periodic reports in letter form to the Personnel Manager down at the Works, telling her how we were getting on and how proficient in office skills we were becoming. We weren't very honest, because we usually said we were getting on great and everything was great. But really we couldn't wait to start work.

College was soon thrust behind us and we began to earn our wage. We were labelled junior shorthand typists, no more the stigma of 'trainee'. We did though have to put up with two further years attending college one day a week, which slowly but surely advanced our prowess in the finger whizzing field. Debbie went immediately into the Typing Pool, because she was a year older than June and me. We two floated about the office block for six months, being taught the ropes as to how various departments were run. Jack-of-all-Trades and Odd Jobber we were. However, meeting people in Personnel, Stationery, Print Room and Cen File, before ending up in the Pool, was an experience to be enjoyed.

I liked being in Cen File, but not when it came to doing the filing upstairs in the Sales office. It was a little room overcrowded with six men. I didn't like men in those days. They made me feel uncomfortable. I had to spend anything up to half an hour daily wedged into a square foot corner, afraid to breathe and rustle correspondence, because they both made a noise, and goodness if I dropped a file it sounded like a thunder-clap to my ears. The worst part was knocking on the door and walking into the room, when men's faces looked up from their desks. And walking out again later, when I got the feeling that peepers were boring into my back, or my bum. That feeling made me forget how to walk naturally. Did they talk about me after I'd gone, I wondered, and if so, what did they say? Ooh, the agony of not knowing. Elderly Miss Davies in charge of Cen File and Patricia were incredibly nice ladies. They had been with the company for years and years. One day Miss Davies sprang out at security guards who came to the Works bank, and held them up with a toy water pistol to prove it could be done.

I felt safe with Miss Davies and Patricia, but I didn't for one minute of my stint down the Print Room, which was overrun with practical jokers. I have since learnt a lot more about them from Des, and I'm relieved I didn't know then what I know now. Doreen was the main offender. She'd go over the Transport Cafe and buy cakes for Print Room staff. Often the Office Manager would ask for a Chelsea Bun, which she would obligingly get for him. One day she tried his patience to the limit and he chased her from the Print Room, the only way out for her being through the window. He defied his age, because temper made him run. She had brought him his Chelsea Bun, but as he bit into it the phone rang and he couldn't answer the caller very well apart from spitfire sounds, as there were black cotton strands wrapped round his teeth. Doreen had threaded together all the currants in his bun. Alf, the chief of staff, was just as naughty. One day in particular he bought Des a ring doughnut. It was her birthday. As she looked on, it was cut into segments, distributed and eaten with relish by each member of staff. Des had one crumb. She was spared from eating a doughnut once before. It had had its cream replaced with convincing white frothy glue. The Office Manager suffered again too. Those pranksters somehow drilled a hole in a Murray Mint, filled it with salt, put it back in its wrapper and offered it to him, which he took without question. They told the Manager it was with Bert's compliments. Bert was the old internal Works postie, who proffered Murray Mints right, left and centre. Doreen got displeased herself on one occasion and acted rather impulsively. A chappie bustled into the Print Room protesting about the Irish. Doreen's hubby was one. She gave this fellow a chance to take back what he had said, but he refused, so Doreen grabbed him by his tie and cut it off with scissors she happened to have in her hand. She did the same thing again to another unfortunate being when his tie caught in rotating blades, but on that occasion it was to save his life.

Undoubtedly, June and I were happiest in the Pool. We embarked on our careers as youngsters sat at the front, under the watchful scrutiny of Scottie, our supervisor – she drummed it into me how to spell relevant – improving our status to senior shorthand typists over three years, and gradually making our way to the back of the room. Indeed it was a motley assortment spread throughout the length and breadth of the Pool. There were small fry like June and me in a strange new environment, inbetweeners, that is girls in their twenties and thirties, a few part time Mums, the middle-aged and oldies near to retirement. I swear there wasn't a bitch amongst us. We all got on famously.

My working day began earlier than most typists', because the Smelting Works was situated the other side of Bristol from where we lived, in Avonmouth. Rise and shine for me was at the unearthly hour of 6am. I shared the bus with dockers. An hour later we came to journey's end. The dockers went off to Avonmouth Docks, and I went traipsing a mile up St

Andrew's Road. A very tiring road it was. It was pencil straight and my destiny was in sight from the outset, but it took ages to draw near. Once the bus ran the extra mile or so just for me when my electric haired, toothless Nobby was the driver, at no extra charge of course. One day the Works Manager's chauffeur stopped to give me a lift up the road, and I felt like the cat's whiskers purring along in the Rover – front seat. Lifts were few and far between except for the short spell when an Irish labourer undertook to give me early morning rides. It was after he intimated once or twice he had six kids and wanted seven that I thought I had better make alternative arrangements, which I did. Back to the buses!

Travelling to work wasn't tedious. If I was tired I went to sleep, simple as that. In my Smelting days I bore an egg on my forehead where so many times in sleep my head fell down onto the seat rail in front of me. I always sat at the back of the bus because, if I didn't sleep, I spent the journey studying people and eavesdropping. Coming home was detestable. The bus did nothing but stop start stop start throughout the main traffic black spots of Bristol. At Totterdown a woman took a dog lead for a walk. She didn't have a dog, but trailed the lead and talked to an imaginary one. I saw her from the bus window. A woman stood on the Centre during peak rush hour directing traffic. She wasn't a warden, but thought she was. I saw her from the bus window. I never got used to the chaos. The most it ever took me to get home was two and a half hours, but that was an almighty fluke of a snarl-up. I read both volumes of Forever Amber at bus-stops (I can't read when I'm on the move). Quite often I had to change buses or catch the train and that certainly did create rather a large hole in my pocket moneywise.

Nevertheless one gets immune to a certain extent over irksome journeys. I could put up with them in the main, because my days at the Smelly Works were happy. Not that I had much sleep during the three years I was there. Dad would come home after night shift and find me curled up on the settee, ears bunged with cotton wool, unable to sleep in my bed due to the bang/ crash that went on continuously throughout the night in the factory yard behind our house. I remember once seriously thinking to myself as I lay awake, still awake after hours and hours in bed listening to the racket, I would go over to the yard and hang myself from the loading bay to voice my protest, and pin a note to my nightshirt saying "I can't take any more".

Dad ultimately got things done regarding the noise, because he organised a petition and complained a great deal on my behalf. Then, when the nights became quieter, we moved here to Brook Road on the edge of the golfcourse, and now I moan about the wood pigeons waking me up early.

But to go back to the Avonmouth chapter in my life, each day began the same. My bus-stop was outside Lin's shop, that is Lobb, the newsagent, was her boss. At 7.15 in the morning I would be waiting, tucked inside the doorway, propped against the ice cream freezer watching for my No.99. I made friends with the men who came in for their newspapers. They played a dirty rotten trick on me one morning though. I was in a rush. The bus was approaching, as I scrabbled along the road. I ran into the shop, asked for a magazine to read, stated I would pay for it the next day, dashed out and swung round the hand rail onto the moving bus. I got a seat, because I was panting and wore a loose swagger coat that made me look preggy, but heaps of people had to stand (lots of factory workers caught my bus). I fumbled in my bag for the magazine, turned to page one and was confronted by nude women in sexy poses. I had been handed Playboy. The woman sitting beside me coughed. I went beetroot and thrust it to the bottom of my bag. I stared fixedly out the window, not daring to catch anyone's eye. The Lobbs, father and son, were jokers through and through. On pulling a thread on my skirt one morning the hem came down, but old Mr. Lobb came to my rescue and stapled it back up. He was a lovely chap, yet as a nipper I was scared stiff of him and would wait outside the shop when Dad went in. Pop was permitted to choose my sweets. Old Mrs. Lobb isn't there any longer. She died a while back. The old couple used to take Lin and me for a drive on a Sunday afternoon and treat us to tea and jam scones. We visited a nephew of theirs once who owned a tumbledown farm of many acres. (He wanted a wife and old Mr. and Mrs. Lobb became a pair of tittering matchmakers that day.) The farm had been a Nunnery in years gone by and beneath the ground lay tunnels used for smuggling of all things. Old Mrs. Lobb I think of as the "Well I'll be damned" woman. It was her most common saying. In the shop I became known as Squeaker and the name has stuck.

The girls and women in the Pool were such a friendly, helpful lot and June, Debbie and I soon became established in the colony. We learnt to control run-away electric typewriters, persevere with crackle-voiced men and queer lingo on Dictaphone belts, also how to devise shorthand outlines for things like, what was it now, hydrochlorofluorobenzine, etc. It was a lively pool. I can picture Molly to this day plucking her eyebrows in the coffee breaks. She has been deported, emigrated is her word for it, to Australia now and is working in a jelly bean factory. Whenever a boss came in, and the supervisor started patting her hair, and looking towards us smiling (her girls we were, whether fifteen or fifty-five), we naturally wanted to know what was being said about us up front. Molly would beckon Barbie over, and Barb being a marvel at lip-reading would watch the moving lips of the supervisor and bossman and tell us every single word being said. When Scottie thought we had overlapped a coffee break, she would call out "Girls, girls, come along girls, back to work" and talking would cease apart from one person's chatter, Barbie's. Deaf she may be, but Barbie is bright as a button and like a shiny new penny she radiates a dazzle.

Barb joined the company as telex operator the same year that Debbie did. She knows the telex inside out and carries on conversations with machines anywhere in the world. Immediately before anyone went on holiday abroad, Barbie would tap out a message to any old foreign company in the appropriate port of call, and enquire what their weather was like. She possesses an uncanny instinct, as she understands immediately when the buzzer goes on the telex and the red light flashes indicating an incoming message. She would hurtle from one end of the Typing Pool to the other and be ready and waiting to answer the caller. Dear Barbie, she yelled across the Pool one day that I was metal and ought to be locked up in a metal hospital, and when I chuckled, I was historical, not hysterical. That's not the only thing she yelled out. Once it was in a very loud voice "Angieeeeeee" – she pronounces it with a tribe of eeeeees – "do you kiss with your tongue?" I deviated from giving a straight answer, because the older women's fingers silently hovered above their keyboards. I expect they were sorry I wasn't more explicit in my, ahem, admission, bless them. When I found my voice I told her "It depends". The other day Barbie said her Mum was going to the Black and White Maternity (Minstrel) Show. The times ever Lin and I have told her our friend's name is Meryl not Beryl. It makes no difference. Barb always always greets her with "Hi Beryl". Diane hates to be called Di, but Barbie says Di unceasingly and Diane is sick of telling her "My name is

Diane". We laugh at Barbie's comical sayings, but she joins in with a hee hee hee too. Last Easter, out for a drive with Des, we passed a Cheap Manure sign. Barbie was all for knocking on the door which we couldn't understand. She explained she would like her nails done properly. I do phone Barbie every so often, but leave most of the talking to her. She does wear a hearing aid of course. I butt in from time to time, shouting from here to kingdom come, but it can be disconcerting as it was yesterday. Not because of Barb's deafness, but because two fully grown eight or nine year old boys were tap dancing on my phone box roof. Perishers!

We had a mobile chest X-ray unit visit the Works every so often, and the girls and I trooped along once to see if we were sound. Letters came later proclaiming our tubes were clog free, not a wheeze amongst us and no reason why we shouldn't take up the bagpipes. I had been worried that I might be asked for a second X-ray, as on the first I had been held together by a safety pin. The hook and eye had parted company in my bra fastener. But the pin must have blended in okay with my ribs.

I had sunstroke after a day trip to Weymouth with the family, and my purple inflated legs couldn't carry me anywhere for a few days. I had to get a doctor's note and go on the club or panel, as Nan would say. The following week I returned to the Smelters recovered, but scratchy where I was skinning. At the end of each day I didn't remove my feet from a layer of rubber dust, well that too, but skin flakes that had peeled away from my paisley patterned body.

One Monday June didn't turn up at the college for day release. I hated being by myself. I thought how could she do this to me even if she was ill. Next morning, going into work, I met one of the girls who told me June's Mum had died that weekend, and June had telephoned work herself to say why she was absent. I locked myself in the toilet and had a quiet howl. I went to see June that evening. It was one of those things hard to believe had happened and harder still to face, but June is braver than most. I think she had known for a long time her Mum was very ill. Debbie and I went to June's for tea before night school every week. We hadn't realised. Her Mum was the type of person to ease other people's pain and disregard her own.

I spent a month away from the office block, working in the Stores out on the Plant. I tripped over the Works railway lines to get there, glancing in many mirrors on the way. It wasn't vanity. I had to make certain goods trains weren't shunting. Stores was a dingy place. Row upon row of large pigeon-holes confronted me, stacked full of tyres, nuts, bolts, tools, rubber gloves, etc. It was like a maze to me. I took half an hour to find the loo on day one.

When a sizeable number of us juniors started work at Imperial Smelting we did have a conducted tour of the Plant, dressed in ankle length brown overalls and tin helmets, but apart from my stay in the Stores that was the only other time I came into contact with the manual back-bone of the industry. Occasionally we would know all about it, should coughing start up in the Typing Pool. That meant the wind was bringing the sulphur fumes our way, but Alf and his ammonia down Print Room got blamed. There was a Mr. De La Mere who brought work into the Pool from site. He wore a Davy Crockett hat.

One rather strange happening occurred at least a couple of years after I had left the Smelters. Barbie mentioned that a middle-aged fellow in the Accounts section had changed his hairstyle. He had gone the whole hog. In my day he had had a side parting with hair combed back off his face and slicked down with grease. Now Barbie said he was sporting a soft fluffy Beatle style haircut with not a hint of Brylcreem. I wasn't amazed in the slightest. A flash of extra-sensory perception had told me this would come about, probably long before even he knew it would. My flashes are few and far between.

During one lunchtime I developed a seething, troubled mind. I had gone over the Transport Cafe for a cob or a bap, whichever I craved. I had given the woman behind the counter a pound note and she gave me change for a ten bob note. It was when I got back to the Typing Pool I discovered this, and straightway ran back to the cafe to claim the rest of my change. The fiend of a woman point blank refused to give me my money and said I must have made a mistake. It played on my mind for the rest of the day. When I got home on borrowed bus fare I went upstairs, still feeling slighted, and caught sight of a pin cushion body of a lady. In my wrath I stuck pins vigorously into the felt body. I closed my eyes and thought "Let that be a lesson to you, you swindler, pocketing my hard-earned cash". The devil was in my soul, because next day she wasn't in the shop. God save me, worry trounced my system. I imagined I had inflicted terrible injuries on that female I had molested. My relief was great, to see her back at her diddling the following day, although it wasn't in me to ask how she was. For my piece of nastiness, I received my just desserts. In the Pool I bent one morning to insert a plug in the floor, and couldn't get up again without the help of June's arm. I kept my trap shut, apart from oohs and aahs each time I moved, but agonies imprisoned me in the chair when I got home. Dolt of a Doc next morning made me touch my toes. I dared not open my mouth lest I screamed, but my face spoke for me. Since then I've slept on a door and now and again resort to an elasticated roll-on for support.

WEDDING BELLS AND CANADA HERE I COME

On the 1st July 1966 Rish and Bob got married. We were all in a bit of a daze, not quite grasping the fact that she was leaving us for good and going to live in Canada. I don't remember having much to do with the wedding preparations. We did have a rehearsal at the Church and coming home afterwards, as I sat in the back of Bob's Mini with the Best Man, I got asked for a date. I coloured up and all I could think of to say was "I'm too young". I was 17. It was polite of me, because I could have told him "You're too old". He was 21. I knew Rish and Bob were trying to hide smirks in the front of the car. Wasn't I daft? I might have been married to an airline pilot now.

Rish and I had to decide a week or two before the wedding what colour I should have my hair. We plumped for blonde rather than dark brown. I think that was the last time I coloured my hair, because thereafter I didn't trust my own judgment.

The Wedding Day was beautiful. It was a Friday. Unfortunately, the Wedding Cars arrived an hour too soon and the guests and I, Rish's only bridesmaid, were at Bob's village church extremely early. Poor Nan and Aunt Olly had to knock on someone's door and ask if they could borrow a loo. Rish and Pop held hands tightly in the car and rode round the country lanes to kill time. The muck spreaders, when asked, stopped their racket in the fields behind the church, so the vows could be heard by one and all. It was everything a wedding should be. Bob wore new shoes with the price tag stuck on the sole, clearly visible when he knelt. Marg, Rish's friend, started the flow of tears at the reception.

Rish and Bob went off to spend the weekend at Bournemouth. It must have been the following Monday that Mum, Dad, the boys and I caught the train to Southampton. Poor Mum. Those were the days she lived in a sort of dreamlike world, a complete fog. Her nerves were shot to pieces. She also had a type of morning sickness every day. The family had bed and breakfast at Southampton. I was in with Mum and Dad and the night before Rish sailed away Mum was up every minute pacing the floor like an expectant Dad. She had to have the bedroom door wide open too, so as not to feel shut in. Although it was their honeymoon, Rish wanted us to be with them on that dreary, overcast day. I haven't forgotten going down to the Docks. Our family, Bob's Mum and Freddie (her partner), Aunt Margaret and Bernard (her man friend) stood waiting to greet them in what appeared to be a huge warehouse. We were allowed on board the Carmania to see their cabin. Nine of us wedged in. We tried to jolly one another along, all talking at once, except Bloss. She was too far-gone sat on their bunk. The double dose of drugs she had taken made her fall asleep. But it was for the best. She wasn't aware of what was happening. We were able to lead her quietly off the boat. We stood on the quayside and watched Rish on deck. We shouted up to her until it became pointless. They grew smaller and smaller, becoming specks as they drifted out into that grey sea, and still we waved. It was drizzling. Al began to cry, and then the rest of us females did.

Mum slowly, but quite agonizingly, got better when letters began arriving each week and she knew Rish was well and happy. Rish did her best to hide homesickness, but we could tell it was there for a long time.

The year following Rish's departure for Canada I became a fanatical scrooge. I scrimped and scraped doggedly. The day she left England I swore she would be seeing me in 1967. I kept my promise. Soon after Rish settled in Canada I joined the Anglo American Families Association. There weren't many members in those days, and we met on the first Wednesday evening in each month in a cold, ill-lit scouts hut near the old Glen. I considered the other members fuddy-duddies and old fogeys, because nobody my age belonged to the A.A.F.A. then. I didn't like going to the monthly meetings unless slides featuring Canada were shown, but it was necessity, due to the fact I could only afford to fly with a charter group.

It was decided I should go visit in October 1967. It seems so long ago now. As the holiday drew near I became a zombie, not knowing if I was coming or going. I can remember rethreading my drawers with fresh elastic, as expenses wouldn't run to new ones. Mum and Pop bought me a watch. They thought I had persevered greatly in my aim to save enough for the trip.

Mum, Dad and Al came up to Heathrow to see me off. I could have broken down and wept, I was that scared of flying across the Atlantic. And I was frightened of being on my tod. I had no self-confidence. I did look over my shoulder, but the family had gone, out of sight. "Press on girl" I coaxed myself. I took my place in a long queue of travellers-to-be. I didn't have the faintest idea what was coming, or what I had to produce first, although my eyes never veered from those being seen to in front. My face, full of fear, must have spoken volumes. Gripping tightly to my wodge of documents, I was propelled through passport check. I nodded and shook my head in reply to questions asked, because I couldn't have spoken to save my life. The departure lounge was chock-a-block with people. I sat and gave weak smiles to no one in particular. A fur-draped woman with a mature young daughter came and sat opposite me. I tried to talk to them, but felt very backward. When I mentioned that this was my first flight, and I hadn't a clue what I was doing, they exchanged glances as if to say "What a boring child". What a horrible pair I thought and uneasiness swamped me. I came out of my shell though when Mrs. Green introduced herself to me. She was also travelling alone to Toronto and took care of me as if I was an infant. She had noticed my nervousness when I left the family. I didn't mind queuing up for duty free stuff (Rish had sent a list) and being jostled now that I had a companion, but I had left it too late to get Bob's Bacardi, because the flight was announced before I was attended to. Out to the Boeing 707 we walked. I couldn't see Mum, Dad and Al on any roof, but I waved madly in case. My friend and I had to separate on the flight to New York. She was up one end of the plane and I was down the other, but we waved to one another as we boarded at different ends.

I sat by the window, alongside a dear old man and his daughter. He and I were tremendously excited. I had been told by thoughtful people to swallow like crazy and crunch a barley sugar on take-off so this I did, but not with ease. I shut my eyes too. Consequently, I couldn't believe we were up when the old man nudged me and said gleefully "We're in heaven". I was virtually glued to the window the length of the flight, except at feeding times. We had a huge meal and no sooner that was over, it was snack time. My magazines and paperback weren't touched. I couldn't get over I was up in 'space'. We arrived over New York near enough on time, but couldn't land for an hour. Isn't Kennedy Airport supposed to be the busiest place in the world on a Friday evening? We had chosen to arrive not only on a Friday evening, but the start of Thanksgiving weekend! Traffic was teeming. We circled and circled, and I got hotter and groggier, but the New York lights fascinated me. Eventually we touched down, but the plane had to wander from runway to runway, looking for a place to park.

We were unloaded and filed into the arrivals building where I paired up with Mrs. Green again. Immigration wasn't too bad. They helped themselves to anything they wanted clutched in my paw. However, customs at Kennedy Airport did put the wind up me. A 'mile' long queue formed behind me. A giant sized black man, who politely beckoned me to open my case, confronted me. Numb with shock, and thinking the end of the road had come, I fumbled for my keys. The case clicked open and a thorough search was conducted through my smalls, etc. Even my packets of oogies were squeezed. I thought if he ripped them apart I would die on the spot. His "okay" hit me like wine gums. One leg of the journey was over.

However, we had missed our connecting flight and had to wait two hours for the next. We toured the airport in a bus. At long last we reported to the Air Canada building and the man at the desk got confused over my name and checked up by phone, to England I thought. I tagged along behind Mrs. Green, not daring to let her slip out of sight for an instant. If she went to spend a penny I certainly did too. We were fit to drop waiting for our flight to Toronto. I was almost a goner. I had it fixed in my mind I was going to stay right where I was. I would spend my holiday in the seat I was sat in in Kennedy Airport. I was exhausted and my nerves were extremely fraught. I was convinced Rish wouldn't be at Toronto Airport to meet me. When she saw that I didn't stumble off the plane I was supposed to come on, I felt sure she would think I wasn't coming and go home. However, something spurred me on.

We boarded a little plane and I was overcome by excitement again. I couldn't understand why the businessmen across the aisle were leafing through sheaves of papers, instead of eyeing the whole kit and caboodle like me. I didn't want to miss a fallen biscuit crumb. I swear to this day I saw Rish and Bob through the plane window as we landed. I was second off the plane and felt like a celebrity waving to balconies swarming with multi-coloured, fly size people. We were hustled into a clinical empty building. Forms had to be filled in, incorrectly due to the state we were in. We went into the Customs Hall and were subjected to a mode of torture. Sliding doors kept opening and shutting. Behind the doors Rish, Bob and a host of people stood. I was able to see them for a mere few seconds at a time and wave frantically. I was blubbering uncontrollably too. Then the doors would shut blocking them from view. It went on like that, with the doors opening and closing, as Mrs. Green and I fell over luggage accumulating on the floor and barged people, as we groped our way round the conveyor belt bearing our cases. We snaffled them and then it was the last dreaded ordeal. I must have looked like a dishevelled hippy with my poxy grease smeared face and black running eyes. The interrogator asked if I was Irish. I gave a blank look, because in my condition thought was impossible. I didn't know whether I was or I wasn't at that minute. He overlooked my dumbness. His next question was a blockbuster. He asked if I was bringing in LSD. I think I must have given a strangled cry, because in the next breath he told me to "Beat it". I needed no second telling. I sent people flying sideways in my haste to get through those infernal doors to Rish and safety. When I did I was stricken with more wails. Grubby Pange had made it to Canada and there followed a never to be forgotten holiday.

I fell in love with Canada, the "golly gees", and "your welcome" after a thank you and just about everything else. Rish greets all her guests with home-made cherry cheesecake. I can understand why. It makes them return. October, in my opinion, has to be the best month to visit Canada, when the Fall colours are at their most beautiful. Seeing is believing. The reds, golds, the browns and orange on so vast a scale captivated me. Wherever Rish and Bob took me I sighed a rapturous "Ecstasy". I never quite knew where we were going until we got there, as Rish kept putting her hands over my eyes when we drew near signposts. I admit the first day in Canada I had my doubts about her. We were on our way to Glenhaffy Conservation Area and she began to give me a running commentary. There was room for me in the front seat of the car between them. At one instance she pointed out the car window and said, "Look at those sods". "Oh dear" thought I, "a year away from home and Rish has learnt unsavoury language. Bob should take his belt to her, or did she pick it up from him?" My rather shocked face glanced out of the side window, expecting to see road-hogs, but instead a lorry sped by loaded with rolled grass/earth mats. I did titter at the sods. On another occasion Rish called me a grockle, which I thought at first was a Canadian swear word until she put me wise.

I was well and truly entranced by Niagara Falls. How many times did I walk away and return for another, and yet another look until I was wringing wet. As far as I was concerned, the green and misty mountainous Horseshoe Falls with its rainbow halo had more magnetic power than a dishy fellah.

Rish and Bob took me for a weekend to Ottawa and the first night we huddled together on benches to see the Son et Lumiere. It was a magnificent sight to see the Houses of Parliament lit up on the Hill, and to listen to the compelling voice explaining the history of Canada. I didn't want to forget it, but I have. Ottawa has the friendliest chipmunks. We couldn't help but talk to them as if they were babies. That weekend we also drove twenty odd miles into Quebec and touched on the edge of Gatineau Provincial Park. The scenery had me in raptures. Forests and lakes stretched far and wide, and the colouring was of a brilliance beyond compare. We didn't get to see their friends at Renfrew because of fog, but I recall their names tickled me; Billy and Roly Bees and their sprogs were Bart and Doug. One day I would love to go back and see Calabogie where wild raspberries grow in plenty, and Mountain Chute. These were wild areas of Ontario where hunters and trappers roamed. I saw the trailer Rish and Bob lived in for three months when Bob was working on the Hydro project there. Poor Rishy didn't enjoy that quarter year. The mosquitoes loved and devoured her, and the ants did likewise with her pumpkin pie one day. I do declare that the Fall colours were unrivalled in that area, and no words of mine can do justice to them. My eyes won't ever again feast upon anything quite so spectacular as the richness of a Canadian Fall – sunshine a necessity of course. The sighs came out of me wherever we went, and I wouldn't like to guess the number of times I said incredulously "I can't believe it". How I wished for eyes in the back and sides of my head as Bob drove along the highways and byways.

I've still got the maps Rish drew for me, plotting routes around Toronto I could follow on the days she was working. Out by myself I was a little nervous. I avoided cops, because they wore guns. I was scared crossing roads. I knew jaywalking was an offence, but didn't know exactly what the word meant and whether or not I was guilty of it. Lots of funny people stuck their arms out, indicating they were crossing the road, and traffic would always stop for them. I found post-boxes peculiar. I had to walk right the way round one before finding the tip-up opening lid. No slits to be seen over there, not like here. I would hand shop assistants silver subway discs, thinking they were money. I did think chaps eyed up girls appreciatively far more than they did at home. Embarrassing when one isn't used to it. I was so nosey listening in on people's conversations. The accent wowed me. What was my favourite advert on the telly? The Benson and Hedges one with the long cigarette, which kept getting in people's way. It had such a hummable tune.

The three of us went to see a drive-in movie, but we had to wrap blankets round our legs because it was perishing. During the intermission there was a mad dash from the cars to the self-service restaurant for burgers, French fries and steaming coffees. What odd things I remember. The powder room was violet and immaculately clean. All Canadian loos are clean without exception.

Bob was working in Belleville at the time of my visit, but he came home two or three nights in the week for college and, of course, weekends. We went to Belleville on the coach one day and had a meal at Gran's where Bob had lodgings. While he was under Gran's roof he was permanently bloated. She looked after him too well, because he put on so much weight his bed collapsed under him one night. I put my foot in it by telling Gran her house was homely, because in Canada that means not very nice.

Rish was so happy one Friday afternoon when a knock came on the apartment door at 3pm and she opened it to find a grinning Bob there. Home for good from Belleville with four bottles of wine in his arms, presented by office colleagues he had left behind. We celebrated and went to the Town and Country Restaurant, where we paid a set sum and ate whatever we wanted, a vast quantity I recollect.

I had clipped my hair up for the occasion, as I didn't want it flopping in my food. I knew I shouldn't have, because the wind had whistled and howled all day long. We ran from the car park to the restaurant entrance, but in vain. My hair needed a quick complete restyle in the Ladies. Rish and I grabbed the metal out and let it hang in knotted wisps. We couldn't waste precious eating time combing it.

Oh my, the food we ploughed through that evening! For starters we had egg salad, chicken salad, potato salad, pineapple and sultanas in a cheesy sauce, yams and hams, tongue, meatballs, shrimps and goodness knows what else. There were so many other things we didn't have room for on our plates. I could see why Rish and Bob had told me not to have a bread roll when a basket came round. After the hour it took to eat our first course, we had placed before us our main course, a piece of roast beef the size of which left me dumbfounded. It would easily have fed a family of four back home. How I do not know, but we managed a sweet and swapped two-thirds each.

Bob ordered a brisk walk downtown following the meal, but it was a slow plod, with a crawl into Sam the Record Man so I could buy Engelbert for Mum. Canadian records were weird. They had big central holes and you had to buy middles for them. I wonder where the book is that I bought? It was called Belly Button and supposed to be controversial. I was quite scared about bringing it home, in case Customs officials discovered it. It was one of those books poking fun at the Newfies (people from Newfoundland).

What was it the Maple Leaf Ice Hockey Team got called, Loafs that was it? Loafers I suppose. In my dictionary it says alongside loaf, a lump or cabbage-head.

How can we ever forget the letter Mum wrote while I was there? We were sat in the lounge and Rish was reading it aloud, but she got so far and couldn't carry on. Tears were rolling down her cheeks. Laughter tears at Pop's expense. Mum said they hadn't been able to go to sleep one night, due to the infernal din over the Transport Yard. Dad blew his top, got up and said he was going over there to give the foreman a piece of his mind. He put his trousers on over his jama bottoms and stormed off. When he returned he was calm, after telling the Transport Depot precisely what he thought of them, and Mum and Dad then managed to get half a night's rest. In the morning Mum was talking over the hedge to a neighbour, who remarked with a chuckle "Some couple couldn't wait to get home last night, cause there's a pair of underpants on your hedge Mrs. B". Mum coloured up and changed the subject quickly, because she had instinctively twigged, at the woman's remark, why Dad had been unable to find his pants that morning. He normally leaves them in his trousers and what must have happened was that in his temper, the previous night, he had overlooked them when he put his trousers on. As he thundered round to Western Transport they must have worked their way down his leg and come out the bottom. Pop was too furious to notice. Mum waited for the right opportunity, when there wasn't a soul to be seen, and nipped out to retrieve one pair of pants off the hedge. Somebody must have picked them up off the pavement and put them there.

Rish and I often went in the bargain basement of Eatons store, as they sold the best waffles. I had my first pizza in Canada at Yorkdale. It isn't the world's largest undercover shopping precinct now, but it was then I think. I tried my first of many things in October 1967. It is all down in my diary: cheesecake, brown beans not orange ones, huckleberry/blueberry pie, pumpkin pie (my favourite which looked vile, but was absolutely delish), Boston Cream Pie, bran muffins and butter tarts, cherry custard ice cream, maple and pecan ice cream and coconut ice cream to die for, giant milkshakes and sundaes even I could not finish, papa burgers (not teen or mama ones), broiled steaks over charcoal and garlic bread, chicken breasts in sour cream, corn-beef on rye (not like our corned beef at all) with dill pickle and coleslaw bunged on top. I even tried caviare, fluffy pancakes soaked in maple syrup, wieners coated in cornflake crumbs with tomato catsup, mustard and sweet relish – I had to have all the trimmings. We set ourselves quite a task going into the Do-nut shop. There were a mere 56 varieties to choose from! We came away with six different ones. At home we cut each one in three and therefore tasted all six. I developed my passion for Chinese food in Canada after Bob rang up for a meal to be delivered. I fell down the stairs in my haste to get to it. I know exactly what we had, because I wrote it down in my diary: egg rolls, sweet and sour breaded chicken with pineapple, beef chow mein, mushroom egg foo yong, and fortune cookies. Food is definitely my main weakness. We went shopping one day, either to the Dominion or Loblaws store, and when we got home we found in Rish's shopping bag several slices of salami bologna and head cheese, evidently belonging to the man who had gone before us in the checkout queue. We ate it for lunch.

Toronto held a British week whilst I was there and Union Jacks galore decorated shop fronts and stores. I walked into Simpsons one day and had a pan of toffees thrust under my nostrils. "Do try an English toffee, they're delicious", the assistant gushed. I smiled and said no thank you. I nearly asked to sample a Canadian one, but thought of my pimps. We went to the Canadian National Exhibition to see something of British Week there. The British Food Hall was hopeless. I hadn't even tasted half the things on display. I was very chuffed to see my own stand in one of the exhibition halls, or to be precise the stand set up by I.S.C. (N.S.C) Ltd of Avonmouth, England. I knew it would be there, because I had typed letters to Canada from Avonmouth inviting big cheeses to attend the stand. Amazing, I thought, to have travelled 3,000 miles and be faced with a model plan of my own place of work. I thought it best to remain incognito, otherwise Canada may have forced me to divulge secrets. Well I did know things like how many vending machines were in the office block.

Canada is a land of sunsets. I'd go out on the apartment balcony and wait for the sky to change colour. I was never disappointed.

Some afternoons I walked along to Alexander Muir Park and sat watching the black squirrels scampering. The robins were extremely large. It was a wonderful life I was leading in October 1967. No cares had I then. I had an hour more than I had bargained for too, because the clocks altered. That pleased me. I experienced all weathers: sunshine, biting winds, fog, hail and snow flurries. I was in my element however God acted up. On my last weekend we watched kiddies and grown-ups ice-skating outside City Hall. Snow began to fall and I think I was a source of amusement to a group of students, simply because I asked, "Will it pitch?" It was there a woman approached me and asked where I was from. She must have thought I was rolling in dough, because she did her durndest to sell me a plot of land in Florida. Persistent enough, she was, to invite the three of us out to dinner. Bob growled at her in the end. No doubt I looked a sucker more than I looked rich.

On my last day it rained. I washed out two pairs of knickers and had to bring them home wet in my case. I also ironed my clothes before packing. A stupid thing to do, but it kept me occupied. I didn't want to leave. I met Rish from work outside the subway. I said I felt queer and she said shush, because queer meant just that in Canada, and not sickified. We had bags of time at the airport, but not a lot to say. Bob bought a News of the World at a kiosk and I bought a Chatelaine. Parting was painful. Moreso because for twenty minutes after, we could still see one another and mouth words. An inch thick glass separated us, and that was all. I wanted to put my foot through it. Turning my back on them and walking away was such a hard thing to do.

I sat with my Mrs. Green on the plane to New York. We were supplied with a chicken dinner on that hour-long flight. I picked at it. I was blue. We had a three-hour wait at Kennedy Airport and I began to feel more myself. I was looking forward then and not back. On the plane taking me home I ate heartily. Lights were switched off and I had a little rest, but wouldn't sleep. My eyes remained stuck to the window. I saw what I wanted to see, the dawn come up. The sky was split in two, one half was black and star-studded, the other streaky red, which gradually turned yellow, followed by a mystifyingly blue. As I watched eagle-eyed I wanted to shout, "Wake up" at the snoozers and dozers "Look out your windows. Don't miss it", but I disturbed not a soul. They opened their peepers to dazzling sunshine.

My diary states we landed at 11.48am. Mum and Dad had got up at 2.30 that morning, caught the 4 o'clock train and been in the airport since 20 past 7 to meet me. They were bushed, but enjoyed the sights to be seen at Heathrow. I couldn't stop chatting and hugging them, and Dave and Al when I clapped eyes on them at tea-time. I needed a hot water bottle in bed that night, as I was missing the central heating, but didn't sleep for a long while. I was determined not to, until I had relived umpteen memories. Many have stayed fresh in my mind. Canada is quite a magnificent country.

It goes without saying that I pined for my sis.

On my first day back at work I went in to Lin's shop as usual, and there was hung a large piece of cardboard with the words scrawled thereon "Welcome home to our dear Squeaker". On the other side was attached a child's manicure set given free with the Mandy comic. That day too Rish was entirely to blame when I showed myself up in front of an MBE boss at Avonmouth. He was a nice man. Getting on in years, but he had a twinkle in his eye, and I got called a variety of sweeteners like cherub, dear heart, honey bee, etc. I was still telling the typing pool about my holiday when he required me for shorthand. He looked at me over the tops of his glasses and asked how I had liked Canada, and I gave him a string of words like marvellous, beautiful, wonderful and fabulous. He remarked what a close family we were and next minute I was blubbering, snuffling and saying I had no idea when I would see Rish again. I couldn't see through two waterfalls to take dictation and I got hiccups trying to curb my quaking body. The poor man comforted me best he could. He was dreadfully upset himself, because he thought he was at fault for me being upset, and told me to come back later. I spent the following half hour locked in the loo crying uncontrollably.

One thing about those loos petrified the girls and me. We'd be sat there and along would patrol a whopping great cockroach. Up would go our legs and we would sit most awkwardly, and shivering in fear and coldness, until the blighter had passed on his way and we could put feet to the floor once again.

IMPROVING THE MIND

The month after my Canadian trip the Smelting Works sent June and me to Hampshire on a week's course. It was a course to improve the mind generally. We left Bristol on a Saturday morning in late November with misgivings, because the Office Manager had told us we were in for a difficult time. We met the other girls on the course at a youth centre in London and ate lunch with mentally retarded boys before journeying by coach to Avoncliff.

What a place! In days gone by it must have been a manor house inhabited by wealthy landowners. It was situated well off the beaten track, which was the whole idea. In a sense it was intended that we be cut off from civilisation. The evening we arrived there was no electricity, so we couldn't have anything hot to eat or drink to thaw us out. We met the course director and two other tutors (women) before being shown to our rooms. There were four or five girls to a room, about seven bedrooms in use. No one berthed with anybody they knew, and actually June and I did little together during the week. We had to mix with complete strangers. We were all in the same boat so shyness soon evaporated. The first half hour was spent unpacking by candle-light. We were far too old to squabble over who got the softest bed. Minor defects and small luxuries in the rooms were noted, but not quibbled over, like some had electric fires whilst others had radiators, some had a wash-basin, others didn't. There were plenty of bathrooms and extra blankets for cold-blooded mortals. We had our first nerve jangling session that evening in the sitting room. Candles were flickering around us. Introductions! It was made less severe, because we had to talk to the girl next to us for five or ten minutes, then tell the rest of the group all the juicy info we had found out, rather than prattle on about ourselves. A bell woke us early each morning. There was a rota for washing up. Seven girls at a time in one very sizeable kitchen! I don't remember any breakages. At meal-times we moved around to different tables, therefore getting to know, if only slightly, all of the girls.

Our first full day there was a Sunday. We spent the morning at church. We weren't asked if we were believers. In the afternoon there was a hike. We were issued with gumboots and they were essential. On that late November afternoon we sloshed, at times, knee-deep in mud and thoroughly enjoyed ourselves. The countryside was perfect: marshes and bogs, woodland, sprawling valleys and hills covered in brown scrub. Frisky ponies roamed the moorland, but no other humans apart from us. The chilly wind whipped colour into our cheeks, as we walked on in resolute steps. We were relying on the tutors to lead us safely back to Avoncliff. I should include the two Labradors and Dennis in our merry band. Dennis belonged to the head cook and was a mischievous laddie who kept losing his duffle coat on the march. Seeing that he only had his head in the hood it wasn't surprising. Sunday evening we began writing our log-books. Also we had to design a cover, which expressed our feelings towards the course, and how we hoped to benefit from it. My drawings were pathetically second-rate.

The hard graft really began on Monday. We were divided into three groups. The curriculum was varied with sessions entitled Getting and Spending, The Occasion may Arise, Improvisation, Personal Relationships, Good Grooming, Current Affairs, Committee Procedure, Airing our Views, Speech and we had to make speeches too. It was hideous hearing my dull as ditch-water, or is it dish-water, voice played back on the tape recorder. I thought I sounded coarse and common as muck, but funny enough the London girls liked June's and my West Country lilt. We had several movement sessions which commenced with us all feeling utterly self-conscious, but within half an hour we had thrown caution to the wind and 'trees' were sprouting out of the hallway floor like nobody's business. I couldn't get the hang of good deportment though, and taking off an imaginary coat and gloves correctly. Throughout the week we had several craft periods. I chose to make a gonk rather than a lampshade or something useful. Goodness knows why. I can't sew. I've been told I hem backwards. I thought my imagination could help me there better than my stitching could. People referred to my gonk as Groucho Marx with his fierce looking face. He's here in the room with me, hanging by a long strand of red wool hair from the key in the wardrobe.

The days were long, but we didn't seem to get over-tired. Three evenings we had guest speakers come to Avoncliff, such interesting people. One woman spoke of her life helping others, that is women prisoners and their families, unmarried mothers and hospital patients. A man to be greatly admired came and spoke of the war, his incarceration in prisoner of war camps (mainly to do with the time he spent in Colditz) and his escapes from them. It amazed me how he had sought and found enjoyment in the most abominable situations. The last speaker impressed me most. She spoke of her devotion to the handicapped. We saw slides of how these poor people cope with their disablement. I was moved, because when I came home I wrote to a welfare bod, asking if I could help take care of the mentally handicapped part-time. He wrote to say he'd come and see me, but he couldn't keep the first appointment, and the second he didn't turn up for neither. Maybe my conviction was being tested. I didn't persevere in my quest to help. Other petty things became time consuming.

Mid-week we were let loose on a spending spree in Bournemouth. We did too have a trip to Poole Pottery where most of us bought dolphins.

Friday was the day we had to put into practice everything we had learnt. We were giving a dinner party that evening for air force pilots stationed at Hamble. We worked like troopers getting the place spick and span. There was flower arranging to be done, tables to be laid. I don't know how, but I fitted in a last walk to one of the two lakes in the grounds for five minutes solitary. I don't think I was dodging chores. We had plenty of time to titivate.

I washed and set Mandy's hair. Every girl who went on that course must remember Amanda. She was like a chirpy little sparrow and a breath of fresh air combined. There was nothing false about her yet she needed masses of reassurance from us. She became like a mascot. Her background was different to ours, partly a reason why we took her to our hearts. She came from a very poor family, was the oldest of a handful of kids (but younger than the rest of us) and worked in a sweet factory. She was on the course hoping against hope to achieve her Duke of Edinburgh gold award. All the other girls were shorthand typists, secretaries and nurses.

We were on tenterhooks come the evening and quite bowled over by the super-duper uniformed men, real men not boys, who walked through the doors of Avoncliff. I was one of several girls who waited on them hand, foot and finger at table. I didn't mind in the slightest. Mandy and I served fourteen. When the Christmas Dinner was finally over, the party began in very high spirits. There was modern and ballroom dancing, musical chairs, pennies balanced between two foreheads, and a stamping game, the conga and locomotion. I fell hook line and sinker for one of the boys in blue, who didn't have volumes to say, but what he did was meaningful. We kept drifting apart in games, but always seemed to get back to each other's side again. The end of the evening came far too soon. There was a draw and I went to get raffle tickets I had left in my purse. On my return from the next room, I found it was all over and the pilots were boarding their coach. I stood on the steps and waved with the rest. The coach was held up for quite a while, because there were men missing. Girls too. Eventually their number was accounted for and off they went.

It was a late night. After the dinner dance, although tired, we assembled in the sitting room for our final get-together. The director said she hoped that we had gained in knowledge about others and ourselves, and that the things we had been told, perhaps seemingly unimportant, we could take away, digest and remember. I don't think any of us slept that night. In the early hours of the morning we were still talking over the events of the week, or popping along to so and so's room to say goodbye. Several of us padded along to Mandy's room and found her full of the giggles. She had overdone it with the punch. We had too. The word that sparked us off was pitch. Mandy said she fell down one once and we wondered what on earth it was. She said it wasn't exactly a ditch, and it wasn't exactly a pit. We were none the wiser, but Mandy surely did make us hoot. In fact the staff came up to see what the commotion was about.

There was one thing that occurred on the course, which I can't explain. I had popped along the landing late one night to go to the bathroom, as is my wont, and strange as it may seem, I wouldn't come out again for ages. Why?

Because a horrible fear suddenly engulfed me. I distinctly knew there was a bod outside the door. And I don't believe in ghosts, and I'm not afraid of the dark. When senses became normal I unlocked the door, let myself out and hurried back to bed. Okay, I'm a clot, but I still think of it as an unsolved mystery.

The Smelting Works had spent a good deal of money sending June and me on the course. I fail to understand what they got out of it, but I enjoyed it. Immediately after the course I ordered the Sunday Times to be delivered each week. Lobb's paper shop delighted in taking the mickey out of me. For a month or so I gamely battled through that monstrous paper, but I got on the family's nerves, because spread out the paper and I took up a great deal of the living room. I came to the conclusion it was wrong that practically the whole of my Sundays was taken up ploughing through the Sunday Times, so I gave it up and went back to reading the News of the World. I did find it more entertaining, especially the week I opened up to find Desmond the hairdresser staring back at me. He was in drag costume. I should have realised what his outside interests were because Flo, next door to Lin, had introduced him to me as "Desmond with the virgin hands". He was rollered up sat under the drier himself the last time I went for a trim.

SLOWLY MATURING

For the first couple of years at work I had little time for boys. Tritz couldn't understand why I was such a late developer in that field. She had been at it for years. Dating I mean. Lin and I didn't become boy mad until we were, let me see, eighteen. But we didn't miss out on fun times. We were still going to the pictures roughly once a week.

I had rather a blushing experience with Lin coming out of the Odeon Cinema. We were going through the exit tunnel, first out with people swarming behind us, and I pushed open a door leading to what I thought was the outside world, but found I had walked into the Gents. Blind as a bat I am at times. But mine wasn't the only red face on that occasion. Other people had followed me in, all men, except for unsuspecting Lin, who blamed me for being so daft. She certainly is short-sighted. We didn't have to be told to "Get lost!"

Lin made a similar mistake up the top of Blackboy Hill. We had come out of the Maternity Hospital after a visit and were waiting at the bus-stop. Lin said she would just pop across to the public convenience opposite, and I was to wait where I was and hold up the bus if it came. She ran across the road, in through one door, and straightway appeared out the door the far end. When she got inside she realised it was a Gents only. I could have told her that if she had only asked. Her luck had been in. Business was slack, because she caught no member of the male species with his trousers down. "Thank God" said Lin and, as soon as the bus came, it was an anguished "Hurry up, hurry up" all the way home.

Other people make bloomers in respect of toilets though. Again in the Odeon Lin and I were sat one day. There was a packed audience. The lights were up during the intermission. A small, middle-aged woman in a gigantic yellow Stetson walked past the screen, up to a wall and tried every way she knew how to get through. She tapped it, pushed it, hunted top to bottom for a knob, which was nowhere to be seen. And all the while Lin and I, and 'hundreds' of other cinema-goers, were laughing at her predicament. The sign Ladies was indeed fixed on the wall panelling, but Lin and I knew, and hundreds of other women knew, that the Ladies in fact was situated through the side exit door. It didn't click with her and she would have carried on and on trying to get through an impenetrable wall to reach her destination if some kind soul hadn't put her wise. Eventually the lights went out, shushing descended and we settled down to watch the film. That is until a huge yellow hat walked across the screen and laughter started up again. Unkind lot.

One hustley bustley Saturday down in the centre of Bristol, where the beetroot and caulis grow in the flower-beds for decorative purposes, Lin and I saw the most bizarre sight. We had alighted from our bus and, for no good reason, I remarked to Lin that the conductor had got off the bus and sauntered over to a ciggy machine to yield to a packet of fags. Lin glanced behind her in the direction of the bus and a flabbergasted look enhanced her normal one. "Quick Ange, look" she said and I also turned to gaze. The bus was moving off. We diverted our eyes to the conductor, busily lighting up with his back to the bus. We stood open-mouthed taking in the scene, which was awkward as people were colliding with us. What a picture of utter disbelief transformed the conductor's countenance, when he revolved and saw his bus beginning to climb Park Street, the steepest hill for miles around. He was getting on in years, but he ran like a deer, I mean a stag, but the last we saw of him he hadn't made it. He was panting and wheezing, haring in and out of the traffic and gesticulating "My bus, my bus, somebody stop my bus" but nobody did. Passengers on the bus must have realised they were missing an essential piece of the works, but nobody rang the bell to apprehend the driver. Some presumably hadn't paid their fares. Lin and I were on our way to the pictures. Methinks it was 'Sound of Music' again. That was the only time we didn't enjoy the film. We weren't well. We had ruptured ourselves at the expense of that conductor.

I used to take my shoes off in the pictures, but haven't since I played footsie with the fellow sat behind me. It should never have happened. I didn't even see what he looked like. It was nearing the end of the film and I found my left shoe okay, but could not for the life of me get my foot into what I thought was the other one. It did, in fact, belong to another person and the owner-man already had his foot in it. I was too embarrassed to apologise and left before the lights went up. Lin told me the film ending when she followed me out five minutes later. One girl at the Smelting Works also takes her shoes off in the cinema, but she lifts strangers' legs when it's time to hunt for them.

Lin puts a jinx on me I reckon. One night, again on our way to pictures, we had to run for the bus, the one and only time I wore my short wig. It was too small for my head anyway. Running made the thing slip sideways so, on top of the bus, I whipped it off and stuffed it in my handbag. It was an X certificate film Lin and I had gone to view, but I can't explain what was wrong with me that night. After seeing a few bloody bodies cut up, stowed in plastic bags and stored in the fridge, my stomach lurched and I had to come out pretty sharpish. It could have been the fault of the bag of salted peanuts I had eaten. Lin came out with me. She had wasted her money more than I because, virtually the whole time we did spend in the cinema, she hid behind her hands.

Lin and I also went every week to Keep Fit class held at the Community Centre. We were hopeless, but enjoyed it. We were instructed to perform these intricate formation sequences with chiffon scarves and, without fail, Lin and I got in a muddle with our left and right and "buggered" them up. That was the word Griselda used. She was a funny old bat, very spry for 72. Mum called her the witchy woman. We weren't thrown out of the class, because we were needed. All different shapes and sizes of womanhood attended and a dozen I reckon needed help to get up from the floor. Lin and I, being the youngest and healthiest, went round as haulage contractors.

Lin and I went on the paddle steamer to Ilfracombe two or three years running after she started work. We got free tickets from her boss. Lin was never seasick on the boat. I can remember disembarking one year and we went straightway to the beach, ate pasties, and up it came over our Macs, which we were sat on. Coming home at dead of night she was perfectly fine. We would sit on the top deck huddled together in the darkness, trying to keep warm. The rest of the passengers were down below, eating and drinking. Lin and I never took chances. If we were rammed at sea, that is in the Bristol Channel, we would be first in the lifeboats.

Lin did bamboozle me into accompanying her to Needlework Classes. For six months I valiantly kept going, but I didn't finish the black dress I set out to make. At home I was even doing a bit to it one day, tacking instead of hemming. I was using yards of thread and it got in a knot. I cussed and cajoled that knot. The cotton snapped and so did my patience. With all my might I threw the dress impetuously across the room and didn't pick it up until the next day. Nothing makes me blow a fuse more than sewing does. At the time I stopped going to the classes I hadn't even learnt how to tailor tack properly. Lin could sew anyway so she stopped going too.

Dave sent me along to Lin's on her last birthday bearing his bright orange skimpy running vest, with the request that as he loved her dearly, would she put a 3" hem in it on her machine. If she refused he would cancel his standing order for Athletics Weekly up 'her' shop, and take his money elsewhere. Lin said she would do it, because she was sure Lobb's couldn't afford to lose Dave's 5p a week. She left his orange vest lying in a paper bag on the table and then we went out for a birthday celebration nosh. As we left her house her Mum was just coming in. We learnt later that when Mrs. H looked inside the paper bag she thought what a funny peculiar present I had given Lin, and it smelt ripe too. Throughout the evening she puzzled over it, thinking it was a new fashion type of micro mini dress. She doubted whether Lin would ever actually wear the 'dress', even if she lost at least three stone to get into it. I wouldn't have done such a thing to Lin, even though Lin and her Mum call me dimpy and laugh at things I do wrong, like yesterday.

Before leaving their house at lunchtime it started to rain so I put a scarf on without looking in the mirror and wondered why they started to laugh. "That Angela is never right" Lin's Mum said. My white scarf resembled a strip toothache bandage going round my face and under my chin, but not covering my head hardly at all. Lin's Mum is a good sport and Lin says she is as dense as I am. I must admit I wondered about her yesterday. She was sat with her dress on back to front. She knew about it. There was method in her madness. During a hot flush she could easily pull the zip down to cool off.

There is another character in Lin's family far madder than her Mum, Aunty Florrie. One day Lin was talking about her love life (mine was non-existent so I had nothing to say) and Aunty Flor, who had come to cadge a free dinner, was all ears. She butted in and said she wouldn't want another man in her life, not even if he had diamonds on his whatsit. "Todger" she said in the next breath, in case we hadn't grasped what a whatsit was. Her second husband Fritz, a German, whose only English was swear words, she lost years ago in a multiple car crash. Now too her daughter has recently died, and she is bringing up two tiny grand-daughters and a lazy sod of a son-in-law on a shoestring. There could never be a replica of Aunty Flor. A rum old bird she is with her dark, smouldering, dart-about eyes, raucous belly laugh and cunning of a didicoi. Whether it's a nervous habit or an invitation to men, I don't know, but she purses her lips in and out non-stop. She only has wisps of her own hair left. Constant dyeing has made it patchy and thin on top, so she usually wears a wig, which is rather on the big side. It's like a black lacquered, matted mass similar to raffia paper. She reminds me of the gypos who come round the houses selling pegs, paper flowers and dish cloths. Anyone who didn't buy from them was cursed. Mum doesn't answer the door to them, nor to the Mormons and Jehovah's Witnesses, but hides until a gate is heard being slammed or shut as the case may be. But Aunty Flor had received pots of money in compensation when her Fritzie was killed and lived like a duchess, but not any more. She squandered it away, so the Judge told her, when her Grocery Shop went bankrupt. It was her own fault. It wasn't as if she didn't do a roaring trade, just the opposite. Customers came from far and wide, simply because Florrie let them add up their own bills. She said she hadn't a head for figures and her finger system wasn't reliable.

There wasn't much of Aunty Flor in height, but widthways she was a barrel of solid muscle. She wore tight flashy clothes. Often silver Lurex with baubles and bangles of imitation jewellery when she came sponging off of Mrs. H. A meal was okay, but Lin did get in a bad mood if Aunty Flor decided to spend the night, as that meant sharing her single bed. I adored watching Aunty Flor come slowly down the road, teetering along on 4" stiletto heels. The shoes themselves were a couple of sizes too big to cater for bunions, and I've seen her step right out of a pair, turn round and hobble on her heels back to them. The toes of Aunty Flor's shoes have always been dagger points, pointing upwards instead of outwards.

I've got this picture in my mind of Lin's family and me sat round the fire one night watching telly. I was having supper with them – fish and chips in newspaper, because they taste better that way and saves on the washing up. Aunty Flor finished her chips, licked her greasy lips and fingers, rolled the paper into a ball and threw it onto the fire without stirring from the chair she was wedged in. Five minutes went by before she said "Better put me teef back in". She had taken her false teeth out to eat, which sounds an odd thing to do, but that was Aunty Flor. She thought she had left them resting on the arm of her chair, but they weren't there. She took the chair apart, that is removed the seat cushion, and was on her knees with her arms down the sides of it hunting, when Lin's Mum got up to poke the fire. There lying in the ashes were the remains of Aunty Flor's teeth. The house became in uproar, as we fell about laughing. Lin's brother John wiped away his tears in the carpet. He was rolling on it, helplessly. Florrie picked her pearlies up out of the fire on the shovel. The plate itself had melted and looked like bubblegum. She gazed forlornly at the remains and then burst forth into a streaming torrent of abuse, wagging her finger at the sticky, sizzling, smoking, smelly mess.

It must be four or five years ago when Aunty Flor threw a party at New Year. She had had a windfall, or to be precise, her husband Fritz's compensation. I was invited. Lin's family I knew so well I too called her Aunts, Aunty so and so. The booze flowed freely, down people's gullets, also onto the floor, into the loo, and bowls and buckets when it came up again. A lot of fixing and mixing of drinks went on and I admit I drank a sizeable quantity that night. But for some inexplicable reason, although extremely smiley, I didn't get drunk. Good stomach lining I must have.

The party began with everyone in such a lively mood, but come the end I was administering black coffee, soothing words and cold compresses to fever ridden sweaty brows, shouldering bodies to beds and standing by with a freshly rinsed po to whip beneath a puffy face which had already filled half dozen others. If I pulled the flush fifty times I'm surprised, because I would have said it to be a hundred. Pange gave her all to the role of Florence, flitting from room to room. The real Flor was paralytic. Lin and Josie had had to retire early to a bedroom, as they were heaving every few seconds.

180

They started with one bowl between them, but fought over it and after quarter of an hour necessity called for one each. I was worried about my pals. They did look awful, Josie especially. Her colouring kept changing from white to green, then yellow to grey. Several of the younger children were sprawled on blankets and pillows, dazedly moaning and groaning, holding tender, wretched bellies. Sleep couldn't come to them. They ached inside too much. Full glasses appearing on the coffee table had soon disappeared, to be replaced within minutes by empties. (Kids at work under the table.) I nabbed a couple, but not in time. They too quickly vanished upstairs to the bathroom.

In one darkened bedroom lay a girl with no senses left at all. She had come to the party with her baby, unbeknown by hubby who was on night shift. With the party drawing to a close, I dragged her feeble frame with a man's help up and down the road outside the house, but she was incapable of breathing in air correctly. Her legs were like sponge/cottonwool and jelly rolled into one, and her body a sack of potatoes. She was sweating cobs too. We managed to get coffee down her. That is, we tipped her head back and poured a cupful down her front. She was fit for nothing and I hope she wasn't sober next morning. Then, if her husband hit her she wouldn't feel it, well only marginally.

I don't think I'll ever forget that party. All the evil spirits at work, knocking my friends down like ninepins. Amazingly, I hadn't wanted to be sick when I had seen the sick everywhere. It had splashed on my face, my hands were tainted, even my bottom smelt, because I had sat in a puddle of vomit that had got on an eiderdown. I could stand the smell, the nauseating stench, the stale sweat, and I could go from one inebriate human being to another and help them fight their drunken stupors without even a tummy roll. Probably the drink in me acted as a stabiliser. That's odd, because if I, myself, feel ill in the night I invariably shout for Mum.

We travelled home in a hearse from the party. It had been converted into a taxi. Nine of us were squashed inside. No room for gloom. I hope we didn't cause any passers-by to die of fright on the ride home, because there were three heads lolling out of the windows, belonging to Lin, Josie and John. Josie was threatening to be sick whenever the hearse slid over a blade of grass growing out of the tarmac. That is when I locked her in a stranglehold and thrust her head out of the window. I wouldn't let it in again neither, as I didn't want Lin's Dad to pay extra if I could prevent accidents from occurring. The grown-ups and I were quite all right. When we got to Lin's house we hauled in the lifeless bodies and dumped them on the floor. They had a lump or two of coal put on the fire for warmth, a blanket each but nothing else. Lin's Mum said "There they stay til morning, and let it be a lesson to them". After the burial, I was carried off home alone in the hearse. I felt like a horror Dame out of an X film. Outside our house I paid 'my man' a courteous "Goodnight" adding Giles under my breath, and walked sedately and thankfully inside. I was slightly fuzzy-wuzzy by then.

Next morning I overslept and had yeast vite for breakfast. I had forgotten to set the alarm. Oh, what it is to be relied on. It meant the brothers were late for work, because it was my duty to get them up. When roused they can come out with terrible inhuman quotes which are best ignored. They'll miss me when I'm gone.

I seemed to be involved in numerous piddly accidents around this period, which I can't for the life of me understand why.

It's a wonder though I am still here, the things I do to myself. I was stood in the kitchen once munching an apple and at the same time drying my hair with the hand-drier. I suppose a loose strand got sucked inside the blades and caused the motor to go wrong. I didn't realise anything was amiss until my nose began twitching. Something was burning and it just happened to be my palm. A flame was flickering out of it. I was stunned and stared aghast at it. Seconds later I decided it was hurting and gave a piercing scream to let Mum know I was on fire. Bonk went the hair-drier onto the floor. I threw it down, because that was the offending article. The lead was alight. I threw my apple same place too. Footsteps came running. Rish called me a stupid clot when she saw the hair-drier lying in bits. I bawled. My flame had fizzled out and I was disgruntled that they had missed it. All Mum said was "You're sure to die after it". I did have a smoky, singed, gingery black hole in my hand, which gave off a most peculiar whiff. I reckon I'm rubbery, as it smelt like our bonfire tyres of years ago.

I do get livid with myself for being a blockhead. I got home from the Smelters one night having suffered in silence throughout the day, but I unbuttoned my lips to the family as to why I had a red stain covering my right foot and bubbly blisters appearing. I had taken a kettle upstairs to wash that morning. The lid wasn't on properly, because I hadn't put it on properly. I stepped back onto the kettle and said "xxxzzz!!! Hell, Fire and Damnation!" when I had a footbath in very slightly off the boil water.

I was trying to round up Lin's dog one tea-time and tried to vault the two-strand wire fence separating Lin's garden from Flo's. Only I didn't clear it. I came a cropper. Soil isn't a favourite food of mine. Dratted mongrel came to lick my wounds.

Lin and I have had more than our fair share of narrow escapes in our time. Going back maybe four years, we took Richard, her youngest brother, to the zoo one day. He would have been about four at the time. I love him dearly, but he did get us in an almighty lather. The afternoon was a pleasant one until we decided to show Richard the bear pit. Lin and I were thickheads. We stood him up by the bars. "See Richard, down there, can you see? Look at the bears". Too true he could see them. He couldn't take his eyes off them. His head was firmly jammed between the bars. We didn't register this at first. He was content glaring down at them for a while. Then he said "Lin I can't move my head". "Rubbish" we said, but Oh Lor it was true. Lin and I didn't panic, but she went pea colour and I had to turn away, blink many times, before looking back and believing what I saw. We gulped in deep lungfuls of air and told Richard to try, try, try and move his head. He said, "I can't". We said "Course you can", but he couldn't.

We tried all sorts. We told him to breathe in and not out, to suck his cheeks in like we were doing, which he couldn't see, as we thought maybe his head might shrink. Lin said he wasn't trying. Richard began to whimper and said, "If you pull my hair, I'll tell our Mum" and Lin said if he screamed she would kill him, but what did it matter, because he was a goner anyway when Bruin caught sight of him. Lin's stubborn coaxing worked in the end. She held Richard's neck. I placed my hands over his ears, damn nuisance they are and should be bitten off at birth, and we pulled as gently as we could with a fierce final tug, and he was free. He was in one piece thank the Lord, although we had had visions of Richard's head falling off and bouncing down amongst the bears.

Richard was quite happy. He still had his ears albeit very pinched ones. But Lin and I, oh how scared we had been. We had to find a bench to sit on.

I mean to say, if a bear had climbed up the pole in the centre of the pit, and extended an arm to Richard, it wouldn't have been to shake hands. It doesn't bear thinking about. Lin and I vowed her Mum must never know Richard nearly became a tasty snack for old bear chops. When we calmed down we thought Richard deserved a laugh, so we went to see the purple and red bummed baboons.

HILARY AND SID

I doubt whether I shall ever in my lifetime come across a couple quite like Hilary and Sid who walked into mine and Lin's life, stayed for nearly a year, and then departed swiftly, ne'er to be seen again save the once. Lin and I were fond of them and their two kiddies, and we had some great times together. Lin knew Hilary from a couple of years before, and she filled me in on certain facts. Hilary had met Sid at the fairground along Woody Lane. He worked the Big Dipper. She willingly got seduced in the fields and bingo Ian was conceived. They married. Sid left the fairground, couldn't settle in a steady job, turned to petty crime and went in clink. Oh, baby Hilary came along in the interim period. Lin and I started visiting Hilary and the children while Sid was away "working". Hilary never referred to him being in jail, but we knew. We didn't let on that we knew.

Hilary's flat was half way up St Michael's Hill, surrounded by boarded up, evil smelling disused houses, except for the tramp gatherings each night. The demolition squad has moved in now. The house we visited was split three ways, junk shop out front, Hilary in the basement and back room and a couple of students had the top floor. Dust, damp and cobwebs were plentiful. Take the shop first. We could open the door an inch, enough to make the bell ring. This brought the old proprietress to the doorway, but it took ages, because she had to squeeze by mountains of rubbish piled high inside the shop. She then busily threw things aside to make an empty space of a foot square so that we could enter. She was a strange occity, and would haggle for hours, but she was good to Hilary and the kids. I bought a cheap ring there, which people remarked on, because it was unusual. It was a dark copper colour with a humbug stone. It had serrated edging, which cut my knucks, but I put up with that. One of the student fellows above Hilary used to visit her. Once, when the students were out, Lin and I egged each other on to climb the stairs and peep into their main room. Hilary had told us about it. It was weird. There were two purple walls and two orange ones. The ceiling was black with a dirty great big sun painted over it. A couple of worn rugs, mattresses and guitars on bare boards were the only things to occupy the room.

Hilary lived in squalor and a certain amount of filth, but seemed quite happy and content. Water trickled down the walls and paper peeled off. Cockroaches lived behind the wallpaper. Naked dull bulbs lit the rooms. Grease lay in globs in the kitchen. The flat was furnished with stuff out of the junk shop, discarded from working class homes: broken chairs with soiled covers, table with uneven legs, chipped cups and plates, no saucers, hard lumpy beds and the like. Hilary classed herself lucky to have found a place at all. Lin and I enjoyed our Sunday visits. We cleared out our wardrobes at home and went with either a bundle of cast-off clothes for Hilary or scrounged matinee jackets for the baby.

We stayed overnight some weekends. The bedroom was vast and freezing cold, but we were hardy. It was down in the cellar. There was a single tiny window vent a couple of inches above pavement level and we could see feet and legs strolling or scurrying by. Hilary and I slept at the head of the bed and Lin at the foot. Because Lin had long toe-nails and we feared scratched faces (and Hilary said she might well have sucked Lin's big toe), we issued her with a pair of Sid's socks to wear. One night in particular I remember. Hilary had a nightmare and began whimpering, tossing and turning. I lay rigid, ever watchful, and wished Lin would wake up, but nothing makes Lin stir. Then little Ian began to cry and Hilary woke up and went over to see to his wet bot. I lay there and pretended to be asleep. We would force down our Sunday dinners. Usually it was a plateful of watery cabbage and Smash with a sausage a piece, or a slice of Spam. In the afternoon we took the children and a case of washing along to the launderette. Hilary hadn't room to swing a cat let alone hoist a washing line outside her back door. Lin and I were about seventeen at the time and maternal, so we pretended, when out, Ian and baby Hilary were ours.

The weeks turned into months and one evening Hilary informed us that Sid would be home the coming weekend. The day after release we were invited for Sunday tea. Lin and I were scared stiff of meeting him and hummed and haahed outside the back door, giggling too, as we decided who should be first to walk in and brave the meeting. God knows what we expected to find, but he looked quite normal, thin and pale with a scruffy goat beard. Crook or not, it was easy to like him. He didn't mention where he had been "working" and we asked no questions, but admired the beautiful varnished jewellery box he had made from matchsticks.

Our pattern didn't change. We tripped up there Sundays just the same, and occasionally an evening in the week as well. A chunk of the time we spent taking the children out and left the lovebirds to get on with it. Lin and I were called upon to become Godmothers at baby Hilary's christening. Sid acquired a puppy for me, which I wasn't allowed to take home – Mum & Dad said no and meant no. I did love the little black scrap with the collapsible legs, and felt proud as punch when people stopped and said "Isn't he sweet" and tickled it – I hadn't a clue as to sex – under its chin. Lin and I were good friends to Sid, because we washed his brand spanking new car quite often. Many new things appeared about the place soon after Sid's release. I can't remember him working. Everyone was happy. Ian's initial shyness with his Daddy vanished.

One evening Lin and I baby-sat. We did frequently. Never got paid of course. Hilary and Sid had acquired a telly and with Cherry Bs, or a Pony, and a pork pie from the Off Licence, Lin and I had no complaints. Having immensely long noses we happened to come across high priced bills on the mantelshelf. Our attention turned to drawers, and we couldn't believe our eyes at the number of demand letters, pay up or else notices and HP payments owing, which filled them up. Our eyes bulged out of their sockets when we found one of a series of letters concerning non-payment of the car. It was worded in such a manner that unless part of the account was settled immediately, court action would be taken against Sid. Lin and I laughed, but nervously, because we imagined ourselves in court summoned as witnesses and having to testify.

Suddenly, the week following our discovery, word came that they had moved far out into the country, Mangotsfield. Done a runner in fact.

Being out of town, Lin and I felt we could breathe now when travelling in Sid's stolen car. We had been frantic that sooner or later we'd be rumbled as aiders and abetters. I'd kept quiet about the car to Mum and Dad naturally. I wasn't a blabbermouth. We were astounded the first time we went to see them in their new home. It was so peaceful there and simply divine. Sid was working on a farm and a lovely cottage went with the job. We toured the farm and saw cows being milked (Sid did know how) at close quarters, clucking hens pecking seed in the dirt yard, even a pig nosing and grunting amongst garbage, with piglets squealing delightedly as they rolled in mud heaps. It was pure ecstasy. Grey clouds had hung permanently over St Michael's Hill, but down on the farm the sun shone bright and warming. Time stood still. Brown speckled eggs were collected from the jolly farmer's wife for our breakfast. Lin and I walked miles to the one grocer-cum-meat and veg shop, stopping to pick primroses on the return journey.

The summer weekends we had on the farm were bliss. We either slept downstairs on chairs and the settee, with baby Hilary in her pram beside us, or we had Hilary and Sid's bed upstairs. The bed was the sole piece of furniture in their enormous bedroom. At night we padded across the floorboards, stooping because the ceilings throughout the cottage slanted, and chatted long into the night about our lives, and what we were going to do with them. Poor Lin though, twice she got up out of bed and stepped down onto things. Once her watch and once her glasses, because our possessions had to go on the floor. We took it in turns to switch off the light. Like Lin would get into bed and in my floor sweeping nightshirt I would position myself by the door, flick off the light and then try to find the bed in that great expanse of room and darkness. Lin was a hopeless guide. We woke in the morning with sun streaming through latticed windows and Ian sat on the bed pummelling us to "Wake up".

It was about that time I began running. At night, under cover of darkness, I raced a hundred times round our back garden, which is no bigger than a postage stamp, spurred on by Dave and Al's taunts and jibes. So it was on Sunday afternoons at the cottage I gave Lin, Hilary and Sid great amusement by loping round their garden, with bursts of speed and snail's pace crawling intermingled.

I washed, cut and set Hilary's hair at the cottage. I found nits, but shut my eyes to them. As soon as I got home I washed mine and used the nit comb.

Rover Sid got itchy feet again. We missed going to see them a couple of weekends. One day Hilary, who was at her Mum's for the day, popped into Lin's shop for a natter. She said Sid hadn't been happy farming. Apparently, she was still at the farmhouse (rent-free), but they were looking for another place to live. She had told the farmer and his wife that Sid had left her. In fact he was up to something, dodgy dealings in the daytime, Lin and I concluded. At night Hilary said he sneaked back to the cottage and when he had given the password, she let him in to spend the night.

Thereafter they faded out of our lives. Since then I've seen Sid once. He rumbled past me driving an articulated lorry and stopped on a double yellow line for a five-minute chat. I learnt that they were living quite near, two more babes had arrived on the scene, and Lin and I must go and see them like old times. But a few years had elapsed and Lin and I had walked out of their lives to stay.

THE START OF
PROPER DATING

It was after the Sid and Hilary episode in our lives that Lin and I started
to go dancing on a Saturday night. Not that we were very interested in the
opposite sex. Generally we danced with each other – handbags at our feet
– and systematically turned boys away if they approached. The Mecca was
our dance hall. Lin and I were self-conscious at first. We'd give chaps the
once-over when they weren't looking in our direction, and if they were, we
averted our eyes pretty darn quick. Apart from meetings with eyes, chaps
weren't exactly in our sights until, all of a sudden, fire kindled inside both of
us practically simultaneously.

Frilly Shirt I met at the Mecca. He wasn't my type at all. I only put up
with him because Lin and Josie went out with his two mates, and we wanted
to stick together in a sixsome. We were right in thinking safety in numbers.
No sooner had the sixsome split up, and Lin went out in a twosome for the
first time, he took her home to meet his Mum and Dad, brothers and sisters,
up the road to meet his Gran and down the road to meet his Aunty and
Uncle. He was so chuffed to have her. After calling on his entire family, Lin's
feet throbbed and her smile was false. She had been greeted with nothing
but insinuations, e.g. had the wedding date been arranged? Lin didn't turn
up for the next date. She hadn't been captivated she said, and therefore didn't
intend to be a captive.

But back to Frilly Shirt, I was bored in his company. And too, he was a year younger than me, which made a world of difference then and was most off-putting. He had a hunch back and walked on his toes, which I could have forgiven him for, but I could not overlook his absurd frilly shirts. They sickened me. Yes, they were in fashion, but his didn't have just frills. They had tinsel and diamante embroidered on them too. I began to wonder if he was one of Them, but I had my mind changed for me. He wanted lots of kisses and things I wasn't prepared to give. He had the cheek to give me a shocking love bite on the neck without asking permission. (It is highly probable I day-dreamed about nice things to eat as he kissed me.) For days I wore the same old stretched polo neck jumper. Mum noticed the bite and tut-tutted with a chuckle, but it wasn't her I was worried about. It was Pops. Another thing which made me want to scream was that Frilly Shirt said "Ya what?" to everything I said. It irked me to such a degree I could have sloshed him. Instead I seethed inwardly, because he did have a car. I think every date I ever had with him I had a cob on, as unfathomable moodiness would descend like a cloak enveloping me. Thinking back he was a saint to put up with me.

One Sunday, on a sixsome date, I had started out as usual determined to be a misery and succeeded splendidly throughout the evening. Coming home we had parked in a car park. Lin and her chap were busy canoodling in the back of our car. Josie and her chap were having a humdinger of a love battle in their car parked in front of us. I knew, because I was watching the skirmish and action going on through their rear window, till it steamed over. I flatly refused to acknowledge the advances of Frilly Shirt by saying I wasn't in the mood. I never was with him. When he realised he had ice in the car he gave up. I sat bolt upright, arms folded, locked my lips and wouldn't even look at him. The minutes ticked by. I was the one to break the silence. I said I was fed up and wanted to go home. Without a word he abruptly started the car, shaking Lin and her fellah out of their clinch, and off we went. The pair of us remained speechless, but noises could be heard inside and outside the car. The noise of plonkers Lin and her chap were exchanging and the noise of tyres screaming angrily round corners. I did feel rotten for being so rotten. I apologised for being me as I got out of the car, but he said not a word and slammed the door in my face. Lin told me that when I got out of the car Frilly Shirt said acidly "You've got a funny friend". Lin said, "I know, she makes me laugh".

There then followed Romeo. I would say there has to be an Italian pop up in every girl's life. He was all that a Casanova is cracked up to be. This Italian bod was very friendly and made me feel first class. However, I didn't believe a single word he said on the subject of love and romancing.

The evening I met my dark and dashing smasheroo, I was out for an evening's dancing with a crowd of girlfriends. It was a birthday celebration I do believe. Methinks Lin and her sister Dinah were tiddly before the evening began, because both of them left their brollies on the outward bus. In the dance hall we bumped into a group of Italian men and paired up. There were no language problems. They were fluent in English, too fluent. They were equally handsome so why was it I had to end up with Angelo. Those Italian geezers thought it was hysterical, and each time one came near to us it would be "Angela meet Angelo" followed by madcap laughter with, it goes without saying, my girlfriends joining in the hilarity. They got worse and out of control though as the evening gathered hours, due to a happening. It came to pass that night, and Lord I hope it never comes about again.

I had worn my long false hair-piece and after lots of spirited, intricate dance movements and head tosses, it had begun to slip backwards ever so slightly. I didn't take much notice, as I thought it would be secure with the fifty odd hair clips dug into my false and real tresses. I continued dancing until suddenly, in the middle of a smoochy one, a crisis hit like a bolt out of the blue. Angelo's hands had been gliding up and down my spine enough to make a girl tingle. He was giving me the jitters. Then the dopey clot went for the tender spot at the base of my neck. To do this his hands had risen up and under my hair-piece, and it simply came away in his hands. His eyes widened and a look of incredibility passed over his face. There it was tangled up in his fingers and there I was, metallic head, with my own hair tightly gripped and flattened at the sides, plus a backbrushed cottage loaf for body on top. I screamed. I must have done. Why did it have to be a slow dreamy number the band was playing? I momentarily fainted standing up. Angelo began to grin and hoisted my wig aloft like a prize trophy. I could have scalped him. Instead I jerked it from him, gave him a push and raced off the floor, not bothering to avoid couples as I sped on my way. As I went I hooked my arm through Terence's and whisked her along with me.

We hid in darkness under the stairs, surrounded by snoggers, while

Terence did repair work on me. She fitted it on as best she could. I forced myself to come out from under the stairs, told myself I looked divine, and walked straight-backed upstairs to the powder room to survey the damage. Boy, when I saw myself in the mirror I nearly fainted again, this time onto the floor. My make-up was smudged beyond restoration where I had been licked, but the wig! Well, I had never seen anything quite like it. The crown of the hair-piece (it's like a net skull cap) was over my ear so it looked as though I had a large mound on one side of my head. The Leaning Tower of Pisa Tritz called it. Also it was dented in two places like rift valleys, and the hair itself was like tumble-weed. I blamed Terence of course for my 'beuteefully' groomed appearance. The cast of Hair had nothing on me that night. I plucked up courage and went back sheepishly with a beaming Terence to Angelo and his mob of laughing hyena friends. They cheered as I swanned into their midst.

Upon reflection it was a pleasurable evening. Fun for some, except every girl said she had a sore tongue next day. To court an Italiano it would be a case of, don't forget to clean out ears before a date, because they do seem to love lugs. They chew and nibble and let sweet nothings pour through them, but better I say to let the real drippy talk go in one and out the other.

SNIPPETS

I wore Mum's grey wig once. It didn't fit awfully well, was far too small to be exact, and I pulled it off on the bus going to the Mecca. I think that was the night I got cheesed off with a chap, so made an excuse I had to catch the last bus home, although it was only 10pm. He did ask if I had my fare, and when I said yes he said, "That's all right then".

Lin says I'm a right softie for getting mixed up with the wrong types. I did have a kind heart once upon a time. At the Locarno one evening I caught sight of a girl being sick in a corner. I didn't know her from Adam, but went over to see if I could be of assistance. She was awfully drunk so I strapped her to me and dragged her outside to take the air. She was a size, and sweating like a pig. Luckily a friend found us and took her off my hands. Lin wouldn't have anything to do with me the rest of the evening, because she said I stank.

I can remember the time Lin's sister had Annie, her first baby. Immediately Dinah came home from hospital, a few days after production, Lin and I went to stay for a week to help look after her, the baby, the high-rise flat and Fred, Di's hubby. Not that I helped much, nor hindered, because I was working during the day. Lin was on a week's holiday or 'the club' I can't remember which. My main job of the day was to do the washing up in the evenings. I swore Lin left the day's dirty crocks until then.

One day we had just finished tea – Lin's a dab hand at making chips – when we heard the ice cream man dinging his bell way down the street. Lovely, we thought, to have cornets for pud, but we would have to be quick if

194

we wanted to catch him. We shot round the flat looking for purses, and I said I would go because I had cheetah legs, and as the patient was bed-bound we couldn't send her. "Hurry up, quick, quick," Lin and Dinah shouted from the bedroom. I bounded into the kitchen, whipped off my pinny, went round in circles but couldn't find an empty space to throw it into so dropped it on the floor, tripped over it, didn't know what I was doing, opened the door and whizzed through. It closed. "Funny" I thought, "it's dark and it's only tea-time" (it was summer). I had locked myself in the larder. There were two doors in the kitchen next to each other, one being the larder and one being the way out of the flat. Being in a dither I had picked the wrong one. I screamed for Lin who came running and wondered where in the world I was. Her ears are remarkable and she sensed where my panic-stricken cries were coming from. She's no detective, but she knows I'm a clothead. She let me out and she was in a worse state than I with her hee-hawing. She held her tummy in her hands as laughter split her sides, crossed her legs and moaned "Ooh, the pain".

I wouldn't let myself laugh right then, but bowled Lin over and thundered out of the right door and down flights of steps. I'm afraid by the time I reached the first floor I too was desperate, trying to hop downstairs with my legs weaved together to curb the flow. As I stumbled from the block of flats I was laughing long and loud. I'm not one to draw attention to myself, but I couldn't help it. The kids grouped round the ice cream van backed away and let me go first. I couldn't speak until I collected myself together, which took at least a full minute, as I went from one foot to the other. Then what came out of me was a spluttering, gurgling mass of tee hee hee giggles. At last I recovered enough dignity to gasp, "Three ice creams, but please please hurry". The poor man sensed it was a matter of life, death or puddles, so produced three 4d cones at the double and charged me 6d each. I grabbed them, stampeded bottom of the stairs one minute and top of four flights and into the bathroom the very next. For all the exertion and agony I went through, most of the ice cream was lost halfway up the stairs. I was going so fast two of the scoops fell out of the cones. Because of my mistake Dinah nearly undid her internal stitching. Thank goodness she had already had Annie. The condition Di was in, as I was released from the larder, Annie would have come out like a bullet from a gun.

I did get worried about Lin though. I can soon calm down after a fit, but when Lin gets going she finds it difficult to stop. She has to be left alone until she starts to choke, then she has to be dealt a hefty backslap, which makes her draw breath and hey presto, she is as right as rain again. Lin will thank a person profusely for administering said treatment, except the time Josie used excessive force and nearly broke her back. Josie didn't know her own strength. I have seen her karate chop a fellah who asked for a kiss in a dance hall. Josie wasn't flattered. Lin and I disowned her on that occasion, and there were others. She was a case. Her favourite word was "Bleeders". Anyone who upset her was a bleeder. Once Lin, Josie and I were on the diesel train, returning home after a day's outing to Weston-Super-Mare. We were making our way through jam-packed carriages, looking for a place to park our rumps, when out of the blue Josie's voice boomed "Bleeden hell, why can't three of these sods stuck on their bloody great asses give us a seat". She didn't get an answer. Lin and I grabbed our wide-eyed innocent Josie and rushed her from the midst of gaping travellers. As she sat on a swaying loo, we gave her a stern lecture that that wasn't the way for a refined young lady to talk. She was sorry for showing us up. Many times Josie didn't seem to know right from wrong, and that there is a time and place for everything. She fainted on us in a crowded store once and frightened the life out of Lin and me. It was so sudden.

Lin and I aren't regular church-goers by any means, but the Christmas Carol Service always did appeal to us. However, one year we got the timing wrong. Lin, Josie and I smartened ourselves up, put each other's presents in brown paper carrier bags, and set off for St Lukes, only to find the normal service about to take place. We stayed, but couldn't get the gist of the Latin, hymns, sermon and Holy Communion. Neither one of us had been confirmed. I can't say we enjoyed ourselves. Al told me afterwards that the Carol Service had been held earlier in the evening. A cluster of old gaffers had gone into church from the Kings Arms. Instead of Rejoice, Rejoice, it was grunt snore whistle. I was surprised Al hadn't been amongst them, but he informed me with all seriousness that he had a helluva thirst on him that evening, and remained propping up the bar at his thirstquencher, savouring every last glug.

New Year's Eve that year the waiters in the Trattoria opened a bottle of champagne at midnight and I was given a glass to be divided into equal sips between Barbie, Joan and me. When we left the restaurant I bought a posy of violets from an old man on the street corner for Mum, but was disappointed because they didn't smell. I gave him a New Year's kiss. I like old men. They remind me of Granfer. Joan drove us home minus her exhaust, but what the heck, it was New Year's Eve.

I experienced an evening around that time which started out so happily and ended without warning on an achingly sad note. Let me begin at the beginning. Part way on my journeys to work in the morning Bernice would sit by me on the bus. Bernice had gone to the same school as me. I only knew her slightly. I used to feel sorry for her, maybe because she was even more clumsy than I, and had bigger feet believe it or not. We had little in common. One morning she asked me if I would like to go to a dinner and dance with her, her parents and an aunt and uncle. The girlfriend she usually mixed with couldn't go. It was to be a posh frocks do at the Royal Hotel. I accepted, but felt a bit out of place when the time came, because everyone wore evening dress and I didn't possess such a thing. I wished I had worn my bridesmaid's dress. However, that is beside the point.

Bernice's Mum and Dad picked me up. It was the first time I had met them. We collected her aunt and uncle and got to the Royal in time for a drink and a chat before dinner. I enjoyed being with them. They were well-to-do people, but nice and friendly. I got the impression Bernice was like me, a Daddy's girl. She seemed to irritate her mother somehow. Her Mum was petite and dainty.

We had a sumptuous meal. I sat beside Bernice's father and we got along famously. He thought the world of Bernice. She was an only child. He told me that same day he had retired and was so looking forward to retirement. He had a host of ideas as to how he was going to spend it. We went into the ballroom after our splendid meal and when the band started up Bernice dragged me to my feet and attempted to teach me to waltz. We were going great guns. As I did a turn, I happened to glance back at our table. There seemed to be more people than there should have been grouped round the table. No one was smiling. In fact they all looked dreadfully tense. That was how I knew something was amiss. A little voice inside of me said "Keep on dancing". We did, but before long Bernice became aware of the strained company round our table. "I wonder what's going on," she said. A greater power than I discontinued our dancing.

We went back to the table and learnt that Bernice's Dad had collapsed and died of a heart attack. Bernice was alone apart from me and her aunt and uncle. She broke down. She shook and I cradled her, because it was the right thing to do. I talked, but what came out was pure nonsense. It was like nursing a baby. I was a relief mother until her own came back from the hospital. Bernice's mother whispered to me "I'm sorry. I wouldn't have had this happen, not for the world". She walked away and my tears came and didn't stop for many an hour.

Bernice's aunt and uncle drove me home. Her aunt came to the door with me and knocked. Mum opened it and I brushed past her, going straight upstairs. Mum, seeing the condition I was in, thought initially that I was drunk until Bernice's aunt explained about the hideous evening we had had. Shocks like that are few and far between thank the Lord.

The next time I saw Bernice on the bus she was okay. I was touched, because she said she was glad it had been me there that night and not her other friend. Bernice is happily married now to a blind man.

I'm learning as the years roll by. "If you can't be good be careful" is sound advice. It was at Debbie's engagement party, and her sister's 21st, I got an inkling that men were not trustworthy creatures, and I myself wasn't to be trusted. The party was bags of fun. I met Ralph. We ended up afterwards at Debbie's house, and how it happened I do not remember, but Ralph and I were on the settee, alone, in the front parlour. Amorous Ralph was more than I could cope with. He must have been, because as we were about our business, bells began to ring in my head. They weren't little tinkly ones, but loud ding-dongers. Immediately I called a halt to sofa capers, straightened and smoothed myself out and returned skirt to knee length, as it had ventured up beyond the line of respectability. I mean to say, how could I have progressed further with that tremendous racket deafening my powers of concentration. Ralph looked perplexed and wanted to know why I had cried out "Cease, right now" to hanky-panky. He didn't find my explanation about the crashing bells satisfactory and tried to worm his way round me, but I refused, mostly, all further advances and would only indulge in necking, distasteful word that and petting sounds terribly olde-fash. I swear to this day I did hear bells. Anyone was welcome to spend the night on Debbie's floor if they wished, but my carriage awaited, glad to say, and I crushed myself into a random person's car with, I'm sure, ten others wanting their own beds. Still, randy Ralph taught me a lesson. If the warning bells sound, be on guard. I don't lay down arms and surrender unless of course I want to, in which case I wouldn't even hear Big Ben chiming.

Something I have just remembered about Debbie's party. I nearly didn't get there. I was waiting to meet June off the ferry. It started to rain so I took shelter in a phone box. When the rain eased I couldn't get out. I pushed and pushed at what I thought was the door only it wasn't. A genuine mistake, because the four walls to a phone box are identical. I was in a mad panic thinking I would die of suffocation, but a man came and rescued me, who had been watching my antics from the street corner. No sympathy from that quarter. He said I had made his day and given him the laugh of the century. I appreciated his kindness on setting me free, but I was blowed if I could see the funny side of the situation. If he hadn't come when he did I would have had to dial 999.

MOVING HOUSE AGAIN

It was in May 1968 the Council consented to our move from the Ford Estate and agreed to rehouse us in Brook Road, a ten-minute walk away, and one bus-stop further from the Smelting Works. We were given two weeks in which to pack, and for two weeks Mum did nothing but moan and grumble. She had wanted to move and now that we were going she decided, after all, she didn't want to. There was too much to do and too little time to do it in. One night she sat on the floor and wept and wept. She didn't know which way to turn, surrounded by orange boxes, trunks, cases, cardboard boxes, brown paper, newspapers, china, glass, toys, junk, rubbish and litter. Bloss is an immense hoarder and will not throw anything away. I remember turning out the larder and coming across eight jars of mincemeat, shop bought, six not opened, two started, dried up and gone off, years and years old all of them. But that is the Blossom we are used to. We needed to move, mainly because of Western Transport who shattered our night's sleep. Also, keeping the massive garden up to scratch was killing Dad. Another thing that would be a godsend in our new home was an immersion heater. At Ford we didn't have one, and it meant the boiler had to be lit in the kitchen and buckets of water carried upstairs on bath night. Poor Dad wore the stair carpet out in no time. Then Rish and I weren't satisfied with the dribble of water and called down for Mum to bring up a few kettles in addition. Mum had less trouble when we were small fry and two could be bathed at the same time.

And so we moved house. Mum as well. No.23 met with our approval and only once over the last four years have we wished we had stayed at Ford

Crescent. It was the evening we had the floods, one month after moving! The whole of Somerset was badly hit and the foot of water, which seeped into our house, was nothing compared with the intake some people had in their homes. It was bad enough though.

How clear that night springs to mind. After a day's continuous rain I arrived home from work to find Dad in galoshes at the bottom of the garden, checking for the umpteenth time the water level of the stream. When he came indoors he said, "Just look at the golfcourse" and indeed it was awesome. Day old rivers were coursing down the hills into the stream. Darkness fell and we could see the rain no longer and hardly hear it when the telly was switched on. I went to bed fairly early. I could hear the rain then pelting down as I lay there. I could also hear voices filled with consternation coming from the lower deck. I went to the top of the stairs and called down "What's up?" Dave replied that the water was coming in. Instinct must have made me put a pair of trousers on and I went downstairs to find the folks staring in bewilderment, as a trickle of water came under the back door. Dad opened it and tried to brush the water out, but it would not stay out. Suddenly a cry was heard at the front door. Upon lifting the stairs and hallway fitted carpet, Dave had seen water forcing its way in there. Ally too, positioned at the French Windows in the lounge-diner saw creeping water. We couldn't think straight, faced by this unrestrained element sweeping in, all set to engulf our home. Even though our brains were numb, our reflexes were sharp. In a flurry we all moved at once. We dragged up the living room carpet, emptied cupboards and shelves. Everything in sight was piled into arms and stacked under chins. In relay style we pounded upstairs and down again for another load. For quickness, some things I threw upstairs, like the framed baby photo of me which shattered, but that didn't matter, although it was the only one Mum had of me as a babe. We toiled and we sweated. My bare chest didn't have time to feel the cold under my flimsy nightie. Still the water seeped steadily in and rose. Mum got frightened as more and more ran in under the doors, and we got rid of her by taking her to a neighbour's. Actually it was a good foot deeper outside and Bloss had to wade.

We fought with brooms, mops, buckets and bowls, not knowing whether we would win or lose. The rains continued. Resolutely determined, we worked on into the night, shovelling forever shovelling the waters out the same way they had come in, yet in again they would come. Untouched neighbours came with tea and aid of further mop-up utensils. Muscles ripped and feet got cold. We're dead lucky the boys are still on this earth. Dave should have had a watery grave. He pulled the telly plug out of the skirting board socket, and was sent reeling backwards as he became alive with electricity. He felt numb that was all, and said he could no longer feel his strained, tired, aching, throbbing body and back he went to work, trailing his arms through the murky water, filling up yet another bucket as we bailed out. Ally as well stood on a piece of wood which sailed in through the kitchen door and got a rusty nail in his foot, but his feet were blue and he hardly felt it at the time. Mum made sure he went for a tetanus jab next day.

And as suddenly as it had begun, the rain ceased. Torrents hammering down became spitty rain, which in turn changed to lulling spots and then the pitter-patter plip plops stopped altogether. Oh the relief felt, to stop for a little rest. Inside the house the water was nearly to our knees, outside it was thigh high. I had found that out when I took Mum's hand and led her away to the safety of a neighbour's dry kitchen. As the waters outside subsided normally, operation mop up began throughout our living quarters. We spurred ourselves on, renewed with vigour, because we desperately wanted our beds, but couldn't go to them until we had drained the house. The turmoil upstairs and down could be tackled when daylight came, which, come to think of it, already had. We'd worked doggedly through the night. So many families wrenched their backs that night in an effort to save their homes and belongings. The watermark on our wallpaper is little more than a foot off the ground. What of those where the water rose to lick the ceiling?

SWITZERLAND

The week after I came back from Canada in November 1967, Lin and I went out for a meal. We had masses to talk about. During the meal we decided we were definitely going to have a holiday abroad in 1968. It was a toss-up between Spain and Switzerland. The Spanish weather appealed to me. The Swiss Alps inflamed Lin. I'm glad Lin won me over. We had to beat a hasty retreat from the restaurant once our minds were made up. Lin was sick outside in the gutter. The Peach Melba upset her. Let's face it, Lin wouldn't have survived Spanish cuisine. Anyways, having settled on Switzerland, we had to determine whereabouts we would have our base. We spent an afternoon scanning brochures in a travel agency and agreed wholeheartedly on Davos, better known as a winter sports holiday centre, but August was the month we chose. We booked.

In the first half of 1968 we were over the moon whenever we thought about Switzerland. Months before the holiday Lin and I hunted for part time jobs, besides maintaining our full time occupations, because we wanted to boost our resources. One evening alone we telephoned four supermarkets in Bedminster and asked if they wanted shelf fillers, but we were turned down. The Ritz cinema as well said no vacancies when we offered our services as usherettes. We were met with refusals from restaurants where we applied as washer-uppers, and offices where we asked to become evening scrubbers: floor scrubbers, toilet scrubbers, any old scrubbers. No deal. No one wanted us. We dialled daily all over the place, but our requests for work were unanimously scuppered. We made do somehow with the income our employers forked out. Six months before the holiday Lin and I looked in her sister's spring and summer catalogue and picked out, oh about ten dresses each that we fancied ourselves in in Switzerland. I think we managed to buy a couple apiece on the weekly.

From here on I read from my diary.

On the 15th August we left Bristol bus station at quarter to one and it rained all the way to London. We got wet spending a penny at Marlborough. At Victoria coach station Lin and I went straight to Bay 18 and sat on our cases. We tried looking at case labels to see who was going where. At long last we boarded a coach and left London for Manston Airport in Kent. Looking discretely around, Lin and I thought that there were no other young people on the tour, but we were mistaken. We ran into thick fog and lashing rain. However, we took off from the airport on time, quarter to ten. Lin was perfectly okay. It was a lovely smooth flight. Noisy some said, but we didn't notice. There were two air-hostesses on the plane to tend to our needs, which were minimal. One wasn't well and had to remain strapped in her seat for most of the flight directly behind Lin and me. The other girl, the chief stewardess, didn't have a clue where we were going and had to ask Lin and me our destination before she could welcome the passengers aboard. We landed at Basle almost midnight. Passing through customs and immigration was no bother, but the nitwit man on the desk asked me where Davos was, and all I could reply was Switzerland. He should have known. Our courier introduced herself. (Rosevita was her name. Ryvita two students called her. Lin and I wondered why, because we referred to her throughout the holiday as Rosenella, and it was only on the last day we learnt her real name.) I took a shine to our coach driver. I thought his name was Billy at first, but found out later it was Willy.

We began our journey to Davos. It was bitterly cold in the coach and I couldn't sleep. Lin did, but as it began to get light I kept waking her, much to her groans, to point out the scenery she was missing. First of all it seemed we were always in Berne, Basle or Zurich, one or other of those. But all of a sudden city life was left behind and lights became few and far between. We made one toilet stop – I didn't like Swiss moths – after which Lin and I played I Spy with the interior of the coach. Dawn began to break as we ate up the miles and I could vaguely see rugged mountains clawing the sky, as my eyes grew accustomed to the dimness. Lin was now wide-awake after serious prodding from me. When we came to Klosters we could tell we were climbing higher and higher. We coursed round hairpin bends, but were oblivious to the fact that we were on the edge of a precipice. We were too intent looking down upon sleeping hamlets to think about the long drop below. There was no traffic, no people, merely little wooden chalets nestling on grassy slopes adorned with carved shutters and flowering window boxes. Towering snow-capped mountains thrust their proud magnificent peaks skywards and we paid them compliment after compliment. Lin and I were mesmerised by the staggering landscape.

Arriving at Davos Dorf and then Davos Platz, Lin and I could have jumped for joy. The hotel and surroundings were far better than the travel brochure had led us to believe. Our arrival time was 5.30am. We were expected, because Giovanni, the Manager, unlocked the main doors to let our party in. 'Omar Sharif' his assistant was also in reception. I nearly had to catch Lin the moment she clapped eyes on him. He had the wow factor. We bundled together in the entrance hall as Rosenella sorted out our rooms. Lin and I were plump tuckered out, but even so took everything in. Giovanni began phoning rooms to tell people it was 6am. We hoped he would spare us the privilege of listening to his 'dark brown' velvety voice relaying the time at that unearthly hour. We were escorted to our room. Lin and I thought it was marvellous. We were in a little annex adjoining the main wing of the hotel. No stairs for us. We could see the mountains, gardens and swimming pool from our ground floor window, and hear cow bells tinkling the second we woke up. After unpacking we went out into the tingling mountain air and made our way to the dining room of the hotel. It was 6.30am. I can't work out how it happened, but Lin and I passed through the empty kitchens, because we got lost.

Lin and I made a bee-line for the table nearest to the one from which the waiters served. Chris and Ken joined us, and Moira with her Mum and Dad sat directly behind. The moment the waiters opened their mouths, Lin and I fell for them. Their "Good morning" sent a ripple through us. My favourite was Antonio who cordially greeted us with "Hello ladies" every morning, noon and night. He was clever with the plates. Lin, Chris and Moira didn't go overboard for him, but admitted he had nice eyes.

Nice! I called them moonbeams. My second favourite was the wine waiter. He looked the odd man out. He had light brown curly hair and blue eyes, whereas the others were dark haired and brown eyed. In the main "Applesaft", which was the only drink our table consumed, looked slightly sad and serious, but boy oh boy, when he did smile my heart bounced. I expect I fell for Antonio and Winery partly because, like me, they were fresh air fanatics. At night, after dinner had been served, they flung the windows wide open, telling us to breathe in deeply the crisp night air. They watched our chests as we did so. I loved taking the air, but the rest of the party were chilly mortals and a breath of air blew them over. Lin and Moira's favourite waiter was too short for me, but apart from that defect he was equally as gorgeous. Ken didn't allow Chris to have a favourite, as they were engaged. Bruno the head waiter was nice, but over experienced. Anyway he was attached to Rosenella. And we mustn't forget the whistler whom Lin renamed Big Ears. Two or three other dishes completed the main attraction at the meal table.

Our first breakfast of rolls went down a treat. We were ravenous. Afterwards it was back to our room for a snooze. That is Lin went out like a light, but I merely dozed off and on until eleven o'clock. Up I got and had a dip in the pool, which made my timbers shiver, but toned me up distinctly. After lunch Lin and I explored. It was a warm summer's day and all was right with the world. I bribed Lin to go in the cable car up Mount Jacobshorn. (I bought her an ice cream with real cream topping on the way down.) It was exhilarating at the summit. Two nuns and a man on crutches thought so too. We clicked busily in every direction, but I think just one photo came out on the mountaintop, the one where Lin looks as though she has been struck by lightning. She has a red shaft of light going through her head and shimmering round her body. When we came down from the mountain we walked through the main street of Davos before we sat sunning ourselves in the hotel gardens. We met two old Welsh ladies and when the evening meal was over they came back to our room and chatted. We were going across to see their room, but Lin was sick. She didn't get up for breakfast next morning. I did, thinking Chris and Ken would be in the dining room, but they had already hopped it. I felt a nit sat at the table by myself. The waiters were jabbering away in German. Telltale looks told me

I was the topic of conversation, but it was the not knowing what they were saying made me blush. The 'sad' waiter let me leave the dining room with my serviette bearing two rolls, butter and jam for Lin.

We had a rainy day, but it didn't stop Lin and me from wandering. We bought a kilo of peaches and spent the morning eating them. (We had taken a box of Ritz biscuits with us to nibble at bedtime.) We went tentatively into the exquisite tiny church behind our room and were bewitched by the splendour of the workmanship. After lunch we did go to the Welsh ladies' room. We nattered and went shopping with them once the rain had eased off. We had tea and cakes then returned to their room for chicken and chocolates.

Our evening meal was by candle-light. A romantic atmosphere, but Lin, Chris, Ken and I were in the wrong mood. We had the giggles. It was Lin's fault. The whistler was driving her insane. He would say "You like chips?" with a whistle, "You like green beans?" with a whistle, but he ceased abruptly when a loud mooing noise came from underneath our table. Only he couldn't figure out where it was coming from, nor could anyone else apart from Lin, Chris, Ken and I. Lin had found a way to shut him up. She had on her lap a cow's head, miniature and squashy, which when squeezed uttered a plaintive moo. She didn't stop mooing throughout the meal. She had bought it for little Richard, her brother. (Unfortunately for Lin, the cow had lost its voice by the time we got back to England and Richard beat her up because of it and said she had to go back and buy another one.) The whistler was used to having the mickey taken out of him, because of his impediment. He didn't mind that. I think he did mind overhearing Lin call him Big Ears, because occasionally afterwards he didn't give her soup or hardly any chips. Once eating and drinking were dispensed with, we tried to blow out the candle on our table, but there was little puff in us. The waiters asked us to stay behind (not Ken) and blow them all out, but we didn't. The meal sunk slowly and when Lin, Chris, Ken and I found we could move, we investigated the cellar bar from which beat music was belting out. We didn't stay long, because it was very crowded and four Teddy Boys approached which put us off. Ken was at a disadvantage there. Instead we went for a walk, came back to our room, kicked shoes off and talked half the night away, Ken and Chris curled up on one bed, Lin and I on the other. We had a laugh about the Hotel

Touriste stamped towel I picked up unknowingly with my cardigan in the Ladies Room, carried still unbeknown to me to the cellar bar, and dropped in the hotel entrance right in front of a gendarme.

Sunday it rained, but Lin, Chris, Ken and I spent the morning climbing a mountain behind the hotel. Squirrels, little birds and pigeons came to eat out of our hands. They didn't mind the cold and rain. I froze to my marrow, and I feel sure if I had been chipped with hammer and chisel, I wouldn't have felt a thing. I didn't care two hoots though that I was perishing, not when I saw a mother and Bambi deer on the mountainside. It hadn't occurred to me Switzerland had deer. The four of us were in dire need of scalding coffees to thaw us out before lunch, otherwise we couldn't have handled a knife and fork. With lunch out of the way, we went to watch skaters at the open-air ice rink. Quite a few were top-notch. There was the ugly bear, the bowler hatted man and the barrel shaped man with the red bobble hat who was dressed in a black wet suit, kept his arms behind his back, bent low and breathed loudly. I said Mum's saying "Red hat, no drawers", but could be that only applies to women.

On Monday a knock came on the door at 6.30am followed by double-Dutch. Lin called out "Come in" and ducked beneath the bedclothes, as a grinning Omar poked his head round the door summoning us to early breakfast. Lin avoided him like the plague thereafter, so ashamed she was of her roller head being seen. We had a coach trip to Lucerne. We loved it there. We ate our packed lunch in the park. Wasps were bothersome, because they made me drop my egg. We walked over the covered wooden bridge and saw, well I can't for the life of me remember if it was paintings or picture carvings describing Swiss history. We also went to see the dying Lion sculpted out of the rock face, and the museum containing glacial things, and the hall of amazing coloured mirrors. Lin and I took a boat out on the Lake for half an hour. I took a photo, supposedly of a view, but Lin's flabby arm and the steering wheel went to make up the print. The day was a long hectic one and I conked out after dinner with a headache. Lin dosed me with three pills. Two were prescribed, but Lin said three wouldn't harm me.

Tuesday we rose early again and set off for Liechtenstein. Luigi drove. Lin had a soft spot for him, and he also had a crush on her, you could tell. He gave her a paper mandarin brolly, the sort you put in cocktails. She thought he was sweet and took his photo. I thought two urchins were sweet and they consented to pose for me with their kites. We would have liked to stay longer in Liechtenstein. We crossed the border into Austria, but spent most of the time in a quaint old town so didn't see the beauty of the countryside. We saw the outstanding beauty of an ancient Austrian church though. We sat by the Rhine with the Welsh old dears, Moira and her parents. Moira has withered legs. It was a super day for sightseeing and a hot one too. Chris and Ken didn't go on that trip. They came to our room early evening to hear all about it before we went down to dinner together. I acted in a very agitated manner. Lin had gone off with an Italian in Austria who had picked her up, I said, and the coach had waited a while, then left her to find her own way back to Switzerland. Chris and Ken were panic-stricken. I said all we could do was wait for her to turn up and pray that she would. Solemnly we went to the dining room, sat there for a minute or two, and in walked Lin beaming her breeches off. Chris and Ken pressed her for details, told her she was a naughty girl and hadn't thought of the worry poor Angela had had. Poor Ange was laughing into her soup spoon. The game was up. What brilliant actresses Lin and I were. Lin had been in the wardrobe the whole time Chris and Ken were in our room. I let my dinner go down and then went for a long cool dip in the pool. The others didn't brave it, but ran off with my clothes. I made an almighty racket yelling indignantly, and beckoning rudely to three figures visible at a window. I thought the figures were Chris, Ken and Lin and the window was Chris's, but it wasn't. Droplet that I was dripped my way back to the hotel room for a rubdown. I dressed up as one of Ken Dodd's Diddymen, with an eiderdown stuffed up my jumper and down my slacks. The four of us went for an evening stroll and I received some gapes and gawks at the sight and size of me. I thought Lin's suggestion that we go into the disco was taking things too far.

Wednesday we left after breakfast for the Fluela Pass (I've got four rocks as mementoes in my jewel box) and St Moritz. Luigi was our coach driver so Lin was happy. I would have preferred Willy to drive us. Giovanni, the Manager, came along for the ride. Rosenella looked strained. She switched on the radio and translated that the Russians had marched into Czechoslovakia at five o'clock that morning. The news was upsetting and I could tell that it had affected Rosenella. Her boyfriend met her at the Fluela Pass – he was a

Czech – and again at St Moritz in his car. They had deep discussions with Giovanni. We had a fabulous time at St Moritz. Mostly we dabbled our toes in the Lake, splashed each other and sunbathed. We had to hurry like mad when we got back to the hotel to make our costumes for the fancy dress parade. Chris, Moira, Lin and I were the aces in a pack of cards. Ken was the joker in ordinary togs. We used the bed sheets and crepe paper. A gross man dressed as Twiggy won. The wine waiter smiled the whole evening and sent zings through me. Later, as I was in the way while the others undid stitches in our costumes and remade the beds, I had a midnight dip. As soon as I had dried off in snowy soft towels (Lin's as well as my own), it was time to pack. It was our last night in Davos.

Thursday we went into breakfast late. It was a sad feeling, the fact that we were leaving. A party of Czech boys came in. They looked haggard. Lin and I wandered through Davos that morning. We shopped, took in the sights and kept camera buttons active. We had an hour to spare before lunch and sat by the pool with Chris and Ken larking around. One thing about being an elephant, it wasn't easy to tip me out of my lounger. Well it was when all three meanies ganged together and heaved ho. We had a mouth watering buffet lunch with eel, trout, duck, fresh salmon and other tasty titbits. Full to bursting with food and melancholy, we loaded baggage and ourselves onto the coach and waved goodbye to the waiters lining the balcony. Why did they look so blooming cheerful? What was there to smile about? Our blues didn't take long to disappear. Mine went quicker than Lin's because Willy, my man, was driving. (Luigi, Lin's man, stayed behind in Davos.) On the way to Basle there was lots to see. All good things except we saw soldiers on the march. It was a military training area we passed through, but somehow with the uprising in Czechoslovakia men in uniform had a disheartening effect. We stopped for a scrumptious sticky apricot pastry and ate surrounded by staggering scenery. I was happy. Willy smiled my way and I could have done a double somersault if requested.

Our travelling band arrived in Basle at eight o'clock. Appropriate, Lin and I agreed, as we were staying overnight at the Hotel Bristol. We had a taste of home, steak and chips. Lin, Chris, Ken and I walked round the town. It was colourful with neon signs indicating night-life for those who could afford to pay. People were out in force. Males and females gave us the beady eye. Before we got footsore and lost our bearings, we retreated to the hotel and had a nightcap in the bar. The telly was on. We didn't have to understand the language. The pictures being shown, and the faces of onlookers, spoke for themselves with regard to the Russian take-over of Czechoslovakia. Rosenella thought it wise for Lin and me not to look out of our bedroom window. Our room was situated at the back of the hotel. We ignored her advice of course. We looked down on the vice street where prossies conducted their business, and naturally Lin and I wanted to see what went on, not that we learnt anything. Agog, we watched the proceedings. Balconies contained lazing females who leaned over railings bantering with one another and gave Lin and me an eyeful of bare breast. But none thumbed their noses, stuck their tongues out or called us names. Our presence was noted as interested bystanders, nothing more. We had the look of novices I expect. I don't think business was booming that night. I expect men, having been threatened with rolling pins, were safely under lock and key in their own bedrooms. Lin and I retired for the night, but it wasn't long before we heard a faint tapping on the door. We argued who should go. Lin conquered her fear and let Chris in. Talk about state to get in! Her room was out back like ours, and she was nervous as a kitten about sleeping there. She climbed in with Lin and me.

We woke up at 6am. The dustmen were out with their carts and it proved pointless trying to go back to sleep with the din of the bins being emptied. We wrote out our lists for the customs, fiddling the price of the articles we were taking home. We forgot about Ken. He was in a lathery stew when he knocked on our door. He had thought about calling the police when he went along to Chris's room and found her bed not slept in, and her belongings missing, but he thought about it some more and came along to us first. He didn't think she had walked out on him. Ken has got a good brain. He was studying Politics and Russian at University. Now he's with the Gas Board. At the breakfast table Chris picked all the dry rolls out of the basket and placed them with tender loving care in her shoulder bag in case we got hungry on the coach.

We had a look at Basle by daylight. I bought cream cheese for Pop in a supermarket. We caught a tram to the town centre where there was a large market. Ken looks lovely on a photo with his head appearing in a bucket of dahlia heads. We went in a museum and up a tower to survey what we could. We had steak and chips again at the hotel for lunch. Immediately after stuffing, we left Basle for Schaffhausen and the Rhine Falls. I even had a paddle in the Falls. Ken was elected to take photos of Lin and me with the Falls in the background. Sure enough, he got the Falls in the viewfinder, but only my and Lin's feet. Mine turn in and Lin's turn out. Ken never quite got over the shock of finding out what size shoe I was. I think my feet fascinated him. We had our final meal on foreign soil, steak and chips, in a restaurant overlooking the Falls and watched them fade out of sight as darkness descended.

We boarded our holiday coach for the last time and took no notice of the driver on the journey to Basle airport. (Willy had taken off with not even a goodbye.) At quarter to eleven we said goodbye to Rosevita – we at last found out her correct name – and Whatnot her mascot. We each had a hug. Our flight home was supposed to take off at ten to one. Hours later we were still grounded. The delay was due to fog at Manston and Gatwick. Lots of weary travellers slept sat on their cases, but there was fun to be had as far as Lin, Chris, Ken, Moira and I were concerned. We played our musical boxes and had a singsong, not a raucous one. I had a huge bunch of dried flowers for Nan that made whoever went near them sneeze and cough. They had had a gallon of perfume sprayed over them while we were mucking about. The perfume had been a present from one of the Welsh ladies, because I was taking duty free fags through Customs for her. The Customs men laughed when I said "Hello" to their "Sprechen Sie Deutsch?" They did, however, question me more thoroughly than the others, and their sniffers were going like the clappers, presumably due to my reeking flowers, which put the wind up me. I was waved on through, the last to board the aircraft. We were eight hours late taking off, but preferred a daytime flight. We touched down at Manston, only to be told a coach was waiting to take us to Gatwick, because that was where our cases had gone. We were tired, but didn't get off scot-free. Questions had to be answered in the Customs Hall and hand luggage delved into. I think I smelt fishy, and probably looked it, with stale perfume floating around my person. From Gatwick we proceeded by coach to Victoria. Sad partings were made, but not until addresses had been swapped. Lin and I were a little bit sick of the sight of coaches, but we had two more legs of the journey home yet to accomplish: coach from London to Bristol Bus Station and then a taxi right to our front doors. It had been a super-duper holiday.

A year later Lin and I went to London one Saturday to meet up with Chris and Ken again. They lived in Kent. We saw the film 2001 in Soho. Going on the train, a man left his brolly behind so I picked it up and carried it round with me throughout the day. Dad was shocked at my dishonest nature, but Dave and Al said "Well done". We nearly missed the midnight train home. We had left Chris and Ken at Victoria underground. They had told us to catch the circle line to Paddington Station. We got on the first train that pulled into the underground. Lin and I were on that tube for ages before we twigged we were going nowhere near Paddington, according to the map over the doorway. We got off, walked out of the station and found ourselves in a dimly lit Jack the Ripper type of street. We hotfoot it back into the same underground again, were put on the correct tube by a kindly Cockney and made it to Paddington in the nick of time to catch our train. We had to go without a snack, but that was our own silly fault.

JADED, BUT
NOT FOR LONG

After Switzerland I found it hard to settle down at work. It wasn't my job's fault, which I loved, but the travelling got on top of me. It had been getting on my wick months before the holiday, so much so I gave myself nose bleeds. I timed them well. Coming home on the bus I would get my knickers in a twist with pent up frustration, as the hour-long journey often became a two-hour one. Night after night the bus inched its way through the Centre, Old Market and Temple Meads, and inched I do mean plus lots of grinding to a complete halt. No sooner had I walked down the garden path into the house, downed a cuppa to unwind, I had to quick march to the sink and let my nostrils gush forth rivers of blood. A member of the family was at hand to plunge the back door key down my back, but it had little quelling power. The Red Sea ebbed when it was good and ready and not before. I could guarantee that nightly I would turn into a flaming red Spotted Dick. (It could have been a belated growing phase. Mum, Rish and Dave have been prone to bleeding noses in the past, although Dave has been fixed now. I thought the inside of his nose had been cut into quarters, but Dave put me right, his nose was cauterized not quarterised.)

However, help was at hand.

Henry and Pat, a married Smelting Works couple, offered me lifts to and from work. I abandoned the buses and the taps up my nose were turned off finally. The morning and evening rides were memorable, Henry's car being roadworthy simply because it was tied together with string. The doors and windows were held on with string, although sometimes I held the door shut throughout the entire journey to prevent it coming adrift. Pat's window did fall out one day as we rattled along. Henry got out and kicked the glass into the gutter as Pat put on a scarf. On several occasions I got to work or home with wet feet. I was supposed to watch where I put them, but on occasions a brick would slide across the floor to reveal a gaping hole up which puddles whooshed. We went too fast in this holey car ever to be stopped by the police. Henry had a habit of going round bollards the wrong way. He was definitely a mad professor type, a distracted genius really. Once we had to stop at Hotwells and Henry had to run half a mile back down the Portway in teeming rain to retrieve his windscreen wipers, which had taken flight. I don't recollect an evening when Pat and I didn't have to push the car half a dozen times round the Works car park to get it started. It was a common sight for us to be diverted around countless vehicles by office staff valuing their property. Even though first out we were always the last to leave. Then, when it exploded into action, it was zoom all the way home with me getting out while it was still moving and remembering to shut the door ever so gently as I ran half a dozen paces beside it.

Henry and Pat became matchmakers. My wedded twosome said they weren't stirring up untruths, but there was a particular boy who liked me, just my looks, because we had never spoken, but he was very shy and couldn't bring himself to make an approach. Apparently, he sat and gazed at me during lunch in the canteen. This news was enough to give me a nervous breakdown each day from twelve till one. As I hadn't a clue who he was, I felt every blumming male in the place was looking at me, and I got in a right pickle eating my food. My hands shook. Peas shot everywhere. Gravy spilled off my plate. Stabbed chips flew in all directions. I had difficulty in raising a cup of tea without losing half its contents. I was even frightened to use the sauce bottle. I made a point of enquiring of June was there anything on my chin (which he would see) before leaving the table. I hated lunchbreaks and persuaded June, if I could, to stay in the typing pool and eat rolls from over the Transport Caf, so that I wouldn't have to endure a miserable hour with chips getting stuck in my gullet, pastry impossible to break and pineapple cubes being chased round and round the dish, because they simply would not sit in my spoon. I hated even walking to my place at table carrying a hot plate of dinner. I was afraid I would drop it and meatballs would tumble into a boss's turn-ups and He, whoever He was, would see me make a fool of myself. I used to turn red just thinking about blunders in those days.

Eventually Pat slyly pointed him out to me one day in the canteen. Oh him, I thought at first, a tiny bit disappointed my secret admirer wasn't somebody else I had set my sights on. But after a few days I got to thinking, following meticulous study, he was very nice indeed with a beautiful pair of eyes. Yes, that chap with the eyes did make me flip my lid and when his and mine met in a head-on collision, I forgot about the piece of gristle in my mouth and went on chewing and chewing for quarter of an hour. I went all of a do dah when one afternoon he telephoned through to the typing pool from his department, and asked if I would like to go out on the Saturday. It was totally unexpected and what was so sad I had arranged to go out with a friend to celebrate her birthday that day. I could have cried. It sounded such a feeble excuse and he must have thought it one, because he didn't ask for another date. Upon thinking about it, he may have been too shy for me. With shy people I tend to act the same and we don't get anywhere. I heard from Henry and Pat that Sean (Seen Mum says) was rather upset at my rebuff, but they told me later, after he had left the Works, that he was courting seriously. They shouldn't have. It made me feel unloved and disgruntled.

JOE, THE TOAD

It was while I was working at Avonmouth I had my first real romance. I had gone to the Towns Talk on the Bridgwater Road with a hen party. Joe was on a stag night. He asked me to dance and we carried on from there. Actually, I had fancied his friend, but within minutes of being together Joe gained victory. He had a Tom Jones quality about him and, come to think of it, the action too. He sang songs like "It's not unusual" and "What's new Pussycat wo wo wo wo" at the top of his voice driving along, clicking his fingers merrily. Joe was ten years older than me and I thought of him as a lively, generous bachelor. I enjoyed our dates. I suppose I was a skittish young filly, but I felt ecstatic when he told me not to kiss him the way I did, because I hadn't seen a man get het up like that before. Joe was foreman on the shop floor of a car sales firm. With a friend he also ran a small garage in Barton Hill, so it was only at weekends and one evening each week we dated. I usually telephoned him at work to see what night he was free, but once he rang me. I was quite put out because, before he was put through to the typing pool, he chatted up the girl on the switchboard. He had asked for Angela and she said "Angela speaking" (true she was one) and he thought she was me, or so he said. I went off that Angela, because he had called her darling and I knew, even if he didn't, that she was very pretty. I said his tongue ought to be bitten off and he asked if I was offering. Men are such twisters. I must say Joe had picked out for himself a grand courting spot. We parked overlooking the Suspension Bridge. It was a magical sight, seeing it lit up with light bulbs in the inky blackness.

During our courtship I met with my 'accident'. To this day no one, myself included, seems to know exactly what befell Pange that October night four years ago. I've still got a war wound as proof of battle with things or beings unknown; a white blotch on my chin. And too, the revolting photos Pops took of me swathed in bandages with a bloody 'orrible face on show to my public. But how did it come about? I have searched my mind, but blank spaces remain. Not one drop of liquor had passed my lips on the night in question, when June and I visited Debbie and the twins, but coffee was drunk by the gallon. We had bid each other a warm goodnight. Debbie waved to us with both hands, as we started for our respective homes, because June turned left outside the garden gate and I went right. I hummed as I walked. One of my feet kicked the other shin, I do remember that. I do it regularly. I expect I called myself a clumsy oaf and walked on.

I did get to my bus-stop on the Portbury, that I do recall, but then for twenty odd minutes Pange had a blackout. My memory waves will not tell me what happened. Fancy waking up with half of me wrapped round the bus-stop and the other half lying in the gutter, truly seeing stars and flashing headlights. I lay there thinking, "Bad dream Pange, better get up and have a glass of water to flood the nerves". It was no trouble whatsoever picking myself up, but why wouldn't anything keep still. Slowly it registered that I was not in my bedroom. I took stock of my whereabouts. I remembered leaving Debbie's, but what on earth happened next. I thought if I was going to die, I wanted to do it in my own bed in peace and quiet with Mum nearby. I felt not quite right and sat down on the pavement for a minute or two. I dillied and dallied thinking "Shall I, shan't I wait here for my bus, or go back to Debbie's for another coffee and a sit down in the warm?" Lurch back to Debbie's I did, but I was a long time getting there, because I couldn't focus on her house and twice reeled past it. Rob opened the door and I wondered why he exclaimed "Good God!" Debbie attended to me, as I flatly refused hospital treatment. She cleaned me up best she could, but I was awfully gritty, dirty and caked in blood where my face had been torn apart in three places: eye, cheek and chin. Dopey me asked for a mirror. I looked into it and instead of crying hysterically, like any other normal human being would have done, I went into peals of laughter. I simmered down soon enough, because I throbbed and ached from crown to toe. Rob's mate gave me a lift home and I chatted amicably on the journey about the weather and so forth. He drove like a madman, as he didn't want me to die on him I suppose.

I wouldn't let him see me to the door. I thought it only fair that I be the one to prepare Mum, and Nan who was staying with us, to face me. I knocked on the back door, but when Mum on the inside tried to open it I wouldn't let her. I shouted, "Before you let me in I've got to warn you, don't look at my face". Eventually I got into the kitchen, after we had exchanged questions and answers through the door. After five minutes Mum plucked up courage to look and gave several shudders. We had to tell Nan to turn the other way in the bed in case it made her ill to see me. In the night though I had to wake Nan and together we hollered and thumped the floor for Mum to come. Rough I was and in need of the blue enamel po that night.

Morning dawned and I had my first visitors. Dave and Al came in to see ugly Pange. My eye had disappeared in the night. I was puffed and blown up, and I looked like a rainbow with shades of red, blue, purple and gold colouring my face. My portrait should have been painted and hung in the Chamber of Horrors. Pop said I couldn't have looked worse had I gone ten rounds with Cass the Gas. I moved only when I had to, because my body felt banged about, and how the deuce my foot got twisted round the wrong way I can't rightly say. Doc had to be summoned and my certificate was sent off to work stating thereon that I had received multiple injuries. June was incredulous, as I had been perfectly mobile when we parted at Debbie's, and she came at a fast pace to see me, demanding to know the full story, which could not be told.

I looked a sight going to work for a couple of weeks. The bus conductors – no lift as Henry was on a course – saw to it that I rested my legs, my good one too. They positioned me so that I could put my feet up. I dragged my leg around with me for a week or two. I got acquainted with remarks like "You've got dried prunes and apricots on your face" and "You shouldn't have struggled", but soon I was gambolling over the canteen or cafe for cheese cobs with the rest of the girls at lunchtime. Afterwards I often experienced the tremors before crossing the road in case I got hit for six. I have made myself believe a car mounted the pavement and didn't see me. I'll not concoct far-fetched tales involving maniacs.

My face didn't put Joe off. I 'phoned him and explained the mess I was in and that same night he came round after work in his oily overalls to see how I was. I soon became fit. We got to the stage where he would put my arm through his on a Sunday afternoon walk. One night he came unexpectedly – he didn't knock on our door, but peep-peeped twice on the car horn to announce his arrival. I wasn't in. I rang him the next day and he snarled. He said he wasn't sure how he was fixed, but he would telephone me the following day. He never did. I wanted to phone him, but I never did. And that was Joe that was. Well not quite. Much much later, years in fact, Lin and I were chin-wagging with Carol, her sister-in-law, whom I learnt worked for Joe's firm before her marriage. I also learnt she could remember him as being a married man with three kiddies. Ooh, didn't I ever loathe and detest him vehemently, the dirty rat. I was hoodwinked good and proper.

PROMOTION

All too soon promotion came June's and my way, and we were turfed out of the typing pool. It meant goodbye to the Avonmouth Works. I can understand one of Glad's customers – one grey, rainy Sunday her husband was driving past the Smelting Works and she took one look and ordered him to stop the car on the spot. Out came her crayons and sketch pad and with starry eyes her fingers skimmed over paper: the chimney stacks, the belching yellow and black fumes, the red brickwork and metal grabs, pulleys, cranes, the furnaces, the overhead cables, railway lines and shunting engines, and the splash of geranium amidst the cobblestones in front of the office block. She captured every detail with a background of dusky, water-laden sky, to paint on canvas the minute she got home. It takes some of us that way. So June and I, too busy to clean out our drawers properly, but not busy enough to say thank you and goodbye to many friends (we didn't cry, but Barbie did), left the Works with beautiful bouquets one Friday afternoon in November 1968, to start work as secretaries in the skyscraper, air-conditioned, centrally heated Head Office building of Imperial Smelting near Bristol town centre. We were to be two out of many new secretaries working for English and American bods who were building a new plant for the firm at Anglesey. Sigh at remembrances.

Three months I lasted there and in that time I changed from being a happy person to a downright miserable, long faced uncommunicative thing. The first month I felt unwanted. I was put into the Accounts Department. We couldn't choose our post. I read the dictionary for something to do. The only time I can remember laughing was when Sue Snivel tipped a bottle of white snopake correcting fluid over the new Royal Blue office carpet. We got through a roll of toilet paper mopping up and rubbing with water to get the stains out. I suppose we did a reasonable job. We thought it was ever so funny and Humphrey did. He said holes would come in it. The three of us kept it to ourselves by moving furniture over the paler square. I didn't like it in the Accounts department. I twiddled my thumbs all day long and I wasn't used to it. The tiddly jobs I was given held no interest for me. Figures, Yuck! June was kept busy busy working for the Chief Buyer. I felt even more dejected when I saw my name on a list of personnel. I was classed as a typist, June as a secretary. Well, at Avonmouth I had typed the Queens Award to Industry! It takes a lot for me to complain to high-ups. This was one time I did, to the Chief Accountant. He saw to it that I was given a secretarial position working for the Chief Design Engineer. Alas I became worse than ever.

Every night I came home and followed the same pattern: ate tea, went to bed early and cried myself to sleep, only uttering monosyllables to the folks at home. I was disintegrating. Many factors accounted for my unsociable behaviour and withdrawn state of mind, the main one being loneliness. June was in an open plan office with lots of girls for company, not unlike the Pool except the work was secretarial. I was deposited in an enormous drawing office with no females in sight, only men, 'millions' of them. I was still at the awkward, blushing, shy, stammering stage when if one spoke I didn't know where to put or what to do with my hands, feet and eyes. I don't mind being teased now, but then I would gladly have loved to crawl beneath my desk all day and every day. My electric typewriter! I can imagine to this day what it sounded like to my ears – each key struck like a deafening crescendo with only the noise made by pencils and rubbers to match it. I felt, undeniably, a multitude of angry faces was glowering at me for spoiling concentration and distracting thought. I got jumpy, nervy and edgy, and thought if I typed slower perhaps the noise wouldn't sound so noisy. My speed dwindled rapidly, almost to the stage of one finger tapping. I no longer pounded the key-board. I jerked sluggishly. When it came to underlining, I absolutely couldn't look up to meet a face. The sound was identical to a machine gun rat-tat-tatting. I felt hated even if I wasn't.

The best part of the day was lunch-hours. Then I met up with buoyant June and we raced into town for a feed of beanshoots and banana fritters, because we had developed a passion for Chinese grub. Dear Terence soothed me nearly every day on the telephone. At threeish in the afternoons I would flee my office to seek refuge in the foyer telephone booth, cramming in coin after coin as I unburdened my soul to her. She was Prudence Patience herself, and was never touchy with me for interrupting her working days for long spells at a time. I didn't say anything to June about being unhappy, but she may have guessed. I was least down in the mouth if my boss wanted photocopying done, because that meant I could take the lift up to June's floor where the Xerox machine was situated and see women, even though I was too busy to talk to them. There were men on June's floor of course, but they seemed a nicer bunch than the lot downstairs with me. They were older family men, like Humphrey who brought in holly, masses of it and full of red berries, just for me at Christmas time. (I caused a disturbance going home on the rush hour bus that night. Almost as bad as the time when Lin bought a television aerial one Saturday, and we took it in turns to fence with the shoppers in town and on the bus going home.) I'm wandering. However, there was always the dread of returning to my corner in the drawing office. Unfailingly, I hated pushing open the swing doors, because a sea of cheeky, smiling faces stared back at me which I mistook for scowling ones. My answering smiles were forced and very false. Every single time I walked the floor to my allotted corner in the drawing office, I couldn't stop myself from thinking I was going to trip over my feet, fall and show my bloomers. Secret fears consumed me, all of them groundless. I hated too having to take round nearly thirty cups of tea and coffee twice a day. Of course I muddled up who had what. My trays were badly in need of draining after serving the draughtsmen and engineers. I was told I wouldn't make a very good waitress. A jest, but I took it as a criticism.

My boss was a kind man. A Russian, but he had made his home in California. He was sad and homesick for America. I could see it in his face and heavy plodding walk. He sat on his own in Woolworths cafeteria at lunchtime. I jumped and got flustered each time he buzzed me on the phone. It was one of those new-fangled contraptions with four connecting devices, and I couldn't for the life of me get the hang of using it. Golly, I once told him in a crowded office of nobs he had a call from Japan. In fact it was from the office block across the road from us behind Courage's brewery. Dumbo Pange. It makes me go red even now to think of it. I must have had a pebble blocking my ear.

Three months crept by and I could stand it no longer. I could stand nothing any more. Not the men – I'm ashamed of myself admittedly, because they were all really nice blokes – the tedious folding up of hundreds of plans daily, each one seeming bigger than me, the sickening pit in my stomach which stayed gnawing from sunrise to sunset, the clock watching, being afraid of my own shadow, my clumsy feet, my trembling hands, my faltering voice every time a person spoke, the smiles which had to be dragged from me. I wanted to come out of the lonesome world I had cloaked myself in, speak again to friends and family in a voice glad to be alive, so scribble dee dee went my hand one evening and with white face I handed in my notice next morning.

I must have caused a flurry, because I had personnel officers come to Bristol from Avonmouth, wondering why my decision had been reached. How the devil did I tell men that I was frightened out of my skin working with men? That I had come from the shelter of a happy, bustling, noisy typing pool atmosphere and been thrown into a cemetery. Cemetery is the wrong word to use, as I was fully aware the men were very much alive. The spacious drawing office floor I thought of more as a lions' den that housed lions which were quieter than mice. I must have made up things to tell the personnel officers, like for instance I couldn't open a window to let in fresh air, I had become an uncontrollable spendthrift working near Broadmead shopping centre, I didn't like engineering work which was partly true. Whatever I said I felt free, if uncomfortable. Three very happy years at Avonmouth, three very unhappy months at Bristol spent with the same firm. The time had come to disengage myself from Imperial Smelting.

This time there were few goodbyes to be said and no bouquet to send me on my way, only my own relieved smile. I missed June. (We'd been buddies for a long while.) I missed my little boss too. I did what he said and wrote to let him know how I was getting on. I hope he enjoyed his stay in Bristol and grew to like tea.

WIMPEYS

The next step in my working life transported me to the Legal Department of Wimpeys and here I've become ground in for three and a half years. Nan tells people I work for Whippies. (Sounds like I work in ice cream.) If I said the firm made rabbit hutches a lot of people would agree with me. I soon became part of the fixtures and fittings along with the other females. We are indeed a happy quartet. I found it a hard life in the beginning, having to revert to bashing a manual typewriter and losing my nails in the process, but I soon familiarized myself with it. In our office we sit surrounded by cabinets slotted with thousands of files, mostly with their pockets coming undone, because we do work hard and overfill them. Oh, and jam jars filled with water, Susan's humidifiers. Good sorts I work with. There are only females stationed in my office. When I first started working for Wimpeys it took time to get acquainted with the women. What a strange bunch I thought. Now I'm as strange as what they are. I'm the baby of the group.

Peggy will pad into Mr. Ede's office for dictation in stockinged feet. I've learnt an amazing amount of stuff from Peg. She is peculiar. If she sneezes three times in a row there is nothing to worry about. That is normal. If she sneezes just the once that is a sure sign a cold is on the way and she will go home and have a hot onion. She is a staunch believer that onions are good for colds. Cheese on the other hand should be taken in large quantities if a person wishes to feel fruity. Mr. Ede, my nice boss, agrees cheese perks him up no end. I must have hidden talents, because I eat nothing but cheese every day in my sandwiches.

Peggy is Mum to four teenaged daughters and cannot do a thing right, like our Mum. Peggy's babies were all born covered in pith. She had craved passionately for oranges throughout each of her pregnancies. Peggy tells us comical stories. One I particularly like about a girl her daughters knew who had a 21st birthday that raised eyebrows. This poor unfortunate being lived in a flat. That is, converted bedrooms on the top floor of her parents' house. The girl's boyfriend called round on the night of her birthday. Her parents presumably had gone out for a meal. The girl and her fellah were skylarking when the telephone rang. It was her mother speaking on the line – could she go downstairs and turn the cooker off, because mother had forgotten to do it before going out. The boyfriend clomped downstairs giving the giggling wench a piggyback. They opened the living room door to go through to the kitchen, switched on the light and there, surprise, surprise, were her parents, immediate family and close friends. Nobody moved though. Mouths opened and shut without a word. Aghast they stared at the 'happy' couple who just happened to be naked as the day they were born.

At 11.30 in the morning Peggy sits with steam gushing round her feet where the kettle is plugged in. We need an extra unofficial cuppa to help us stand the pace. Wimpeys tea ladies are lovely, but they do not make good tea. It either comes out the urn grey or very dark brown, and I had to return a cup one day because it had stew floating in it, that is bits of cabbage and carrot.

During my first week at Wimpeys I had three phone calls one afternoon. Peggy, overhearing my greetings as I answered the callers, thought I was a flighty miss with three boyfriends named Dave, Terry and Jack. I convinced her Terri was a girl, my best friend, and Jack was Jackie. Only Dave was a real live fellah. My brother! With regard to boyfriends Peggy's advice to me is simply "Keep 'em walking". She remembers following this policy herself with one in particular who got hot under the collar and lustful. She merely clamped his arm to hers and walked and talked until she got to her front door. Only then did she stop awhile. She is nutty. She went out with a boy when she was sixteen and the first time he brought her home he said he would give her a ring the next day. She built up her hopes, fully expecting a ring to be placed on her finger, but they were dashed when he phoned. The wrong kind of ring she realised.

The most off-putting thing in our office is the heating system. Sometimes it's like a bakehouse. Peggy dries up like a sultana and smothers handcream on her face two or three times a day. I blot my face with a tissue a dozen times a day, because my pores open like a colander. You could do chips easily in my daily output of grease. I haul and scrape my hair back in a pony-tail in sweltering heat, because if I don't I get extremely annoyed with it, scarfing my neck and shoulders. On the other hand the office can be like a fridge. The first winter I was there the dopey firm ran out of fuel and, stingy lot, they didn't replenish stocks. We sat typing in overcoats and we put feet and legs in huge cardboard boxes to keep out the draughts. (Susan's brainwave.) Even Mr. Ede had a box for his legs. It was frustrating, as impossible to type well with mittens on and if we removed them, fingers would not bend because they were frozen stiff. We sat and swore non-stop at the errors made.

Mattie, as Scottish as they come, made up the number when I joined the ranks. She grew fungus in a saucer of cold tea and ciggy ash on her window sill for six months, because she liked the pretty colours which appeared, as it got more and more germ riddled. Mattie came in an hour late one morning and didn't even know it until we spoke up.

Edie isn't such a bad boss. He's a man. We've shortened his name to Edie or Mr. Ede. He doesn't mind. His surname is a mile long. I've a soft spot for him. We discuss a great many things. He's my confidant and counsellor and advises me when I have boyfriend problems. He calls me mugwump. He doesn't mind my prattle. Mind you, tears nearly poked through the other day when he called me a cabbage, because I knew he was right. He has been known to pinch my Cosmopolitan to read whilst signing his post, then complaining it wasn't as good as Penthouse regards illustrations and titillations. He says we take advantage of his simplicity. We do threaten to bash him at times. Yesterday he held the door open for me and said "Dirt before the brush" as I walked through. Naturally I countered "Beauty before the beast". Mr. Ede doesn't collect antiques, but one he saw in a Scottish castle last year he said he would dearly love to own. It was a tongue scraper. At least twice a day Edie gives us a rendering of "All things bright and beautiful". He has lent me one or two good books, like Cider with Rosie and Copsford. He's a Londoner and gains great delight in taking the mick out of the Bristolian accent. He swears somebody once said "The Gurkhals from Indial". He insists that I say "Vodkal and Lime". I'm sure I don't. Mr. Ede has taught me a string trick, and I ended up with Chinese burns to both wrists, because I wouldn't divulge it to Dave and Al. I soft-soaped Mr. Ede the other lunchtime to drive me home, because it was raining. On my return I told him what Mum had said when I announced who had brought me. "My goodness, I hope he didn't see your drawers hanging up on the kitchen line!" I even like the men who work at Wimpeys, and the drawing office crowd is the best. Maybe it's because they don't take advantage, like one day Mr. Ede was dictating to me and my favourite salesman came in and sat down on my lap.

My main boss, Old P, is a bit of a sod. He's not old actually, middle-aged I reckon. I can't figure out why, but I prickle and my bodily hairs stand on end whenever I enter his room. To be honest he isn't that much of a nuisance. He is an exceptionally clever man, and I don't know why it is he needles me. He's a work-aholic. Our little team is extremely conscientious, but he isn't one to praise our efforts and by gad we have sweated for him. He does leave us alone though. By this I mean he rarely steps inside our office. Only twice can I remember him treading over the threshold into the legal typists' room. Once was to dictate to Mattie. She had difficulty in walking that particular day, because one of her horses had stood on her foot. The other time was rather embarrassing. I was watering our potted plants with the kettle last Christmas Eve. I don't know where the dickens the rest of the office was. You could have knocked me down with a feather when Mr. P walked in to wish us Merry Christmas. I was so taken aback I carried on with my watering and flooded the plants. He's ever so smart, really really smart in his dress sense and quite an attractive man to look at, if he'd just unbend a little. He's very brisk. We usually do receive compliments of the season from Old P and shortbread from Mr. Ede. Before my time Peggy dropped hints to a boss that the legal typists didn't ever get a Christmas box, like chocolates. The next morning they each received a hanky, boxed, with lacy edges, which did so touch them.

Another thing that riles me about Mr. P, he keeps his ear to the wall. Every time he hears my footsteps walk down the corridor at 12.30, the time I go to powder my nose, etc etc, he phones through to the office for me. It's handy that the loo is next door to our office, because Peggy can knock on the wall to let me know if my presence is required, without moving from her seat. To be honest, there is no earthly reason for Mr. P to use the internal telephone. As our office adjoins his, we can hear his voice through the wall as well as on the phone. I like to use the informal touch when answering the internal phone, but once when I said "Hello, Angela speaking" a voice replied "Who would that be? Miss Burborough?" I knew then it was him, and I knew darn well he knew it was me. He was merely driving the point home to me that I should answer calls as Miss Burborough. I ask you, what a mouthful! There was one occurrence when he came on the phone instinctively I wanted to say Angela, but stopped myself as I knew that wasn't being correct. For a moment I got flummoxed and said Miss urhum Burborough. I had forgotten who I was besides being Angela. I apologised to him when I saw him, and he appeared to be human, because he smiled.

Occasionally I use the Dictaphone. Now I like listening to Old P on tape, because I can answer back. I harmed him once, quite unintentionally, but a stabbing all the same. It was my nail that wounded him. I didn't draw blood. One day I did want his blood. He made me hopping mad. A day in November it was. I asked him for two days leave and he didn't think I had any more due to me out of my annual quota. He said I had used up my last two days in February. I easily checked on that and next day went into work equipped with my personal diary – an entry in February read "Sick for two days, really billious. Ally phoned work for me." Boring stuff in my diary, but it pays to be boring at times. I prevented him hoodwinking me.

What was it I did wrong one day? Mr. P was having a house built and I transcribed the shorthand he had given me to read that he wanted a violet barred gate. He politely informed me the word should have been vertical. I do some terrible outlines. Talking about that word violet, I wore violet eye shadow to work one day and nobody talked to me nearly all morning. I was told later they thought I had been crying over something or someone and made myself ill. They thought I would come round in my own good time, but until I did I would be better left alone. Charming! My lids haven't seen that colour since. It did nothing for me. Mr. Ede didn't like it. He said at first glance he thought I had picked up a couple of shiners.

The girls and I enjoy the work, but wish there wasn't quite so much of it. We come across amusing things from time to time. I had a house purchaser whose Christian name was Primrose. He was a long distance lorry driver. Then there was the man selling land to the company who introduced himself to one of the bosses "My name is Ham, I'm the best part of a pig."

Working at Wimpeys I don't have to rise until 7.15 am. Ecstasy! It does mean though that the family gets in each other's way, moving around Bloss's piddly kitchen. It's rather too early for fun and games, but they do occur. Only this morning Dave left home for work. Half a minute later he came back through the door, supposedly crying and wailing, "Mum, I've got the sack." He was bringing in a sack left on the hedge by the sack man. Collection day. He sings 'The Laughing Policeman' at 7.30am.

Mum doesn't know what she is doing first thing in the morning. She does get in a pickle with Ally's sandwiches. One day she sandwiched two pieces of bread and butter together, forgetting to put the cheese in. Another morning she made his sandwiches, but instead of putting them into a paper bag and putting the half pound of cheese back in the fridge (M/D bought a fridge a short while ago, at long last. Dave is mightily chuffed. No more bits on the milk in summer he said.), she did things the wrong way round. Ally went off to work with a large lump of cheese in his brief case. Sandwiches are the only thing he carries in it. His greeting that night, as he came through the door, was "Bloss is a stupe." She didn't have a clue what she had done until he produced the cheese – a stinky lump of grease – from his case.

Lunchtimes are enjoyable. Once a week I go down The Pilgrim with Tritz for a roll and a pint of cider. Last week she informed me they were having a new recruit join them in War Pensions. A Civil Servant named Mr. Bacon. He would go down well with Mr. Egg, said Tritz, who has been in her section for donkey's years.

Usually the rest of the week I take my sandwiches along to Lin's, which is a short four minutes walk from Wimpeys. Fifteen minutes it takes though if Buttercup is out in her garden pruning rose bushes. Her face reminds me of a walnut shell. She reckons I am just like her, unlucky in love. Her lodger last week left her after twenty-five years. At Lin's I can have two cups of tea if I like. Lin's break for lunch is the same as mine, so we have plenty of time to chat.

Lin was telling me the other day about a chap she met at a dance. He brought her home and she invited him in for a coffee. It was very late and she hadn't particularly wanted to, but he had kept on saying how thirsty he was. Anyways, he went and ate her Mum's dried peas in soak. Then Penny the dog did her business on the front room carpet, which Lin had to wipe up. Before the evening drew to a close, Lin had to raise her voice not only to the dog. Her Mum woke up and called downstairs "Behave you two". Lin had had enough and decided to turn her beau out. She didn't give him a reason why she didn't want to see him again, but she told me he had a flat nose. Flo, one of the neighbours, was in the sitting room at the time, and gave Lin and me sound advice to follow with regards to boyfriends. "Keep your hand on your tuppence". Her wedding night with 'Arry was spent with his sister sleeping in between them. 'Arry was incapable anyways so it made no difference. Stoned out of his tiny mind he was, Flo said.

I'm forever telling Lin's Mum off. She is supposed to wear a steel ribbed corset all the time, but keeps it on for five minutes only on alternate days. Often Lin, myself and Mrs. H can't hear ourselves talk, because John and four or five of his school mates troop upstairs to the box room and put Slade on the record player with the sound full on. Mrs. H yells, but they don't hear. Flo pounds the wall from next door with her broom, but they don't hear. We're thankful when it is time for school and they charge out of the house in a whirlwind. John and his mates are at the difficult trying age of fifteen. Little Richard is too at six. He was sat in Lin's bedroom window (she would have killed him had she known) lunchtime today when I left the house to return to work. I waved and got the V sign in return and he didn't intend it to mean victory neither. His grin said perfectly "Up your kilt".

At ten to one, the time I arrive at Lin's, the key is in the lock for me to let myself in. As the door opens I announce my arrival with an "ooh ooh", then they know it's me. Richard imitates with an "ooh ooh" back. The things he comes out with. He saw me coming twice last week and let me in, because he had important things to tell me. On the first occasion it was "We've got two new mugs, but you can't 'ave one for your tea. They're for when Lin brings a chap home Saturday nights." The next time it was "We've got a gurt big fish in the baff" and I was hauled upstairs to see this shark. To be precise, it was a pike, which John had caught that weekend and was keeping until every single one of his friends had seen it. John keeps his live bait in the fridge, a tin of writhing maggots, which Richard will place before me when I'm eating. Lin can't clout him in case he tips them out onto the floor.

Richard is always into mischief. I can remember when he broke a bone in his arm and had it in plaster. His other wrist was bandaged too. He sustained these injuries climbing a painter's ladder and missing the rungs on the way down. Injured or not, he could still manage to wield a gun with caps in it, causing me to have a misfortunate occurrence with my new laid eggs one lunchtime. The blighter came into the sitting room one day last week with the poker stuck in the barrel of his gun. Mrs. H raised her hand, but lucky for Richard he tugged and the poker came out "pimps", was the word he used. He is a real boy, no doubt about it. He hates being molly-coddled unless he has got bronchitis. Kissing isn't his scene. I have seen him kiss his Mum once. We called him a cissy, but he was in a good mood and didn't retaliate with fisticuffs. He merely grinned and asked if he would turn into a girl. Richard never has been fond of school. I recollect walking into Lin's one lunchtime and he came running out to tell me he had been to school. "Good boy" says I, "but I'm not bloody going s'afternoon" said Richard, and he didn't. He locked himself in the toilet, didn't he, said he couldn't go, didn't he. The school bus came and went before he did come out. Lin pretty near killed him. It tickles me, because John calls Richard Freck and Richard calls John Ginge when either of them is in a taunting mood, as it never fails to provoke anger. Actually they are both freckle faced and ginger haired. Richard pulled a tooth out the other day and said he would put it under his pillow, as it would turn into a sixpence. I remarked that it would be the work of fairies. Richard looked at me as though I was some kind of a nut. "Not fairies, mice!" Richard rebuked me for being dumb.

I see my godchildren, Annie and Kate, nearly every day. They're my poppets. They live right round the corner and are often at Nanny's lunchtime. It's funny to think that Richard is their uncle. He is six, Annie is four and Kate two. Richard calls Kate Spring, because her curls spring back into place when he pulls them. He is home from school today with a blotchy body. He isn't diseased, only allergic to his sore throat medicine. Trust him! He belted a cricket ball through the open window lunchtime and his screech of "Duck", which accompanied it, proved to us his throat couldn't be that bad. He was a demon today. He swiped Kate and when we looked out the window, hearing her cries, we saw him telling the lawn mower off for doing it. The cheeky moo told his Mum, "You can't hit me. I'm bad". Kate came indoors crying and presented herself to me, sobbing for my lap. Annie had to come and sidle up close as well, thumbing all the while. She is going through a phase of sucking her thumb and a button sewn onto a piece of cloth at the same time. One day she said to me, completely out of the blue, did I kiss Ben? I said not any more and she said, matter of factly, rather than consolingly, "But you will when he comes back".

The kids do like people to listen to what they have to say, like Richard's jokes. He certainly keeps the stream flowing when he starts. I know better than to say I've heard them all before. Anyways, he doesn't wait for me to answer. Today he rapidly asked me "What dog don't have legs, hot dog, and why didn't the skeleton cross the road, cos he's got no guts, and Mum can I have the topper off the bread?" Sat down with his buttered crust, he began to relate to me what had happened on Saturday. The girls couldn't get a word in edgeways, although they tried. He went to Weston for the day with Mrs. H, Dinah, Annie, Kate and John. He said "Never again, Weston is a load of old cobblers" and to back up his statement "Nobody would come in the Crazy House with me". He had gone in the slot machine booth to have his photo taken. It didn't come out too well. "Our dopey Mum told me to stand up right when the red light flashed" Richard said, and that was why the photo showed a hunchback. Richard said that John and him had been on the pier and looked through the rudey-nudey machines at ladies with big pom-poms. Bazookas he called them in the next breath when I smiled. After his tales about Weston he turned to a different topic. Lin was going to get him a rabbit, a white one with black markings. I asked if he had a name in mind for it. "Snow Black" he said. Lin and I hid smiles and tried to get him to change his mind to Snow White or Blackie. He gave us thunderous looks and decided to leave us, saying he was going to see Baldy Head for his pocket money. Flo's husband 'Arry he calls Baldy Head. He came back five minutes later with money in hand and said he would call his rabbit Fluff.

Lin's Mum and Mrs. Flook (Flukey, Richard calls her, but then he calls Mrs. Fog next door, Foggy to her face) were sat talking of muggets the other lunchtime. I asked to be enlightened and was told they were pigs' toilet things, which were soaked in brine and later boiled. Messy things to prepare and clean, but tasty when cooked. Dad said the poor people from Monkey Town ate them.

My lunchtimes at Lin's are not what one would call relaxing, but I prefer them to sitting in the canteen with a plate of stodge. I like to get some midday fresh air into my lungs too. One thing I must remember not to do in future is hang my coat up in the kitchen if we have yellow smoked fish for tea. People in the lift with me today didn't half wrinkle their noses, and a cat followed me right the way down the road into Lin's garden, and only beat a hasty retreat when Penny barked. On my way back to work I passed the old lady who can barely walk the road due to her tree trunk legs. She thanks me for my smile. I've got plenty to smile about compared with her. Into work I came and politely told the young man stood pressing the lift button it wasn't working, to which he replied, "I know love, it will be in a minute, I'm the lift engineer". Why do I bother?

Oh yes, I settled into Wimpeys quite happily and then, when was it, the beginning of June '69 my life took a further upward trend.

MARTIN, MY FIRST LOVE

I went to a dance with Lin one weekend and danced with Martin. We only had a couple of dances and some small talk before he drifted off, much to my disappointment. The following Saturday I was there again and so was Martin. He asked me to dance, but didn't recognise me at first, because my hair had gone from very short to very long (my switch) in one week. We stayed together for the rest of the evening and my heart leapt. I learnt he had been in Bristol just for a few weeks and was in lodgings. He was buying a house, which would be finished in a couple of months. He was Office Manager in a do-it-yourself firm. Before coming to Bristol he had lived and worked in Reading, but had asked for a transfer when he heard a new branch of the firm was opening up on the outskirts of Bristol. He was five years older than me. Unfortunately, Lin didn't fancy his friend Gordon. Gordon had a car. Martin didn't. Martin had only been acquainted with Gordon a week or two. He had met him at a dance. They got talking propping up the bar. Gordon was a sad, moody sort of fellow, always with an air of gloom about him. Most of the first month Martin and I dated Gordon came out with us too. I felt sorry for him. He wanted company and did take us out lots in the car. The most convenient place for the three of us to meet was The Hatchet, the 'funny' women's pub, but after a swift half we moved on. Invariably, the next stop was The Chequers down by the river. Gradually, we began seeing less of Gordon until he faded out of the picture altogether.

June and July were loved-up happy months. I fell hook, line and sinker for Martin. We drank in the cellar bars, ate in Chinese and Indian restaurants, danced at The Mecca and Tiffanys. He loved music and was always finger tapping on table-tops. Drumming was in his blood, because his father had played before the Queen and backed international singing stars. Everything was right with my world.

(Interlude)

There was one weekend I didn't see him. The girls and I went camping, a never to be forgotten experience. Let me see now, what did happen? What didn't is more apt. There were muck ups from start to finish, but it was still great. We hired a Mini with Des driving and set off from Bristol on a Friday night headed roughly in the direction of Bournemouth. The tent, a good one, I had managed to borrow for a small fee from work. I had joined the Sports and Social Club the week before for that sole purpose, because only members were allowed to borrow the tent. This we fastened onto the roof rack and laid our four sleeping bags across it. The four of us (Lin, Barbie and I hefty lumps, but not much of Des to speak of) squeezed into the car with pots and pans, tins of beans and can opener, and off we tootled. We did a mile or two. Happy as sand-boys we were. Then, on a fast dual carriageway, a passing motorist beeped us. Boy didn't he ever beep us! Road hog we muttered, but he didn't look like one. We couldn't figure out why he was using his horn like that. We knew we were four raving beauties, but he stood no chance with his missus sat beside him, and she was laughing. Good job Barbie was turned round in her seat chatting to Lin and me in the back, because suddenly she hollered for Des to stop the car. "Don't be ridiculous" we said, and Lin added "Oh Barb, you should have gone before we left." Barb though had seen out the back window a couple of sleeping bags dancing in the wind. It took Des a minute or two to decide exactly what to do. She halted the car a good way further up the road on a gravel shoulder, and off tanked Barbie back down the carriageway tittering as she went. Barb was tons bigger then, before her milk and banana diet, and she was a picture as she attempted to hurry back to us with two squashy sleeping bags gathered up in her arms. The toots she received from drivers! They were shoved in the car between me and Lin and the rest of our clobber. That was the beginning of things to come.

We carried on regardless and, before we knew it, blumming darkness had descended and we were still on the road. Nearly 10.30pm we came across a campsite, close to Salisbury I think it was, but upon enquiring for a square of field we were told "Sorry full up". Our dejected faces made the warden relent and he said he just might be able to squeeze us in. By this time the fires were out and people were in their tents mostly snoring. There was bags of room round about the spot allocated to us, and we failed to understand why we had been told a different tale when we first asked for a space.

By torchlight we unloaded the tent and turned the car headlights on. We nearly cried, because at the end of half an hour we were still absolutely clueless how to put the durn thing up. We had a diagram to go by, but it wasn't that good. I had drawn it the night before, as I watched our neighbour, Mr. Willy, put up the tent in our back garden. It was very complicated with two rooms. There was a groundsheet, inner tent besides the outer one, plus loads of pegs and small horseshoe type things to hammer into the ground. We were near to despair. It was awfully dark and we had chilly bumps. Then a knight in shining armour, I should say striped pyjamas, came to our rescue from the tent next door, although it was situated quite a distance from us. He probably thought he had better, and then, with a bit of luck, he might be able to get some kip. He was marvellous and with issued instructions, we had it up in no time at all. We thanked him profusely and would have kissed him if a woman hadn't been peering through his tent porthole.

He left us and in dim light (one torch had died on us) we found what was needed next: Barbie's Dad's wartime oil stove, saucepan of water, mugs, tea bags and milk. Somebody had forgotten to bring sugar. I didn't mind, but the others did. Barb said to light the stove we had to blow on it. Blow it we did, taking it in turns to get down on our benders. We went through a box of matches, but not a glimmer could we raise. We had come to the end of our tether and couldn't be fussed with it any more. We had our breakfast, a bowl of cornflakes minus sugar and half dozen biscuits. We had a bedtime drink of cold water, wiped a Quickie over our faces and jostled together into sleeping bags. We had hardly a wink of sleep between us. The ground was bumpy with hummocks and stumps. Stones jabbed us in the back and the countless stings we had received whilst raising the tent itched.

That wasn't all. We had almost succeeded in our efforts to go to sleep when suddenly the four of us sat bolt upright in astonishment. The ground shook beneath us and a train thundered past the tent making the flap flap. We were amazed to find ourselves still alive once it had hurtled by. Even hard-of-hearing Barb said, "I heard that" in an incredulous tone. After three or four had again disrupted the stillness of night, we could stand it no longer and by seven in the morning we were up, dressed if not washed, and ready to depart. No wonder our sleep had been disturbed. In daylight we could see we were not only parked a few feet away from the railway line, but our tent was erected on a nettle patch twenty-foot square. The reasons were obvious why no one was camped near to us. We did perk up instantly when Des blew the fire into life with a gigantic puff and we could have a cuppa.

We were securely packed up and all set to go before anyone else on the site had stirred. Into the Mini we climbed and told Des to start her up and let's go pronto, but go we could not. The car had an unhealthy cough. Des tried again and again to get her going, but the battery was flat as a pancake. No amount of coaxing, cajoling and swearing would make her change her tune. So out we clambered and pushed. Now you would think that with me, Barb and Lin built like tanks, and with our shoulders to her stern, we could have got some life into the old girl, but no. There was movement in the camp by this time and a bit of muscle, solid not flabby, and brawn was called for. We summoned assistance from the campsite warden who was patrolling and three or four beefy men. Thus, with Lin, Barbie and me on the sidelines shouting encouragement, we watched as they pushed the car round and round the tents. Heavy breathing and a little slope did the trick and our Mini spat into life. It was "In girls at the double, quick quick quick". No time for a thank you, just a cheery wave. No time to pay the warden neither for our night's tent space and the site amenities. I mean to say we dared not stop, not for anything, once we got started, and we had had an uncomfortable night.

Onwards the car sped. We gave it its head until we reached Bournemouth. A hearty breakfast was next on the agenda. The car played up every single time we made a stop and wanted to restart, but Des complained to the hire firm on our return to Bristol, for lumbering us with a duff car, and we got a refund.

We had the sun on our side and enjoyed Saturday window-shopping in the town centre. We walked along the beach and paddled, but didn't brave the sea. Late afternoon we drove out of Bournemouth, followed the A Road for a short distance and came off when we saw arrows pointing to another campsite. This one was smart, we could tell, and although costly we didn't mind, because we had slept rent-free the previous night. Aid wasn't needed this time. We had the tent over its scaffolding within minutes, about sixty I would say. Des went great guns with her huffing and puffing and we ate a hearty meal of tinned Beef Roma. We each paid a shilling for a shower. Des, Lin and I got scared though when we couldn't make Barbie answer that she was all right. We kept banging on the booth door, especially when steam started to creep under it, but out the lobster walked, grinning from ear to ear and said "That was lovely". She had removed her hearing aid of course. We each washed a pair of pants under the shower and hung them on the guy ropes.

We put our faces on, dolled ourselves up in pretty but crumpled dresses, and went out to do the town with wet hair. We did a couple of pubs instead. At closing time we had to run round the car park behind the rotten old car, flexing our biceps, before returning to the campsite. We changed into Bell Bottoms and being starving Marvins went in the site restaurant and had chicken wings for supper followed by a singsong.

At midnight, with overloaded bellies, we hastened along in the cold night air to find our sleeping quarters. Barbie nearly intruded into someone else's privacy, but we grabbed her shirt-tails in the nick of time and made it safely to our own shelter, which looked exactly like twenty or thirty others. The give-away was the knickers hanging outside.

We had to rid ourselves of the giggles before seeking rest. Barbie began moaning that there was something hooked around her big toe. Out she crawled from her sleeping bag with a moth ring nestling round it. Into the bag she burrowed again, and once more, panic stations. She swore her monthly had come. Out she got for a second time, stepped over our bodies and went into the outer lobby to inspect her Dad's jamas, which she was wearing. False alarm so back into the warmth she came. Peace descended for five minutes, then Barbie's voice called out "Angieeeeee, are you asleep?" Torches were switched on, because none of us were. "What now Barb?" was the question. "Well I think I had better go to the John and put something on, in case something should come in the night" she replied. That made sense so out came the crawler for the third time, walked over us, rummaged for her doings and raced speedily off to the Ladies. She was a darn sight happier on her return. That is until she got into her sleeping bag. She said she could feel something with legs. After much gyrating and worming, she pulled out an enormous black spider and with a squeal threw it at us. We didn't bring the tent down around our ears, because we were responsible. It was Lin's brother's joke one. Oh yes, she was cold too and said she wished she had fur like cows and sheep had.

At long last we drifted into slumberland but damn me, poor Des had the screaming 'abdabs'. Chronic claustrophobia. We had to let her get out sharpish and take some air. When she had calmed down it was all change, as we had to let her sleep by the door, with her head hanging out, otherwise she would have died on us. Barb had to pick Lin's sleeping bag up by the feet, whilst I got her under the armpits, and gently we dropped her senseless sleeping frame out of the way, thus enabling Des to kip by the door flap and feel a breeze on her face. Nothing can wake Lin until she is good and ready to open her eyes.

Next day was a heat wave and that morning we did little, other than laze in the sun and nibble non-stop. Fresh air we blamed for our enormous appetites, but one only has to look at the framework of Barb, Lin and me to know fresh air had nothing to do with it. My God, my dewlaps! We took idiotic photos. I've got one of me with Lin on my back (in her rollers) and she is holding a pair of sneakers in such a way it looks like I've got donkey's ears. We mailed postcards. I have no idea why, because we were only gone two days and one arrived at home on Monday morning before I left for work. We spent the afternoon driving through the New Forest, which was a pleasant interlude except the ponies galloped off when they caught sight of us.

We made good time on our homeward journey and stopped off at Longleat Stately Home for a couple of hours to have a gander at the house. We didn't bother to drive into the Lion Park in case the car got scratched. We had done enough damage by sitting on the bumper to have our photo taken. Poor Barbie got a stern reprimand in the courtyard, not that she was aware of it. We were stood admiring a highwayman's coach as the guide, a woman, spoke of its history. She had told us not to touch, but Barb didn't hear and approached to have a good look inside. She heaved herself up onto this priceless object, peered inside and called to us to come and have a look. Not on your nelly. The guide went spare and denounced our friend for contaminating the coach. We hastily shunted Barbie away, to her surprise. Anyone would think she had fingered the Crown Jewels the way that stroppy guide acted. That coach had no feelings, but Barbie had. As she says, bless her, "I get easily hurted". Before we left the grounds we thought we must have a photo taken of the four of us together, to bring back memories in our dotage. We chose our spot with a glorious rose bush in the background and proceeded to pick out the man to do the deed for us. He was selected with care out of the hundreds of geezers wandering about, because he had the most complicated, expensive looking camera slung round his neck. We thought he would do a grand job with my little Brownie Box. Huh, he cut our heads off. Our cheesy grins had been in vain. He snapped us from our linked arms downwards. Big feet and unflattering jeans at half-mast made up most of the picture, and who the devil moved our pink bush at the last second, I'm blowed if I know.

BACK TO MARTIN

Martin's and my courtship blossomed. He picked me up and carried me down busy Park Street – no mean feat – one evening in light-hearted mood, grunting under the strain. He moved house. I bought him two china ducks. I was at the house when Martin's TV was delivered and the wiring man thought we were newly-weds. Martin emphatically put him wise. We didn't go out much in September, although it was a fine month. I took him to meet Nan and she gave him two pillow-cases. He came to tea one Sunday afternoon. Mum and Dad liked him. I showed him family photos. Rish's wedding album he skimmed through in half a minute, hardly glancing at me in my bridesmaid's dress with my yellow coloured hair.

I met people he worked with like nice Sam, Hubert married with children but a wolf, Mrs. Whats-her-name, Martin's secretary. I met wives and girlfriends belonging to the office/warehouse workers and liked them immensely. I saw Martin's office and could picture him sat there when he phoned me at work. We had a coach trip to Guildford for a firm's football match. Martin took charge of a bucket and sponge. He wasn't the sporty type, not like my brothers. There was a buffet dance later on and I met a lot more people who knew Martin. I remember he fell asleep on my shoulder coming home in the coach. Another Sunday the men played football in Gloucestershire and I helped the women cut sandwiches and make tea. I went to an exhibition, which his firm held, and was introduced to high-ups. Martin said he was proud of me. We also went to the firm's annual dinner and dance.

Wanting to please, and in an effort to look glam, I bought a flimsy see-through dress for this posh occasion, but what a performance it was, getting essential accessories like 'spoons' that didn't glare through the white filmy material. I figured my best bet was to opt for a backless bra. Into a shop I went, whispered my request to the assistant who, armed with a couple, ushered me into a cubicle. I hate overbearing females hovering as I disrobe, so I whipped them off her, smiled a firm "Thank you, I'll try these" and she bustled away. Boy oh boy, I wish she hadn't left me alone. What the heck was I supposed to do with the things? I picked up a pair. There were two cups and certainly I knew where they went, but otherwise all it consisted of was yards and yards of strippy straps. Half naked, and frightened to death the assistant would burst in at any second, I struggled for what seemed like ages trying to fathom out what went where, and nearly strangled myself in the process. I twisted straps round my middle, round my neck, round my shoulders, round and round my back too, although common gump was telling me to leave my back alone. Just about everywhere they were wound round, except for my ankles, but in the end I had to give up. I did feel a twit.

Mum told me off later and said why on earth hadn't I called for help, but suffering in silence was preferable to appearing a foolish cracker. Immediately I had finished flinging my clothes on, the assistant's head shot round the door. Feeling crushed I said I would take it (this monstrosity), as it was a perfect fit, very comfortable and exactly what I had in mind to go under my see-through. She assured me I would feel relaxed on the evening, in the knowledge that nothing was on show from behind, and asked me, was I sure I didn't prefer the other one and why didn't I take them both? I had forgotten the other squid like bra lying on the chair.

I left the shop feeling hot, bothered, flummoxed and fed up to my back teeth. I got home, off came clothes again, and in the isolation of my boudoir, behind locked door, I had a further stab at conquering this awkward, puzzling pair of dub-holders. Half an hour went by before, hey presto, I had mastered the art of getting things in their rightful place, I think. Easy peasy really, but what an irritating bra it was. Straps went criss-cross over my front, which I could observe through the dress in the mirror, and looped together at the back on my waistline. It cut me raw. I am positive it was made wrong, because one should never have elastic round a midriff making red rings and stopping the flow of internal juices. I suffered enough with tight garters round my long socks at school. Also my dubs were nowhere to be seen in the wrinkly spoons. Didn't they ever pucker up! Far too much material had been used in their assembly. Both dress and dub protectors were thrown in temper to the back of the wardrobe to rot, and I wore a plain old thing to Martin's 'do' which he said I looked nice in.

We went to people's homes occasionally with other couples, but of course we had to rely on someone for transport all the time.

A wet and windy autumn turned into a bleak winter. I started going to Martin's three nights in the week and Saturday and Sunday afternoons. He couldn't come into Bristol, because he worked late each night. I was a silly lovestruck girl. I left work at 5.15pm and got to Martin's roughly two hours later after catching two buses. One night in November it was as late as 8.30 when I trudged up his pathway. That was exceptionally late due to a firework display at the Rovers ground, which caused a traffic snarl-up.

Another night in December I shared a taxi from the bus station with three women who wanted to go to Yate. Three buses in a row had been taken off the route, due to a severe snowstorm. The taxi driver dropped us at Yate shopping centre and left on my tod I got disorientated and well and truly lost. I tramped in the snow wearing shoes, because I had no boots. Stupidly, I didn't have my brolly, so the snow did what it pleased, and swept and swirled into me. Buffeted I truly was. I battled along in what I thought was the right direction and the tears rolled down my cheeks. I was so miserable, icy cold and wet through. When I finally found Martin's house, quite by chance, at 8pm he didn't answer my knock on the door. I sighed wearily and cried some more before setting off towards the launderette, hoping against hope that was where he would be. I saw Martin before he saw me and tried, in vain, to run. He had been out with a torch scouring the streets for me. Later I sobbed in his arms, strung up and unco-operative, but he understood.

The elastic broke in the waistband of my tights one Saturday, as I was making my way to the bus station to go to Martin's. They came down and down and I was convinced my gusset was visible to hundreds of shoppers. I thought walking slowly might help.

Martin didn't have a lot of furniture, just essentials. For months his bedroom was taboo. The first time he took me in there was to show me fitted wardrobes and dressing table the carpenter at work had put in for him. We were in and out in a flash. The second time was when I arrived one evening to find Martin in bed with a high temperature and sore throat and I sat on it. He would bring the eiderdown off his bed downstairs and we'd snuggle under it on the settee or have cushion fights to keep warm. Perhaps the next day I would smell Martin's aftershave on my clothes and that would make me glow. We sometimes ate tinned meals out of saucepans to save on the washing up, but usually I made do with bread and butter for my tea. Martin ate a cooked lunch and hardly ever wanted tea. He always phoned me at work during an afternoon to see if I was going down to Yate. He never took it for granted that I would. He always had the kettle boiled and two mugs standing ready for coffee as soon as I arrived on his doorstep. We had coffee and brandy if it was an extra cold night.

There was one afternoon when he phoned, he asked me to get a tube of toothpaste on the way down. I said I would, but realised once I had put the phone down that the shops would be shut by the time I left work. I got to Yate about seven o'clock. As I walked by a shop a man came out with empty milk bottles. I asked him if he was shut. I knew he was. He said yes, but was it something urgent I required? I replied that it was actually, and he invited me to come along in. I felt a fraud inside the shop simply asking for toothpaste, but he didn't turf me out without it.

At Martin's I pulled the bathroom light string out of its socket. I took it to him with a host of sincere apologies and he didn't wrap it round my neck.

Martin met all my friends at 21st birthday parties in 1969. There was Terri's, Deb's and Meryl's. I was so proud to have him for my boyfriend. He slept in my bed at home four or five times. He thought I had an extremely hard bed. Dad forgot to remove the door on top of the mattress. I slept on the floor downstairs, because I felt generous. I wouldn't let him get up until lunchtime, but I kept him company. I offloaded the Sunday papers on him, but not much scanning went on. He ate whatever Mum put before him except the Yorkshire Puddings I had made.

I cut Martin's hair. I sewed on his buttons. I bought him a pink knitted poodle at a bring and buy sale, which contained a bottle of shampoo, I don't know what for. It was hideous. I administered his eye drops. I couldn't stop myself falling for him.

One Saturday in November we travelled to Reading on the train. I met Roy and Clare, whom Martin had known for many years. It was Roy's 21st and there was a party that evening in the pub where he worked part-time. Again I met a number of people, friends of Martin, and liked each and every one of them. Roy, naturally, had too much to drink. I danced with him and he came out with the strangest things. Amidst slurred words, I heard him say that Martin thought the world of me, but to give him time, because he was scared of getting serious. Then something was said about Martin being married to a bitch. I didn't think I had heard him right, but nevertheless an icy fear welled up inside of me. I excused myself and went to the outside loo. Sat there, over and over again I told myself it couldn't be true. I felt frightened and far from home, but knew I had to ask Martin about Roy's disclosure, drunken stupor or not. The cold night air revived me enough to walk and I returned to the party. The cake had been wheeled in. I found Martin. He took hold of my hand and smiled. Then he noticed I had the shakes and asked if I was unwell, because I looked ghostly. I asked him to come outside, and there on the pub steps I blurted out what Roy had said, that he used to be married to a bitch. He told me not to take any notice of Roy, that he was completely blotto and unable to think straight. I felt so relieved to have his reassurance. We rejoined the party and stayed unseparated the rest of the evening, except for one instance. Martin went to have a word with Clare's Dad, who came across and told me how stoned and insensible Roy was, and not to pay any attention to what he had to say. I thought no more about Roy's statement.

We struggled back to the flat with Roy in the early hours of the morning. He flaked out on the settee. Clare insisted Martin and I have their bed. I would now class it as a poignantly sad and cruel night. We didn't sleep. We lay together resting in each other's arms and watched the darkness turn to light. The time would have been right to talk of a great many things. I wonder why nothing was said. I can now partly understand how his thoughts must have been in conflict throughout that long night, wanting to shift the weight on his mind, but unable to bring himself to do so. But that was Martin, a closed book at times. He stood alone so often in the time I knew him. Clare brought us a cup of tea and plate of biscuits in the morning. She said Roy was like a bear with a sore head, but had gone down the road to serve in the pub. After we got up Martin went off to the pub, and I helped Clare get the dinner and change the sheets.

Roy and Clare accompanied us home that Sunday evening. They too had decided to pack up and move to Bristol. They were going to stay with Martin for a couple of days, and scout round to see if they could get jobs and buy a house in the area. We had a drink in our favourite pub before I caught the bus home and they headed for Yate.

Mum and Dad had staggeringly sad news to give me on my arrival. From Lin's boss they had heard that her Dad had died Friday afternoon, soon after I had left their house at lunchtime. He had been all right when I saw him and I had received my usual greeting "'Lo Ange" as I walked in, but he had had a very bad asthma attack in the afternoon and he ran out of breath for the last and final time. How he had suffered over the years, but never a moaner. Lin said working in the butter factory for umpteen years had affected his chest. I cried myself to sleep that Sunday night and asked the Lord God Almighty why it had to be him. Monday morning at work I had a dull ache in my heart. I dreaded lunchtime coming. I couldn't say anything to Lin's Mum. I could only hold her hand and kiss her cheek. Lin and I went upstairs and both of us cried. The next Sunday I went to a service held in his honour at the Community Centre. Mrs. H is afraid of churches. Little Richard mentioned his Dad to me just once. He said he wouldn't be going fishing with his Dad any more.

November turned into a wild December. Whenever I set off for Martin's the weather seemed to strike with a vengeance. It seemed to work itself up into a dreadful fury. I strived against the wind, rain, snow and bitter cold. I went through tempests to see 'my' Martin, but I did become tired. I turned into a real Slim Jim, but also began to look drawn and haggard. I was taking two hours to get to Martin's and the same to get home. I kept getting one cold and cough after another. There were those worse off of course. Going to Martin's one Sunday a handsome young man got on the bus. He sat on his own. I felt hurt for him. I tried to imagine him making love. He had artificial arms. Martin's health was poor as well, because of working so hard. We comforted each other's tired and worn out body, like two old codgers really.

The roads and pavements hadn't been built, not properly, on Martin's estate. I stood in mud at the bus-stop. I had to, otherwise I would have got knocked down. There was no street lighting, because it was a country bus route. Martin didn't always come to the bus-stop with me. I always wanted him to, but half the time I said there was no need, as it was pointless for him to come out in the cold. Waiting for the bus, which took me halfway home, I couldn't help snivelling some nights. I tried to console myself by talking sympathetically. I would say things like "Don't worry Pange, things will get better", but they never did. I tried to buck myself up by singing one or two songs at the bus-stop, either 'Pick yourself up, dust yourself off, and start all over again', or 'Give a little whistle, whee whee, give a little whistle, whee whee'. I loved Martin, but he lived so far away. I often had to have a taxi home from the bus station, because I missed my last connection. I would dart from the bus station to the centre of Bristol in the hope that I would catch the last No.1. There were occasions I walked from Bris bus depot to our house, which was a good few miles. It saved me some coppers and I don't mind the dark, never have done. I find it quite soothing. Spooks didn't exist.

Christmas came. Martin said he didn't have a card for me. I said it didn't matter, but deep down it did. I would rather have had a card than a present. Mum said she didn't like him any more. He went to stay with his parents at Brighton over the holiday period. Christmas Eve I went dancing with Lin and Meryl. It made a nice change and I enjoyed myself. I wasn't on the look-out and wanted nobody to take Martin's place, but I did meet an interesting fellah. He told me I was a speciality. That day he had returned from spending three years in Guyana with his parents. I was the first white woman he had danced with in a long while, so he said. Naturally I gave of my best with the flirtatious rigmarole and wheedled compliments out of him, which I think he would have given to the back of a bus if it had been a cream coloured one. He was a jovial sort, only in the region of twenty-four years, but he had a sergeant major bombastic way of talking, "What hey chaps", that sort of thing. His father must have been one of our lot in the army out there, if we have an army there. I was never a bright spark with regard to current affairs. I didn't particularly want anything to do with Stuffy except to hear about far-away places. Kissing was definitely out of the question, because I was Martin's girl.

The first week in January, Roy and Clare came to stay with Martin until their new house was ready for them to move into. I was glad Clare would be able to see to Martin's needs regarding cooking and cleaning, and they would be company. Martin was a solitary man the nights I didn't see him. It was then that I began frequenting Martin's bedroom for a kiss and cuddle in private. "Would you like to see my etchings?" Martin cheekily whispered in my ear and, of course, I answered back a hushed "Yes Please". We made it so obvious to Roy and Clare. If Martin or I went to the toilet, it was a signal for the other person to come upstairs as the flush was pulled. I wouldn't go into his bedroom though without being invited. I sat on the top stair until he came out of the bathroom and led me to a soft spot.

When I had flu a beautiful bouquet of flowers was delivered with a 'Get Well' message from Martin. Between moments of extreme exhaustion there were moments of carefree bliss. We enjoyed snowball fights, even an indoor one one day. I remember we had a funny five minutes at the bus-stop one particular evening, and instead of kissing me goodnight as the bus approached, we shook hands instead. I couldn't wait for our next date to demand and receive an extra ration of kisses.

But for all our desires, frustrating bus journeys took their toll of health, happiness and pocket money. In January I told Martin that until the better weather came, I didn't think I could continue going to see him in the week. I hoped he would understand and still want to see me at weekends. He did and we tried this for a few weekends. Then he went home to see his family one weekend and the prospect of not seeing him for a fortnight seemed dismal.

On the Saturday evening I went dancing with Barbie and Des to cheer myself up. I did considerably. I thoroughly enjoyed my evening and allowed a fellah to take me home. I let him kiss me and suffered excruciating shame afterwards, because I had responded. On Monday I phoned Martin and said I had to come and talk to him that night, and so I went to Yate with my guilty conscience. Martin and I made the usual pretence to Roy and Clare of following each other to the toilet and we met in the bedroom. We sat and talked like we had never done before. I told him what had happened on Saturday. He said as I was being honest with him he would be honest with me. That was when I learned about the break up of his marriage. He had divorced his wife for adultery. I was the first girlfriend he had had since his wife. After the divorce he had come to Bristol to try and start afresh. He was at that time a broken man, mistrustful and not wanting to give anything of himself to anyone, because he was so afraid of being hurt again. I had known without a doubt there was something holding him back. He knew he had been hurting me by not revealing his past life. He wished he had told me everything at the beginning of our courtship. I wished he had too. Things might have been different. He told me his 'life story' on that Monday, and gave me until Saturday to think about it in depth. I could let him know then if I wanted to continue seeing him. He could promise me nothing, no future, because he had no real thought as to what he wanted out of life.

I came home with my thoughts in turmoil, desperately wanting to talk things over with Mum and Dad. They were at loggerheads, but they listened when I broke down and said I had something to tell them. Dad thought I was pregnant at first and gave a great big sigh. Martin did fill my thoughts hour after hour that week. I knew there could only be one answer.

It was snowing when I went to Yate the next Saturday afternoon. I walked very slowly along Eggs Hill Lane, which Martin and I called Egg Shell Lane, very slowly across the football field and through the monstrous housing estate, half of which was still being built. I recall I swept up snow into my gloved hand off the top of a wall, crushed it into a tight ball and watched it disintegrate as I plodded on. I was left with three snow crystals lying in my palm. They had no real significance, but I remember sighing and thinking "In three years time look back Pange and remember this day". Martin, Roy and Clare were watching telly when I arrived. Football! Martin's team was Watford, Roy's Chelsea, and they bantered endlessly on the weekend about respective matches. Martin was lying on the settee. I sat and put his legs over my lap. We had tea and watched the Cliff Richard show on telly. He sang such romantic songs. 'The girl that I marry' was one and 'The Twelfth of Never' was another. I haven't forgotten. But Martin and I had to talk. Pressure on my hand was acknowledged. This time we went upstairs together. I told him I only wanted him and couldn't bear to leave him. We loved then. He was so precious. I had made the right decision, the one Martin wanted me to make.

Two weeks later I reversed my decision and my whole world fell apart.

My 21st birthday was coming up in February and I had booked a room at the White Hart with a buffet laid on. I bought two dresses the week before and Martin chose which one I should wear to my party. It was to be on the

Saturday evening, because my birthday fell on the Sunday. Late on Friday afternoon I had a phone call at work from Martin, saying he felt rotten and didn't know if he would be able to make it on Saturday. I prayed he would, but a telegram came from him on Saturday morning wishing me Happy Birthday. I knew immediately Martin wouldn't show. I couldn't cancel my party, although I wanted to. That afternoon I wept and wept in my bedroom. I was so unhappy. Everything had gone wrong with my life. The party went on. I mixed and mingled with my friends. I acted a part to the best of my ability. I came close to breaking point as I cut the cake. I escaped to the loo, but Terri and Lin had been keeping a watchful eye on me, and came in with words of comfort. I kept my chin up, as Dad had said, and saw it through to the end. I came home and saturated the bed with an overflow of tears.

Sunday I got up knowing full well what I had to do. Martin had said for me to go down to Yate and we would have our own little party with Roy and Clare. The whole day I spent writing a letter to Martin, and that was how my 21st came and went. In that letter I unburdened my soul. Oh yes, he knows I loved him, but he could also see in that letter how unhappy I was. I couldn't carry on seeing him, because I was tired right out, tired of thinking and wondering, tired of being afraid. I had run myself into the ground, trying trying to understand, trying to make him happy, make him smile and I couldn't go on any longer. I caught the bus into town and posted my letter in the central post office, making sure it would be delivered to Martin on Monday morning. It was.

He telephoned me Monday afternoon at work. He called me Angela for the first time. It had always been Angie before. All he said was that he had received my letter and would reply to it. It didn't sound like my Martin. The voice sounded harsh and bitter. His letter wasn't a bit like that. I loved him all the more for his words and wrote back to tell him so. What a booby. He wanted to know what he could buy me for my 21st and I asked for a cross and chain.

For many months the going was tough, but the two of us won through. I wrote to Marje Proops, the agony aunt in the newspaper, page after page of distress, just wanting to talk. It would have taken her a month of Sundays to read. I didn't send it. I began going in bookshops, wanting to read up on Divorce and how it affects people. I asked one young assistant serving in a shop if he could recommend such a book to me and like a Swift his eyes flew to my left hand. Martin is gone, but not forgotten. I popped his photo, after kissing it, inside Rish's Bible, which I acquired after she left England.

Every six months for two years Martin and I wrote long letters to each other saying how we were getting on. I saw him twice in that time. One summer, when I was happy to learn he had got himself a fiancée and a car, and again that same winter a short while before Christmas. He phoned me in December. He was leaving Bristol for London and wanted to see me before he left. We went to our old pub and talked over old times and our hopes for the future, separate futures. My coat lining got stuck in my dress zip and Martin had to come to my assistance. We kissed goodbye certainly not as lovers, but as friends. The end of 1971 was the last I heard of Martin. We didn't write in 1972. It would have been wrong to do so. Martin planned to remarry in December 1972. Looking back, the first time I ever stepped across his threshold I knew that little house in Yate would never be my home. Girls do think of these things with a serious boyfriend.

AFTERMATH

After Martin and I split up, I was unlivable with for a time and started spending evenings and weekends in solitary confinement behind my locked bedroom door. I'm a great one for wallowing in self-pity. In my mind I chattered away endlessly to Martin. I must have become totally dull and boring. I woke up to the fact one morning and decided to try my hand at socialising again. It wasn't so difficult to do. Barbie, Des, Lin and Meryl took me under their wing and all of a sudden I found life was quite enjoyable. Undoubtedly, I missed Martin desperately at times, but inbetween I did begin to notice other fellahs.

At the Spa one evening I saw a chap who had been in Rish's class at school, and I brazenly introduced myself to him as Rish's kid sister (although he didn't know me from Adam). Rish and her friends won't have forgotten Doug, as he was hot stuff, a real dish. It was a big mistake to go home with him and I told him so sat on his lap in the car. He said I was different. At the time I took it as a compliment. When I got out of the car with his phone number I forgot my brolly. Years have since passed and I've seen him a few times to say hello, nothing more, but wonder I do what became of my brolly. He probably used it himself. It was a black one with a point. He was a very good-looking chap, but I feel sorry for him if I see him at a dance. It's odds on that a handful of the Grammar School boys he teaches will also be there, and Monday morning he will be greeted with "How did you make out on Saturday night Sir? Did you score?" He told me it often happens.

Barbie gave this same fellow a big surprise once. He drove her home from a dance and, when they were canoodling in the car, a startling thing happened. Barb said, as he ruffled her hair, pulled her to him, told her she had exquisite eyebrows and did she pluck them, a loud whistle suddenly interrupted the romantic moment. The clinch was broken. He looked at smiling Barb in astonishment and asked, "Was that you?" Barb nodded. She explained. He had leaned on her hearing aid and it didn't like it. Doug told her he had thought for a minute the police were going to converge on the car.

In May of that year I met Max. Without a doubt he is the handsomest fellow I shall ever have the privilege of dating, and he was sincerely nice too. It was hard lines I met him two weeks before he was due to fly to Spain. Every summer he worked on the Continent as a courier. In wintertime he found jobs to tide himself over. He told me of the countless far away places he had seen and how he had fared. He had spent years hitch-hiking and camping with chaps and girls alike, taking jobs as a barman, milkman, postman etc. when money ran out. He looked for the sun always, and found his happiness in hot spots. He came home with a shilling in his pocket from one exotic place. There was no settling in him. He had permanent itchy feet. At the time I met him, he wanted desperately to get to Bolivia. He seemed to know a great deal about the country. He told me that I thought too much, that I should act and think less. He also said I had to wake up each morning and say to myself "I'm beautiful". I said I probably wouldn't, and he said in that case I must say, "Well, someone thinks I'm beautiful". He made me very happy and I laughed readily and easily in his company.

We saw each other two Saturdays following at the Spa and he arranged to see me the Wednesday evening before he went away. On my way to keep that date I made a sixpenny bet with myself that he wouldn't turn up, because there was an important Cup Match on the telly and I knew he loved football. He was outside the Hippodrome ready and waiting, so the first thing I had to do was cough up sixpence. He was a perfect gentleman and put me on his inside as we walked. His arm went round me too which I liked. We went in the Locarno ballroom, but didn't dance. I pleaded with him to talk to me, and after a warm-up kiss he did. A lovely talker he was. I made him say things to me in Spanish.

I learnt he swam like a fish and had been beaten up by thugs as a youngster. His family lived in Glastonbury in a huge house. His family included parents, grandparents, sister, brother and family, uncle and aunt. They all had flatlets in the house. Max said he had the skylight room. He had had a cartilage operation on his knee, his tonsils out and his appendix removed. Later he kindly let me inspect his scars, on condition he could view the beauty spot alongside my belly button, perfectly permissible, as I had a jumper and trousers on.

We left the Mecca after an hour and strolled on the Downs, talking and laughing all the while. I do remember sitting on a bench and we began smooching by holding hands and kissing Eskimo fashion. He made me feel funny all over. What does a girl say but "Wicked" when he said he would like to go to bed with me, and only me, for a minimum of five years, and that would mean loving in the mornings, afternoons as well as evenings. It sounded exquisite even if he broke my heart after five years. He kept telling me to give him big smiles, because my teeth, which got polished and polished, even my large jutting out one, added character he assured me. I remember he called me Mog, probably because of my purring. He squeezed me with the intention of breaking my ribs, and I'm sure I pleaded gasping for "More, more".

He wanted to see what I looked like without my false piece, so I pulled it off and flung it over my shoulder. He said he preferred the real me. To say my own filthy dirty short locks looked windblown was the understatement of the year. Now if he had said I looked as if I had been pulled through a hedge backwards, that would have been nearer the mark. However, he enjoyed mussing it and smoothing down my greasy fringe. The fright I must have looked! I dropped about thirty clips as he was kissing me and giving me love bites in my lobes. It was passion's fault. What on earth his father thought, finding umpteen hair-grips in his car I can't imagine. I recall Max ripped the sleeve of his shirt. We had taken our coats off, because it got awfully warm, and put them with my 'dead rat' on the back seat of the car.

We heard the footie results on the car radio. His team won so that was the cue for more rejoicing. I felt free, with no inhibitions. I loved him talking to me. I loved him kissing me and I wanted to please him. He said I must never do anything to please other than myself. I might easily have lost my head completely if it hadn't been for good old faithful period. He was undoubtedly a man of the world and I shall be thankful I had him all to myself for the brief part of an evening. A whole night wasn't meant to be for this girl.

Driving home he held my hand when he could. He stopped on the corner of our road and said he wasn't going to let me go until he had had a dozen more kisses. I was only too happy to oblige and gave him thirteen, one for luck, because I'm not superstitious. Some things are delightful to look back on. Even if he didn't mean it, he said he would remember our night as one of the happiest in his life. We didn't do much to be truthful. He said he hoped I would remember his face and that one day we would run into each other again. I think not. He had a mission to fulfil, Bolivia, and a lot of wanderlust and sun seeking still to work out of his system. What a divine creature he was though. I reckon he was really a teacher and his subject was 'Romance'. I told him to come back and dance the fandango for me.

I wished he wasn't going away, but it was better for me that he was. He was mature and knew about life, whereas I was an ignoramus. I said I would remember him (and so I have), but he told me not to for too long. He had dozens of hair clips, a sixpenny piece and a hairband to remember me by. I have reminders galore of that wonderful gorgeous man who so easily stole my heart.

What a sexy looking devil I clapped eyes on at the Dug Out one night. He truly was the spitting image of Scott Walker (who is unquestionably divine to look at), but he had lazy speech. No matter. Talk wasn't necessary. It was enough for me to feast my eyes on his handsome features and sexy bodily bits. We danced and talked when the music permitted. That is, I talked normally. He drawled. He asked for a kiss. People kissed publicly in the Dug Out. I told him I had forgotten how to, but undeterred he got one all the same. Jumping the gun, I thought he would make an ideal boyfriend, but then age cropped up in conversation. You could have knocked me down with a feather. He was a mere eighteen year old. At twenty-one I was past everything and near to senility, so his look said. Me, being ancient, was a burden he couldn't stomach. He vanished on the pretext of going to the loo. Mind you, I was relieved. I felt a baby snatcher, although Des said she thought he was a bit of all right too and she was twenty-five! Des said what if he had danced with her? He thought me a Granny. By his reckoning she would have been a great one! I would have said he looked about twenty-six. I spent the remainder of the evening, not much was left of it, with someone more suited to my age group, a forty-plus wooer. He was persistent. He wanted to know what part of Bristol I came from and when I said a small part he replied that wasn't a good enough answer, so I gave him Terri's address. My evening had been ruined, a complete wash-out. I was an old has-been.

To tell the truth chaps played a small part in my life for several months after Martin and I broke up. I preferred my own company. When the mood took me, I went off wandering, usually either to Weston-Super-Mare or the Downs. Weston I adore out of season, when the sands are deserted and there is a strong wind to whip and blow the wishy-washy cobwebs away. With Martin gone, I had to set about restoring the balance of my mind, and walking in squelchy mud on Weston beach was an ideal place for contemplation. Many times I paddled in gloop and had to wring out soggy trouser bottoms before coming home.

I went to Cabot Tower once and surveyed the City from the Crow's Nest. When I decided to come down to ground level, I couldn't get out through the turnstile. (I was pushing instead of pulling the release handle. That was all.) Dusk was swiftly approaching and, for a few ghastly moments, I thought I would be spending the night alone in that eerie dark and damp, twisty-staired turret and boy, didn't the sweat beads trickle. I was all set to go racing to the top and wave something white when I realised what I was doing wrong.

I paid two or three visits to the Grand Spa on my tod in an effort to lose shyness rather than get acquainted with the opposite sex. I can remember leaving there one evening at midnight and walking across the Downs. It was lovely, lovely, with not a soul around, just darkness, wind and trees. I decided to walk home afterwards, all of six miles, maybe more. Goodness knows what time I put the key in the door. I was fagged out, but had enjoyed the exercise. My dance shoes were a write-off. My feet were covered in blisters the next morning. Bloss and Pop don't hold with me roaming the streets in the middle of the night, and think it's a wonder I've not been set upon or picked up by a policeman before now.

It was in the early hours of one morning I walked by trellis-work laden with roses. I went back, stuffed my nose right inside rose after rose, taking deep sniff-fuls of scent. The following day I walked the same road in daylight and thought I would do the same. I found that the roses were covered in blight and minute creepy-crawlies. I wanted to have my nose deloused, but thought the Doc would say codswallop to such a request.

In the dance hall I loved to watch people stood at a crowded bar, trying to attract the barmaid's attention. I adore eavesdropping too, which I'm fully aware is a major weakness of mine. I don't mean to be rude, and I try to be subtle about it.

Going to Barbie's 21st Birthday party in April I nearly lost Lin off the bus. It swerved as she clattered down the stairs and I only just managed to save her by grabbing a handful of coat. After the smashing party Des and her boyfriend drove Lin and me to Dinah's flat where we were staying overnight. I ran into trouble getting out of the Mini. (Minis were everyone's favourite car in those days.) I tried to be ladylike, as Mike got out and pulled his front seat forward to let me out. One foot made it to the kerb, but the other one, under cover of darkness, got well and truly twisted up in the seat belt and brought me to my knees half in/half out of the car. Try as they might, they could not budge nor untangle me for five minutes, until I stopped making the horrible noise that was my laugh. It is a miracle I didn't leave a foot behind in the car. As it was, I had to sit on the kerbstone and get a cold bot while Des, Lin and Mike worked on me. At last I was freed and, full of apologies for my unglamorous exit from the car, I bade Des and Mike goodnight. Lin let me hobble across the green before she realised she was holding my shoe.

Once in the flat we turfed Annie out of her child-size bed and carried her protesting into Di and Fred's room. She cuddled up to Mum. It was left for Fred to sort out the problem of where he was to sleep when he came off night shift. Lin and I slept that night with more body hanging out of the bed than in it. That is, I didn't sleep, but Lin did. Throughout the night I listened to her repeating my name in otherwise garbled sentences. I gave myself ear strain trying to catch the gist of what she was saying about me. She sounded cross going by the tone of her voice. I gave her what-for next morning. "In future" I said, "before you go to sleep zip up them there lips, buttons leave room enough for Angelas to pop out".

I crop up in Tritz's sleep too. One night, not long before she married Rob, Tritz woke Sandie, her sis, from a deep sleep with her shouting and bawling.

They slept in the same room in twin beds and Sandie could not believe her eyes when she opened them. Terence, sound asleep, was leaning out of bed, with her head touching the floor looking under it. And in a very angry voice she was telling me to come out. Oh yes. She was indignantly demanding, "Angela, come out from under my bed this minute. Do you hear me? Come out immediately". On and on she went, telling me off for being under there, then with a smug smile of satisfaction, back beneath the sheets she slithered. Sandie said the contented look on her chops revealed that my lurking shape must have fled out the window. Terence had no knowledge of her nightmare next morning.

But to get back to the night of Barbie's party, Lin's voice did eventually croon me to sleep, but it was short-lived. Annie got her own back on us at an unearthly hour. She shuffled in and was pleased as punch to find both mine and Lin's feet sticking out the bottom of her bed, so she went and got Mum's feather duster didn't she. As if hangovers from the night before weren't enough to put up with! Annie dragged Katie from her cot, dumped her in between Lin and me, and continued to empty her large box of dolls, teddies, animals, books, etc. on top of us. She also installed a toy phone on the pillow next to our lugs and, as she sat on my knee pyramid, kept on for me to converse with her about the weather, the atrocious price of food, and when was I getting married, because she wanted to be a bridesmaid and wear blue. She wanted to know too why Lin and I had black eyes. (Had we washed our faces the night before, the cistern would have been noisy and probably woken up the household, so we had had some thought for others as well as being lazy a-rabs.) And, she enquired, what were those awful dirty marks on the pillowcases and should she tell Mummy. Blumming kids notice everything. Lin said she would brain her if she did, because she herself was going to mention the marks to Dinah. Whether she did, or whether she didn't, I forgot to ask. Annie turned her attention to our clothes strewn on the floor and wanted to put my bra and tights on, so Lin and I had to get up. Thankfully breakfast called Annie and Katie away. I know I couldn't put one foot to the floor, on account of it nearly being wrenched off by three pairs of hands the previous night, and that set off Lin's built-in alarm, because there then followed a three minute laugh.

Des, Barb and I were in the Bierkeller at the Hawthorns one Saturday evening, quietly drinking and minding our own business when a coach-load of Welsh nits descended on the place and started a fight amongst themselves. The poor accordion player went out of tune, as a man was flung against him. When 'our' chaps tried to intervene and calm the rabble, they turned on them and struck intimidating blows. It was sorely unjust. Fists flailed in all directions and we girls were forced to press ourselves tightly against the wall, a hard job for Barbie who is big of bust. Des turned her face to the wall too. I wanted to, but couldn't. As the violence raged across the floor, as tables and chairs were thrown, as kicks and punches landed viciously, I witnessed the bloody battle. One fellah went spinning across a table-top and landed in a drowsy heap. The table, which had been ours in the centre of the floor, was now behind the bar. I saw one of their number drop one of ours by crashing a beer mug onto his skull. I joined Des then with my nose to the wall. Police and dogs came and the brawlers were thrust unrepenting outside where the fight began again. The Leeks would not behave themselves. My ears waggled in disbelief at the worse than gutter language. We had seen such horrific behaviour, we forked out for three brandies and Babycham when we got to the Spa to calm our frayed nerves.

The girls and I went one evening to a select, rather posh club in Bath. We went because we had heard it was good, an 'in' place. We weren't members, but indulged in a spot of blarney with Paddy, someone who was something at the club, and he admitted us as friends of a friend. We stayed an hour. It wasn't our cup of tea. The young people were upper class toffee-noses, the swinging jet set. Even the ones older than us were too too precise and formal. It made me want to go to the centre of the dance floor and scream a rude word to see the reaction. I didn't. We left instead. We heard later from a passing acquaintance that the club had been raided for drugs later that same evening. It just shows the goings-on that do go on anywhere and everywhere. Gosh, imagine if we had stayed and my friends and I had been put against a wall and frisked. I always carry a couple of aspirin in a tissue in my purse. I'm glad we came away when we did without waiting for male money-bags to whisk us off our feet.

As it turned out that particular evening ended on a splendid note. We drove back into Bristol from the Bath club and were cutting into pizzas when the pizzeria was taken over by a gang of men. They were burly, barrel-chested men, armed with magnificent vocal chords. The Bristol Light Opera Singers were out in force on a stag night, and the unannounced free performance they put on for us, and other diners like themselves, was very well received. They roared their way through Gilbert and Sullivan songs. I loved the solo, way-down-low rendering of the song containing deedle deedle dums, which the others joined in with deep-throated choruses. The atmosphere was fantastic. They sang and danced on table tops, wove their way in and out of noshers, used whatever props came to hand, like the coat stand, string of onions, Barbie's brolly. Those men were the tops in entertainment. Talking of tops, we girls used to dance on table- tops on hen nights, especially at the Beerkeller. It was the done thing. I wouldn't do it now.

Des arranged to pick me up one evening at a convenient bus-stop. As I waited, passers-by, both on foot and in cars, gave me 'funny (peculiar) girl' looks. The buses were on strike. Everyone in the city knew they were on strike, including me so I wasn't the dumb ass they thought I was.

At this point I should give Dan a mention. I was courting him the week before my bus-stop pick-up point. Dan and I didn't last long. He was an unreliable twerp. I waited in Brislington Village for nearly an hour one Sunday evening, but he stood me up. Oh yes, I knew where he was and what he was doing. Preferred the blumming fish to me, didn't he. He idolised them and was an enthusiastic angler all day Sundays. All night too I shouldn't wonder. He never knew what time of day it was. I stormed home in a temper and bad mood.

I decided I wouldn't stay in for Dave and Al to poke fun at me, when they came home from the boozer and found me left in the lurch. Therefore, I told Mum I was going for a walk, and told Nan, who was staying with us, that if Dan did chance to knock on our door to tell him to drop dead. I also asked the boy next door, who was sat on his gate when I left home for the second time that evening, to puncture all four tyres of a blue car, couldn't remember the make, if one stopped near the house. Dan stuttered anyway, far worse than I ever do.

I walked to the village again and had it in my head to go up near the 'sea' walls and have a 'blow' to cool me down. I waited in the village this time for over an hour. I knew Bristol Bus Service was lousy, and on a Sunday moreso than in the week. A girl I knew came along. I thought, "How stupid can you get" when she enquired, "What are you waiting there for?" I'm glad I didn't say "Christmas", because in her next breath she informed me the buses weren't running as from that day. A strike! I stalked home in an infernal rage, breathing hell fire and damnation.

June was a divine month in more ways than one. Rish came home for a holiday. That was the best thing that happened. Bob was eager to taste English faggots and big fat pork sausages again. Every member of the family went to meet them at Heathrow, except for Al who couldn't get time off work and Nanny. Mum and Dad went to London by train, Bob's Mum and Freddie in their car because they were driving Rish and Bob back to Bristol, and Dave drove Aunt Margaret and me there and back. Before driving into the airport we got confused by signposts and Dave went four times round a busy roundabout before we espied the right turning. Instead of paying an extortionate amount for the use of a public car-park at the airport, we skulked into the busmen's park. I caught sight of Rish first, behind those glass partitions, and knocked people aside in my hurry to get to her. The rest of the family was doing likewise behind me. I saw her mouth the words to Bob, "Where's my Dad, where's my Mum and Pop?" It was a grand tearful reunion. Little Nan enquired of Bob, when they went to see her, "You don't hurt her, do you?" She gave Rish two pink bedsocks she had knitted with her in mind.

Whilst they were here I took my summer holiday. I lounged in the garden mostly, enhancing my tan. One day I popped up to the shops and bumped into Sib, one of hairdressing Glad's customers. I hadn't seen her, or 'my Bill', her husband, for a long time. She asked me to go back to the flat with her for a coffee and cheer up Bill who was poorly. Sib called me his girlfriend, but I thought of Bill as similar to Pops in many ways. That is why I was so fond of him. When I worked at Glad's on a Saturday morning he would pick up Sib and me at lunchtime in his big hydraulic diesel car, and we would go to the pub for a noggin before going home. Bill didn't look at all well. He had lost an incredible amount of weight. He was told to, because his legs got very ulcerated – what the Japs did to him. Sib said he wouldn't talk about the treatment he received at their hands, but he often cried out in his sleep. I sat at my Bill's feet that afternoon. I could tell he was in a great deal of pain. He sent Rish and Bob his best wishes for a happy holiday although he didn't know them. I never saw Bill again. He died of cancer a couple of weeks later. He was riddled with it. I went to see Sib after the funeral, and this time sat at her feet as she talked of her man. She cried, but it was better that she did. My Bill was a war hero. Sib showed me the Samurai sword he collected when he escaped a prisoner of war camp. He had killed the owner with a single chop. He had had to. I saw a letter too which his men (he was their sergeant) wrote commending his bravery. Bill was loved. The garage where he worked laid down tools and lined the pavement when his funeral car went by as a mark of respect.

ADORABLE MICHEL

And it was during Rish's stay in England I met Michel, my French boyfriend from Marseilles. It sounded rather silly calling him a girl's name, because I pronounced it Michelle. I was with a hen party the night I met him at the Mecca dance hall. He was an excellent dancer. A mover. He made me move quite sexily too. The first song we danced to was 'Yellow River', so it became our song. I did become a weary being that night. My brain couldn't stand the intense exercise it was getting, because I had to think hard before saying even the shortest of sentences. I liked him immensely, but I'm afraid we were pardoning each other throughout the evening due to misunderstood statements. We got on famously though at the end of every dance. I said "Merci beaucoup" and he replied, "Thank you very much". Sign language worked well. When I borrowed his hanky to dab at my brow he raised an imaginary glass to his lips, and so we toddled off to the bar. I drank rather heavily that night: five vodkas and lime and one vodka and orange. I don't know what made me change over. It was a couple too many though. Come the evening's end, I felt that I had a head but no body. I could feel my head floating around the dance floor, but nothing else from the neck down. The orange did it methinks. It is strange, but when we were sat having a drink he rubbed his trouser leg, as if he had an itch. (He did have turn-ups, but was dead trendy.) And then he mopped his face – it was roasting hot – and I spotted a minute tablet resting on his tongue when he next spoke. I wonder about that white pill, and if it came from his turn-up. He did seem exceptionally hot, so I expect it was a little something to cool him down.

It could have been a sucked down polo mint. I mean to say he didn't go crackers or hallucinate after taking it.

We got by that first evening quite well. I found out he lived in Marseilles with his Granny and dog. Michel was twenty-seven. I'm not sure if his father was South African or just lived in that country, but his maman lived in France with his younger brother Claude (18) and sister Claudine (8). I called him my French computer, because he worked with one teaching a programme to Bristol engineers. He had been to many different countries with his job. He didn't look like a frog, nor did he wear a beret and have a string of garlic tied round his middle, as so many people were to ask me in the coming weeks. He did look French from a mile distant. His hair was jet black and curling onto his collar. He had a little black moustache and ticklish beard. But the eyes had it. They were a mystifyingly soulful pair of dark brown ones, which made me putty in his hands. Eyes are my downfall always.

There was one thing that put a damper on my evening. As I left the dance floor with him to rejoin my friends, one of them, most decidedly merry, pounced on us and insulted him. She was rabbiting on and wagging her finger under his nose, spouting forth about hot-blooded Italians (she thought he was one) and all they did was rape, rape, and rape. Bless his cotton socks. He smiled his sweet, disarming smile and said "Merci". I growled at her in the taxi going home. I thought he wouldn't turn up for our date after what she had said. I was in a flaming temper when I came indoors, stormed upstairs and woke up Mum. She called out "Is that you Pange?" Whoever else she thought it was at 2.30am I have no idea, because Alan was too young to do late nights in those days and our Dave, being an athlete, had mostly early nights. I then had to chase pell-mell round and round the bedroom in my undergarments, trying to whack the living daylights out of two massive moths. I don't usually kill anything, except ants, but I had it in for them. I fell into bed exhausted. It must have been 3.30am. Next morning Mum wanted to know whom I had let in through the window the night before. She was referring to the hullabaloo.

It was rather an odd relationship Michel and I had for a couple of months. Now that makes us sound like a couple of queers, but it was nothing like that. In the beginning I was sad in his company, because I still pined for Martin. But then I became aware that Michel was quite a sad person for reasons I would never know, and I did my best to cheer him up and myself in the process.

Although Michel had a limited English vocabulary, and my French revolved around a smattering of words remembered from school days, we rarely gave up on an explanation until it was made clear. An exception springs to mind. We went to see the film 'Carry on up the Jungle'. When the title came up on the screen, in small print underneath were the words 'I'll fill your water hole if you feel mine' or words to that effect. Right from the word go the audience fell about laughing. Poor Michel looked blankly at the screen trying to puzzle over the words and he whispered, "Please explain". That I couldn't do, in speech or actions. We gesticulated frequently. Some evenings we visited the Central Library and under his tuition I translated the titles of French books into English. We sat on College Green after, outside the Council House, and intimately shared new-found words. He would though call his shirt a skirt. He discovered the word rubbish and it became a favourite. He called everything rubbish, me included. When I introduced him to Rish he said, "You are rubbish?" Rish and Bob liked him. The four of us ate at The Trattoria, which has been overrun by mice now I do believe.

Michel had many fine attributes. He was kind, considerate, sensitive, gentle and he treated me like a princess. I feel he may have been a little lonely, in a strange country with a difficult language and aliens to comprehend. I did meet a work associate of his, Gillette, whose wife and child named Bulldozer had joined him in England. Michel's smile was reward enough for my perseverance against the language barrier. I am glad I didn't listen to people warning me off French Romeos who wanted only sex, sex again and more sex. Utter twaddle! They want it no more, no less than the rest of mankind. He did have a way of kissing though which made me want to emit a "Wowee".

We used to go for lengthy walks. A whole Sunday afternoon was spent thus – I met him on the cobblestone quayside near the Old Duke jazz club where he went for a ploughman's most days. After a hello kiss we moved on to the Centre, up Park Street, along Whiteladies Road, climbed Blackboy Hill, walked across the Downs and Suspension Bridge, into the golf links at Ashton Court. There we had a brief sit down. I chewed a blade of grass and Michel chewed a match. Then out we came for another mammoth walk across the Downs, through Westbury Village, Coombe Dingle, Sea Mills, onto the Portway, along to Hotwells where we branched off and trailed a footpath leading guess where, the Downs again. That was some walk that was.

It was there in the long grass I lost my cross and chain which Martin had sent me. Why oh why didn't it fall into my brassiere. I had my treasured keepsake of great sentimental value for such a short time. In the weeks that followed, I hunted high and low in Bristol's jewellers for an exact replica. I would have paid any price. The cross I bought in replacement isn't like Martin's really, but in my heart I've convinced myself it is identical to the one he chose for me.

Michel didn't like to eat alone so I had slap-up meals several evenings a week, with goblets of wine to wash them down of course. Michel asked for a blue steak once and the waitress didn't know what he meant and I couldn't help him out and explain to her, because I didn't know what he was on about neither.

We climbed Cabot Tower one night to see the city lights. Bristol was bewitching in the moonlight. It was a very romantic moment and when Michel kissed me I was moved to tears. He tenderly brushed them away. I was so emotionally aroused I choked and he had to thump me on the back to get air down my windpipe. We came down from the Tower and walked on Brandon Hill. Michel suddenly stopped and sniffed. I stopped and sniffed too, and a sickly aroma came wafting out of the bushes. They were being rustled. Michel took my hand and pulled me on. At the bottom of the hill he said in precise English "Pot". Lurkers in the shrubbery were smoking it. I hadn't come across anything like that before. Michel said he had in the Sorbonne. I'm nosey and wanted to investigate, but against my will he prevented me from returning to the scene of the crime, if one can call it that. A fit of passion soon interfered with my natural spy-like tendencies.

Besides our strolls, we went to restaurants, pubs and dances, and got rid of a small fortune in pennies on the one-armed bandits in the gaming rooms under the ice rink. I went flat hunting with Michel. I'm glad he didn't get a place and stayed well looked after in the Hotel. I knew he was to be a here today, gone tomorrow boyfriend, and not one to get overly fond of.

One night at the Spa Michel didn't seem quite himself. We were halfway through a dance when he said he didn't feel too good and did I mind if he went back to his hotel, a stone's throw away. I said of course not, and that a rest would do him the world of good. He was concerned how I'd get home, but I told him I would be okay as the girls were there and we could share a taxi. I walked him to the door, and with those dark brown mournful eyes he looked at me and said "I go back to the 'otel. I also go 'ome, back to France." I had a kiss on the stairs to tug at the heartstrings, and without another word he walked out of the ballroom and I walked back in.

I took a firm grip on myself and didn't look back. I stood and watched the dancers, smiley happy couples. A photographer friend of Des approached and asked me to dance. He had a penetrating look, which said "I see you in the raw". I was scared of him and he knew it, because I had admitted the same to him at some time or other. He was a nice enough bloke, but I withered under his scrutiny. I wanted Michel. I couldn't have Michel. Michel was already as good as a thousand miles away. He had a measly photo of me. I didn't have one of him. Cry-baby that I am felt my eyes smarting. I sniff sniffed at the photographer and ran away without a word. I went back to the old routine. I bolted the nearest loo door and hey presto, I turned into a weeping willow. I composed myself after half an hour and went to face Joe public, that is, I sat down in a dark corner, alone with my thoughts and remembrances. Dear Des and her fellah, one of her favourites, spotted me and invited me to come and dance with them. They could tell by my downcast features I had lost mon ami, my shining star. When we left to walk to the taxi rank it had been raining. The taxi driver remarked to my friends "She looks like how I feel".

That's life, made up of gains and losses. Looking back, that is the one time when that phrase, 'Parting is such sweet sorrow' really applied regards boyfriends. Other partings have been sodding unbearable.

Mind you, it was only a week or so later I could have sworn I glimpsed Michel with a stunning blonde on his arm.

So Michel had, possibly, gone back to France and by this time Rish and Bob had returned to Canada. I missed Rish terribly. I can remember the day they left England to go home to Canada. Rish woke Ally on their last morning and he had a tear, which was the cue for Mum and me to begin, exactly like he did in 1966 at Southampton Docks when they first set sail for Canada. For Dad she managed a watery smile in the garden before breakfast, clutching hold of Bob's hand, as he took their photo with his potted frangipani at their feet, and we all know what Dad's long thin frangipani looks like, which instead of flowering preferred to remain in its dormant rude looking state.

That day Dad ate bananas which gave him chronic indigestion. Nonetheless, he struggled into town with Mum and, after buying curtains, they found a quiet seat in the Registry Office car park. For half an hour they sat and gazed skywards waiting to see Rish fly over, and they swear to this day her plane did fly directly overhead. I expect they quietly murmured "Goodbye my darlings". It is possible the droning silver bird they saw had Rish and Bob in its stomach judging by the time. I got over Rish's leaving and Michel became a pleasant memory.

I soon met Peter at the Town's Talk, the country club on the Bridgwater Road. Mhmm, yes I admit he was a good-looking bloke, blond and bronzed, but as Mum says "Looks aren't everything". When he offered me a lift home I asked him, "If I say yes, you will take me home won't you?" He said I made him feel protective, so I felt at ease with him and accepted his offer. Then, oh-dearie-me, as we talked in the car I found out he was a murderer. No, it's wrong of me to label him that. He had killed two men, but in self-defence. He had recently returned from spending six years in Rhodesia as a policeman, private detective, estate agent and a driver of oil tankers through deserted plains (I don't know in which order). I wonder if he was asked to leave the country? He said he wanted to go back as a mercenary, but I'm unsure what he meant by that. Although it was two black men he had killed, I got the impression he was on their side.

As we neared home he nodded to the Imperial Ground and asked, "What's that?" I began to say "A private sports ground for Imperial Tobacco Company" but, by the time the word "Company" came out of my mouth, he had swung the car through the open gates, driven across the football pitch, parked behind the shower rooms and turned his lights off. Well, I ask you, the nerve of the fellah! We were on private property and any minute the gates of the ground could be locked up and we would be caught, not in the act, but like rats in a trap, or worse still, not caught but imprisoned all night long. This stranger didn't seem so nice all of a sudden. I consented to sit in the back of the car with him in Ironmould Lane, if he drove out of the Imperial Ground immediately. He did so and in two minutes flat we were in Ironmould Lane. He did become rather attractive again.

The thing was though, after only a couple of dates he kept on for me to do things I didn't want to do, not with him, and I felt strung up whenever he squeezed my knee as we drove along, because isn't pressure on the knee one of those signals, "Will you, or won't you?" As I hadn't a clue what I was supposed to do to answer him no, I had to watch my step. Even in the pictures I had a job to cool his ardour and wished I had worn trousers. He was nice enough, but with that suntan, phew! He was too hot for Pange to handle. Had I been emancipated and a flibbertigibbet he would have been quite a desirable catch.

INTRODUCING BEN

And so the month of August came bringing Ben into my life. He stayed with me for quite a while. What bittersweet memories I have. We met at the Spa. He didn't ask me to dance. He claimed one that he said was owing. Quite true. A month previous I had been dancing with him at the Spa and thought how nice he was, but Michel unexpectedly arrived on the scene looking for me, and I upped and left Ben in the middle of a dance with a not very plausible excuse. Downright rude behaviour I admit, and he said much much later it was his intention to leave me on the dance floor halfway through a smooch, to give me a taste of my own medicine. He didn't though. He also said, a 'century' after we met, that in the beginning he had no intention of dating me, but something went horribly wrong.

He took me home from the Spa that night. He had a Sprite sports car, which I had trouble getting into because it was so low on the ground. Outside the house, when he asked to see me again, I asked if I could sort myself out and phone him. I thought he was absolutely gorgeous and did fancy him like crazy, but I was seeing a chap that week who was okay, but nothing special, and thought it only fair to finish with one before making plans to date another. Ben gave me a feather light goodnight kiss, as he said that was all friends were allowed to do, but oh boy, if I had been the type I would have beseeched him there and then "Take me, I'm yours". He tore the top off a box of wine gums and wrote down his home telephone number for me. I popped that little bit of card into my purse all of three years ago, and there it remained for a long long time.

By Thursday of that week I had politely dumped the other man, whoever he was, and went along to the phone box at the end of the road to call Ben. (We didn't have a phone in our house.) I was nervous and became moreso when his mother answered. I had written a load of nonsensical things on a piece of paper, because I was sure I wouldn't know what to say to him. He knew who I was, which was something in my favour. The first thing I said was that I had wet hair, as I had just washed it. What the hell did he want to know that for?

We did find lots to talk about, because Ben said he was leaving home that coming weekend. Home was a tiny hamlet called Nibble. He was moving into Bristol and going to live at a place named Fairleigh. Fairleigh, I learnt, was one of those huge, old, Victorian or maybe it was Georgian city dwellings divided into wings containing single bedded rooms for single businessmen and career girls. Staff ran the house and prepared meals and cleaned rooms.

Ben asked to see me Sunday afternoon and I agreed readily. I forgot what time he said he would come though, and wasn't ready when he tapped the front door. I ushered him into the living room and tore round swearing, donning clothes and finishing off my face. Eyeliner went on in squiggly lines that day. Ben must have thought I lived in a morgue. Mum was the only person at home and she stayed put in the kitchen, ashamed to show her face, because she was a scruff with rollers in her hair.

We had a heavenly first date lazily walking along a river-bank. I wished later we hadn't sat down though. The gnats or some other pesky biters bit us to bits. As regards legs, Ben didn't fare as badly as I. He wasn't wearing a micro mini. However, that day I did pass on to him my graveyard cough, which he didn't thank me for. As we were driving through the country lanes on our first date, I couldn't understand why Ben grinned at the simplest of questions. Why oh why did I open my mouth and let out a monstrosity of a big bloomer, one I was never allowed to forget. I asked him what time the cat's eyes were switched on.

And so we began dating. I earned the nickname Tosh, either that, wench or hooligan. He used to come and pick me up then. Following a greetings kiss his first words to me were "Belt up". No offence meant. It was said with a twinkling eye and wicked smile. He was thinking of my safety, yet he wouldn't wear his own harness in the car. We saw the summer through and were happy bunnies. A lot of frolicking went on.

Tortworth was a magical place that will remain in my memory for all time. I hope he won't ever take another girl there. Tortworth is an untouched area of natural beauty, where some people may fear to tread because there is no human life for miles around, except in the adjoining prison. I have often thought I would like to be a recluse and have Tortworth for my hermitage in its wild and overgrown state.

Ben and I walked round the lake one Sunday, stopping to watch swans glide across the water. Their beautifully arched necks occasionally dipped into the surface making their bodies tip over into small gentle whirlpools. We would stray from the path and wander where maybe no one else in this day and age has trod. Our feet left faint prints on soft crumbly peat mixed up with a million brown fallen leaves that had no crispness. Grubs hid under dead bark, which had snapped off white coated decaying trees. Fungus and springy moss grew abundantly, because dampness reigned supreme. Light was blotted out altogether, as we tunnelled our way through twigs and branches entwined and interwoven into density over the years. I was given a helping hand up hillocks, but slid on my bot down mounds on t'other side. We pushed our way into a small clearing where sunlight filtered through, spraying a carpet of gold. An edging thickly green had built up all around. Here we lay and rested, and it was here I stopped being a mere slip of a girl and learnt how to become a woman. The world was indeed a truly wonderful place. It always was when we spent an afternoon at Tortworth.

I had a spanking in the sand dunes at Brean, because I cheeked him. Then, when I refused point blank to say I was sorry, Ben tossed me over his shoulder like a sack of spuds and lowered my head closer and closer to the sand. I screamed "I'm sorry" and, when he heard it, he simply let go and dropped me head first into a perishing dune. I pulled it clear and ran after him blaspheming wickedly, as I spat out sand. As I drew near, and he heard my unsavoury language, he stopped and turned to face me. I thought I had better stop several yards from him too. He asked me to repeat what I had said and full of smiles I replied that he was an absolutely adorable divine man. I could never win. Ben was always right and I was always wrong, but I suppose I liked it that way.

We paddled at Burnham during August Bank Holiday weekend, after which I lay flat on my back beside him on the sands, intent on improving my tan. Before many minutes had passed, not one of the sun's rays could get to my body. I was packed in sand. All Ben's own handiwork.

We had trips to Weston-Super-Mare of course. One day, as we strolled along the beach, a 'hurricane' sprang up. The wind whipped my hair band off and carried it out of reach. We got caught in a torrential downpour. We raced to the car and sat wheezing, soaked to the skin. I laughed when Ben leaned behind to pick up, what he thought was a towel, brought with us to dry our feet. I coughed "ahem", but he continued rubbing his hair on not the towel, but an oily rag. I came home wearing his slippers that evening. My sneakers were mud-caked and the soles had come apart. For sentimental reasons I haven't chucked them out. They remain in our shed.

An early autumn Sunday afternoon we drove to Weston. As usual the tide was out when we got there. We walked towards the visible line of froth far distant from us. The vein-streaked firm sand turned into chocolate spread mud and we began to sink. We had expected this and I had removed my tights and Ben had rolled his trouser legs up in readiness. Kids let us dip our legs in their paddling pool later, because they were only sailing boats on the water, not bathing in it. We could have counted a million worm holes in the damp compact sand. Although Ben gave me a head start he won the sprint race, because a minute before the off he kissed me enough to take my breath away. Full of cunning he was. We went for a Chinese meal when we got back to Bristol. It was early evening and business wasn't brisk. A Chinese family who lived upstairs ran the restaurant and, as we ate, half a dozen kiddies trooped in wearing nightgowns and jamas and dragging teddies. They had come to say goodnight to their parents and to receive a kiss each. I wonder what has happened to them, because the restaurant had to close. It was found out that they served cat food.

Ben settled into Fairleigh. The inmates had to abide by the rules, one of which was no guests permitted in bedrooms. Ben told me a funny story of how, in the early hours of one morning, a man decided to pay a call on his girlfriend living there. He somehow sneaked in, no doubt had had a key cut, stealthily climbed the stairs, crept into his girl's room, murmured "Guess who my cherub", switched on the light and found her in bed with another man. There was a disturbance. Not a minor one. A punch-up ensued, and then he fled to the kitchen and went on the rampage. Being berserk, he created havoc and woke everyone up throwing pots and pans at the walls. The three persons involved in the fracas were asked to leave the premises immediately. Ben said two people had committed suicide at Fairleigh. I always got it wrong and told people he lived at Farleigh, which is the mental hospital on the Weston Road. I didn't have a screwy boyfriend, whatever people may have thought.

One night in October when Ben picked me up he said he would give me something to worry about. He explained he had asked the staff for a bigger, warmer room and his request was to be granted the following week when such a room became vacant. The thing was though it would be situated in an adjoining house, a house where boarders' guests were permitted in rooms. I did worry, sort of, but I had fallen hopelessly for him. I wanted him to want me. I wanted him to teach me all about sex, how to love him properly, to make him perfectly happy and I knew he would look after me, because he wasn't irresponsible. We hardly went out when he changed rooms. I was blissfully happy. I hoped he knew I was. It was our place of love, rest and whispered talk. The walls were terribly thin. We needed a rest after heaving the chest of drawers against the door, which was necessary as there weren't any locks. Sometimes we sat on the bed and played Knock Out Whist. We could watch telly or play ping-pong below stairs if we wanted.

He did suggest going to a dance one evening when we met up, but it was too early to go straightaway. We went back to his room to play cards. I took my dress off, because I didn't want to crease it, and put on one of his jumpers. He didn't mind. I wasn't going to stretch it in the front. Ben did try hard to improve my worthless fixture. He looked on as my coach, commanding me to say, "I must, I must, I must improve my bust" whilst I did three backward arm swings at a time. He wouldn't hear of it when I said couldn't I, instead, make a cleavage with dark tan Pan Stik make-up. Ben would criticise me in a kindly way, but he couldn't break me of my two bad habits. I hunch my shoulders and screw my nose up in a gurn a thousand times a day. I did stop poking my tongue out at him. He caught me doing it once. In disgust he told me to "Put it away, you don't know where it's been", but I didn't so he gave me a good hiding. He often remarked the only way to control me was to thrash me, the noisiest, chattiest, most mixed up girlfriend he had ever had.

In November Ben decided he wanted more independence, and Fairleigh food wasn't agreeing with him, so he began looking for a flat. He found one within a matter of days. Ben rented a two room, furnished basement flat from Mrs. S, a widow living with her teenage daughter in a house far too big for their needs. It's just popped into my mind, the night before he left Fairleigh we were laying at the bottom of the bed for some odd reason, making out a grocery and essentials list.

On day of removal we happily shopped in town. We walked the length and breadth of a Tesco store with an empty help-yourself basket. We didn't put anything into it, because there was no food to be seen on the shelves, just clothes and bits and pieces of kitchen/bathroom equipment and utensils for the home. We asked another customer, not an assistant, as we didn't want to appear foolish, where the tins, packets and fresh food had disappeared. She put us right. We were in Tesco Home 'n Wear. Tesco food supermarket was further down the road. I didn't leave Home 'n Wear empty-handed. Ben bought me a pack of dusters (to be left at the flat) and a pair of tights for consenting to be his skivvy. I said I didn't mind charring as long as I got paid in kisses. He said wasn't his company payment enough to which I replied certainly not.

Laden with food we entered the flat. I loved it on sight. I cooked the first meal there: steak, Brussels and mashed spud. I wouldn't say I passed that test with flying colours, because I got a whopping blister on my thumb, which I hid from Ben and slithered about the butter dish when he wasn't looking. Mighty painful that was.

I remember getting in a panic the first time I returned to ground level after climbing two flights of stairs to the bathroom. I had the choice of three doors to go through, and only one would lead me to Ben. I took pot-luck and stepped into the broom cupboard. I turned to the next and opened Mrs. S's kitchen door. I carried on turning in a half circle and found the correct door, through which steps led down to the basement.

By the afternoon of the day Ben moved into the flat, I had a raging headache, watery eyes and a runny nose. But within a few days I was feeling the happiest I had ever been, and tried my hardest to be as domesticated as

Ben. He had more practice than me, actually living there of course. The only thing at Fairleigh Ben preferred was the colour television. At the flat he had to mess about with plugs, leads and wires, and give the old box a couple of hefty whacks, with me holding onto its injured leg, to get it to go.

I became a good duster at the flat. I took pleasure in 'doing' for him. I should never have dusted the Airfix model ship Ben had made, because I cack-handedly lowered all its sails. I had a habit of making blunders. Like the time he sent me into the Grocer's for sugar and I came out with a diddy one pound bag. That wasn't what I had asked for neither. I had asked the man behind the counter for a half-pound bag of sugar, only to be told half pound bags were no longer in existence, if ever, and would madam like a one pound or a two pound bag? "A one pound bag will do fine" I replied, but as he handed it to me I thought "Oh no, I should have had a two pound bag, because that's the normal size one, the size Mum buys". I didn't have the heart to ask the shop man if he could change it for the larger size so went back to the car and told Ben I had saved him some money. He said I was stupid when he saw the size of the bag – he smiled as he said it though – and I think I am too, because I owned up and told him the full story. I kept mum on another occasion when I went into the butcher's and asked for two lean beef chops. I have also been known to ask for venison breasts. The butcher was a stranger so I didn't mind him thinking me a dimwit.

Ben must have despaired of me often. He said I was nuts, because I washed out empty jam jars before I threw them in the dustbin. I wonder if Ben has kept Ferdy Fox, the pincushion I bought him to go in his button tin? It cost me only a few coppers at a Bring and Buy Sale. I sewed on a button for him once. It was off again the following week. I'm not brilliant when it comes to sewing. In fact I hate it. I know full well I shan't improve with age. Ben spoilt me on Saturdays. For services rendered he bought me a treat. Sometimes it was a meringue full of real cream for tea. One afternoon he went down the betting shop and came back with a packet of Maltesers, all for me. I laid them out on the bed and, as I went from room to room with my duster, I greedily popped them one by one into my mouth. I didn't offer Ben any, because he had a packet too. He did confiscate one of mine. That was when, as usual, I hit the telly leg off. Always, always, as I brushed the mat and crawled underneath the telly in my thoroughness, one of its back legs fell off. I then had to yell for Ben to come and screw it on, as I balanced the telly on my back in an effort to stop it crashing over on its side. Ben got used to me wrecking the joint on Saturdays.

His bed suffered somewhat. In anguish and excitement I pummelled it, as I stared transfixed at the screen when wrestling came on the goggle box. Ben made me a fan. We took part in bouts of our own after each match. He would say, "Let's see what you've learnt today" and my resistance was shattered, as I got caught in armlocks, strangleholds, Boston Crabs, half nelsons, etc. I tried to give as good as I got, but my "Give" was invariably followed by an "in". The cheater took advantage and used unfair holds and tickled me to helplessness. That is until I cried out "submit". I was then forced to my knees and made to beg for mercy before I was cast aside, accompanied by "Get off me woman". I got thrown once and missed the bed where I was supposed to land. I cut my eyebrow ever so slightly, but enough to cause some raised ones at work when I explained how I received it.

I met his Mum and Dad at Bath races. They were quite elderly. It was so easy to like them. I said to myself I bet they rarely, if ever, lose their temper. The first time I went to his home I was nervous and asked him if he had a garden shed. When he said yes, I told him that if I went missing that's where I would be, but my shyness didn't go to that extreme. I loved his family home. It was a large stone cottage. I think he said it was 300 or 400 years old. The old people lived for their garden. You could get lost in it. It was stepped in a downward slant from the house. There were nooks and crannies for everything, because everything grew. I loved the lavender that filled the rockery, the roses that Ben's Mum lavished care on and they truly were a sight to behold, the flower-beds, the trees which dotted the sloping lawn and the vegetable garden that bore only the very best pickings. It was a haven in which to sit and dream on a summer's afternoon, to take tea in the early evening and to walk slowly round at day's end looking at life in the soil. One could gaze across the surrounding fields and see far in the distance the road into Bristol carrying matchbox size cars. I envied Ben's sister Laura, being able to sit on the window sill with the lighted ships' lanterns, one red, one green, either side of her, and look upon the beautiful garden as the sun went down.

Usually there was an evening in the week we visited his family. Invariably we would catch his Dad unawares snoozing in the chair, and he would wake with a start and hurriedly remove his knitted bobble hat. Ben took his washing home. Each week, as we dropped off laundry and collected fresh clean clothes, his little Mum would tell him to unpack his case and hang up the shirts the moment he entered the flat. I would maybe see him three days later and find the case exactly as his Mum had handed it to him. He did once wash a couple of shirts himself in Fairy Liquid. I smiled as I approached the washing line. There were no two pegs in each tail the way Mum does it. He had both shirts hanging differently with half dozen pegs per shirt. One he had pegged the collar to the line, hoisted up the shoulders and pegged, lifted up the sleeves and pegged them too. The other shirt had the line for its backbone, pegged in four places, the sleeves of which had been stretched out front and pegged together using two pegs. I wished his Mum could have seen. I like eggs. Ben's Mum got him new-laid ones from the farm and often I boiled a couple for tea. On two or three occasions I beheaded a bad one, never Ben. He would dispute the fact and wouldn't even sniff the yolk to confirm my story. He told his Mum about my bad eggs in such a way I felt a real fraud. His Mum could tell by his roguish smile that I wasn't making a fuss about nothing.

I loved to hear stories relating to Ben as a little boy. He had had a pet goat. His Mum told me he didn't like meat at one time, and it has been known for her to find meat and gravy stuffed into his school blazer or trouser pocket. He absconded his first day at school. Nobody was home when he got there except George the gardener. The teacher came to retrieve him and as soon as Ben saw her coming he got behind George, clung hold of his trouser leg, crying vehemently "Save me George, the bugger's come to take me back". What an awful five year old he must have been. He ran away from home once, after ducking to miss a well-deserved swipe from his Mum. When his Father left work that evening he found Ben sat on the wall outside his office, simply waiting to inform him he had run away. Following a man-to-man talk they returned home hand in hand to sort out the problem.

Ben himself told me about the money-making schemes he dreamt up when he left school, like mending old cars and selling them at a handsome profit. He was very mechanical and loved to tinker. I had to take an interest when I was going out with him, because the car bonnet wouldn't stay up on its own and my arms became hour-long supports. If they became lumps of lead I merely had to request him, just the once, to move his head instantly or it would be sliced off, and he did. In his teens Ben one day came home with a tray full of newborn chicks, which he reared himself before selling them and making a few bob. There was one thing, however, he lost out on. He became a barman. It was extremely hard work the first evening he pulled pints. Next day he telephoned the pub landlord and asked how much money he had earned the previous night. When told, Ben replied, "That's good. You can keep it, because I'm not coming back". Ben preferred to be on the other side of the bar.

He loved a quiet drink at The Moon. The locals at the pub had known him since his youth and they made me so welcome. I had my favourites amongst the regulars. Mr. and Mrs. Poynter, the baker and his wife, I was most fond of. They came into the lounge one evening looking very posh, after attending a wedding. Mr. Poynter pointed to his shoes and chuckled. He had brown laces in black shoes. Mrs. Poynter told us he had too cleaned his felt trilby hat, also brown, with furniture polish. Lloyd was a lovely man who teased me terribly. I thought the world of him. He was a good man who took care of mental patients. Ben often said he would willingly give me away to Lloyd for free. Ben, being a corn merchant, held many long discussions with Alfie who had the thickest blend of Gloucestershire accent I have ever heard. Alfie owned a vast acreage of farmland and was fast becoming a millionaire. He was a man of great character, a clever and shrewd businessman, an ageless wispy haired man with a cigarette butt permanently stuck between his lips. There it stayed balanced throughout every conversation. He was a bit grubby, but so what. I found him thoroughly entertaining, when I could understand what the deuce he was saying.

Ben and I were sat in the public bar on one occasion listening to two old boys' story telling. One puffed out his chest and smugly told us he had been Lord Monty's chauffeur in Palestine and Jerusalem. These gaffers (brothers-in-law) were merry, because their wives had gone off together for a week's holiday leaving them to fend for themselves. They were as pleased as two sandboys at the thought of no bickering and nagging for seven whole days. Nothing but ale, peace and quiet lay in store for them, and what more could men their age want they questioned. One said, true as he was sitting there, he had seen a lady in Scotland wipe her dog's behind when it had concluded its business. I thought dogs had self-cleaning bums. The other chappie asked the Lord to strike him down if it weren't true, but he had seen piglets at a cow's udder. He wasn't struck down in the pub, but I wouldn't have been surprised to learn that he had fallen to the ground after he left.

Once at The Moon my bra came undone. It didn't come undone by itself. It had help, and I thought Ben was being affectionate with his arm round me. He had been working a fiddle through my skinny rib. I had no need to worry about a floppy chest, but my padded bra sagged towards my waist giving the impression I had a droop, even if it was imitation. Ben, the culprit, was full of hee-haws. I said no, he couldn't put his cold hands up my jumper to do me back up. Someone might have seen. Uncomfortably and embarrassingly I made my way to the Ladies and sat across the table from him on my return.

There were other pubs we frequented. Apart from The Moon, my favourite was The Crown set deep in Somerset countryside. I liked to go in wintertime on a cold and frost-glazed evening when breath steamed and my nose turned ruby red. Get me inside the warm interior and I immediately began to tingle and thaw until I was taken over by a rosy glow, and that was before a drink! It was better if we got there early, because we then managed to capture seats on the settee. We sank so low into the squashy chintz covered cushions we had trouble getting up again. The sofa was to the right of the roaring log fire and we would later leave the pub with a ruddy cheek apiece. That was my cosy pub. During one visit Ben gave me a penny and said for me to go out into the main bar and put it in the nickelodeon. I went and did as I was told, put money in the slot, stood waiting and watching, but no music filled the pub. I went back to Ben and told him I couldn't understand why it hadn't played a tune. He questioned my intelligence. There can be none so dumb as I. I had wondered why the thing I put money into had looked like a dog. It was a dog, a china one, collecting contributions for the RSPCA, but he didn't wear a collar saying so, none that I could see anyways. Not far from the dog was a juke-box, which I suppose did look like a juke-box. Ben wouldn't entrust me with any more money.

We, more often than not, stopped in a lay-by halfway home from the pub, but Ben never fancied the idea of a walk across the fields in the moonlight. He said I might accost him, but I could go alone if I wanted and he would wait for me in the car.

One evening Ben took me to a different country pub, which he had heard was a popular place for young and old alike. It was heaving with people, but we managed to squeeze into seats. Within five minutes of our arrival Ben said didn't I want to go to the Ladies. I said I didn't think so. He said I normally did and I said I didn't. Why the heck he was harping on about such a boring topic beat me. In the end I relented, perhaps I did want to go. Ben positively beamed, the funny man. I thought he had probably seen a female in the pub whom he knew and wanted to chat up, so I left him to it.

I fought my way through the masses to the door marked Ladies in a corner of the lounge. Inside a woman was waiting for the loo before me, so I stood idly and glanced around the Ladies thinking, "What's so wonderful about this one?" Then I caught sight of a man wearing a kilt. A cardboard man, that is, pinned on the wall. There was writing above his head. When the woman in front of me had gone into the cubicle and her predecessor had walked out, I edged across to this wee man and read the words "I dare you to lift my kilt", or something similar. At that moment the loo door clicked, as it was unbolted. I jumped away from the wall and, composing myself, nonchalantly turned my back on temptation.

Sat on the lavvy I had time to think and wonder what exactly was beneath his kilt. I came out with my mind made up. No-one else was in the room so I walked up to the man and brazenly pulled up his kilt. "Oh is that it?" I thought, as suspenders and frilly drawers bearing the words "You rude thing" greeted my eyes. "Huh", I thought, and jauntily walked out.

There was no horde of people outside the door. A pathway seemed to have been cleared for me and, as I walked towards Ben, I felt sure every eye in the place was on me, and noticeably the whole gathering was smiling. Some were in fact laughing out loud. I coloured up. I seemed to be the joke. I knew a petticoat couldn't be round my ankles, because I didn't have one on. I couldn't be losing a false lash, because I wasn't wearing any, so why on earth was every single person looking at me and grinning in that awful 'open' way. Where were their manners? I had simply been to do an every day normal occurrence.

Upon reaching Ben, near to tears I asked him what was wrong with me. He unkindly told me to hop it, as I was an embarrassment to him. He said it though with a smile plastered across his chops. My puzzled question as to what had I done to disgrace him (and myself) did receive an answer eventually. The rotter informed me that when I had lifted that offensive Scottish gentleman's kilt, I had triggered off a bell which had loudly rung throughout the pub, and the place just happened to be full of regulars who knew what the bell represented. They also knew I had been the only female in the damnable loo. "I hate you" three times over I giggled to Ben after my acute shame waned.

I chuckled along with the rest when newcomers entered the pub as the evening wore on, and fell foul prey to that outspoken highlander. One poor woman, in particular, a well-to-do prim and proper middle-aged madam, dressed expensively in mauve. She committed the sinful act and walked unknowingly out of the Ladies head held high, only to lower it down and down a bit further as she became conscious of smirky stares.

The pub was a joke one and Ben had been well aware of the fact. Throughout the evening we watched as spiders fixed to elasticated strands dropped from the rafters onto unsuspecting heads and shoulders. Upon discovery men and women would be overcome by 'funny' five-minute fits, as they squirmingly brushed themselves down. Ben laughed the other side of his face when he ordered drinks at the bar and couldn't pick up his change. Coins were glued to the counter to confuse customers. Although noisy in the lounge, we couldn't fail to hear klaxon horns from time to time, summoning kitchen girls to take hot soup orders. But a worse sound showed us the door. No ordinary "Time gentlemen please" from the landlord. He stood in the middle of the floor and blew a hunting horn.

We stopped once for a quick one in the Butcher's Arms down the road from Nan's. I had taken Ben to meet Nan. He guessed which bungalow in the row was hers, because he knew she had a parrot on a perch in her kitchen window. Not a real parrot. It pleased Nan to show Ben over her home. She says she has more now than she has ever had in her life. She is immensely proud of her old people's bungalow, and has every reason to be. She told Ben she pays a mere shilling a year for her telly. Ben fancied living there himself. He liked my little Nan. Besides a drink in the Butcher's Arms, I had a smacker too in front of the yokels. He had said I looked nice in my colourful gypsy blouse (Nan liked it so much I bought her one the same) and did I want to make a bet that he wouldn't kiss me there and then in front of the locals. Gambler that I am did bet, because I was positive he wouldn't brush my lips. It wouldn't be like Ben to do such a thing in a public place. I didn't mind in the slightest losing that bet, and we didn't get thrown out neither for acting in a manner likely to cause a breach of the peace. It was most subtly done.

Once when Ben asked me where I would like to go I suggested the Pucklechurch pub, the scene of hairdresser Glad's annual binge night. Ben wasn't impressed and neither was I. Without the atmosphere my lady friends created, the bar was grim and foreboding. The two bar electric fire in the grate wasn't plugged in. The light bulb shone dismally. The bare wooden chairs and tables littered the huge room in higgledy-piggledy fashion and the floorboards creaked. It was early and we were the only customers. There was an air of gloom. I had sensed a quiet, not very good mood about Ben when we met, and through me bringing him to this joint, this 'battlefield', it was getting worse by the minute. I rummaged for things to say until I got stumped for words. A few dreary faced people entered who weren't interesting to look at, and in their wake a man came in and mounted the platform. He began caterwauling and made a brave attempt to play the piano, but unfortunately half the keys were missing. That was enough to make Ben sigh, "Let's go". I don't think my "Sorry love" was an acceptable apology.

We drove around, not speaking much. We ended up parking in a field entrance at the top of Lansdowne Hill. Stretching below us was the city lights of Bath. We got out of the car for a blow in the wind and walk in the dark across the racecourse to inspect the jumps. I pointed out to Ben Moby Dick, a perfect whale shape of stars in the sky, but he couldn't see it. After walking in the cold night air we went in the nearby pub for a warmer-upper. We were happy again, because this pub was okay, all warm and cosy. Ben had a picture of Kathy Kirby stuck on the wall to gaze at, and I diligently watched the ugly sucker as he shoved his nose round the bottom of the fish tank.

It was at Lansdowne that I lost my cameo ring, Mum and Dad's 21st birthday present to me. Ben knew I was upset. The next evening after work he not only took the car apart searching for it, but when it was put back together he drove out to Bath and hunted in the grass for a long time. He knew what it meant to me and was hoping to surprise me with it next date. It was, however, a hopeless quest. I couldn't bring myself to tell Mum and Dad of my carelessness. I fobbed them off with excuses when they noticed I had stopped wearing it. I went into town one Saturday morning and bought an identical ring. I couldn't help but exclaim "Well I'm blessed!" when I walked into the jeweller's. There was a 20% reduction on any ring bought that day.

Ben got on well with the owner of the house and flat, Mrs. S. He was like a son to her she said. She told me she liked to treat him to home-made cakes once in a while. She was an excellent cook and I failed to understand why he gave them away to me or to work associates without sampling himself. I suppose he wasn't into cake. I was and am.

We had just made a cup of tea one evening when Mrs. S called downstairs for us to go up and see what she was doing. Out of politeness we did, and Ben nearly brought his boots up. She was skinning three fish and disgorging them of their innards. Is that a word? Mind you, I too felt squeamish as she bludgeoned their backs until the spines came away, wrenched off their fins, chopped their heads off and hacked their tails off. If she had gouged out their eyes I'm positive we would have fallen into each other's arms in a coupled faint. For a sweet little old lady she was a bit swashbuckling sadistic. We stood our ground though and pulled sickly faces at one another, me wanting to say "Steady my lad" and Ben's worried frown telling me "Steady old girl", as Mrs. S deftly went about her work with the carving knife, chattering happily all the while and filling us in on detail. I seem to remember Ben had a brainwave, which was slow in coming, and told Mrs. S the kettle must be boiling dry downstairs. Mrs. S's departing words, as we backed out of the kitchen, were "You must taste when they're cooked". Two cold cups of tea lying in wait on the dresser downstairs weren't quite the pick-me-up needed. Mrs. S didn't forget her promise. The next evening, as I was enjoying roast lamb at home, Ben was stealthily dumping newspaper-clad fish in the dustbin. That reminds me of the time Ben drove round for two days with a sack of fish-meal in the boot of the car. He had gotten hold of it cheaply for his Dad's garden. All the cats in the district were to be found sniffing greedily at his rear.

Mrs. S had a heart of gold and Ben repaid her kindness by helping her make his rooms damp-proof, after which they repainted them. The walls had to be scraped, patched and sandpapered first. I was allowed to help. Ben handed me a kitchen knife and Mrs. S handed me a pinny, which she said I could keep. Ben hated me wearing it and called me an old washerwoman. It was hard work for Mrs. S and Ben. I was tea maker-in-chief and brusher-upper. A halt was called at nine in the evenings. Mrs. S would then go off for her bath and I was needed to help my painter and decorator unscrew his weary, tensed up muscles. He had fine, chalky paint scrapings in his hair and eyebrows, old paint daubed clothes on, he was full of yawns, but as he lay on his bed parked in the centre of the room with his eyes closed, it was me he wanted to hold. To look around the room, it couldn't have looked worse had a bomb dropped. To look at my worn out Ben was to love him all the more and I kissed his eyelids.

We held hands lying side by side and sometimes we did driving along, even if we shouldn't have. It seems to me though men in general are quite able to drive one handed. I don't know if women are that way inclined. Words simply weren't needed at such times. Come ten o'clock of an evening, I forlornly left the warmth of our nest to go and make a cup of tea. But as I was waiting for the kettle to boil, I would pad back to where he was prone, walk round the bed tucking in the corners, study his beautiful face, sit down beside him and lay my head on his tummy, the best pillow a girl could have, even if it did move up and down underneath me. I dribble when I'm asleep. Ben was forever waking up in the chair with a soggy jumper on, because I had snuggled into him. I have also got odd legs Ben said. In bed sometimes my legs would jump and twitch, resulting in cramp. Although I didn't want to, I would have to get up and disturb him to walk on the cold floor. He possessed two pairs of slippers, one new pair, one old. The toes were out of the old pair so those were allocated to me, because he couldn't bear draughts. It was hunt the slipper on my arrival at the flat. They were often to be found under the bed out of my arm's reach. He had usually hidden the broom too. But if ever I sneakily found one of his and went to put it on, the matching slipper was nowhere to be seen. Nobody but Ben could take off a slipper in the kitchen and discard the other one in the bedroom.

Me and my little paper bags each month. Of course Ben suspected when I skedaddled upstairs more often than usual once a month, with a slipped muscle protruding at wrist point, or to be exact a rustling bulge underneath my cardigan sleeve. In those days internal protection made you faint, or so my friends and I were led to believe by well-meaning older ladies. Ben was very understanding at these times of the month. On several occasions we would be sat watching telly and I've had the cramps come, and had to ask him if he minded me borrowing his hot water bottle to hold next to my tummy for a while. "Again?" he would question and I would nod. He would smile a sympathetic smile and a short while later ask if the ache had gone. He cared then. I know he did. I got overtired once and stupidly started to cry, because I could not go to sleep no matter how hard I tried and wanted to. He cuddled me until I did. One afternoon I developed a migraine at the flat and he tucked me up in his bed, darkened the room, and sat out in the cold kitchen reading the newspaper for the remainder of the day. I don't get so many head boomers nowadays, but they were quite frequent when I was courting Ben.

A saucepan came down on Ben's head one day. I had stacked them on top of the cupboard wrongly. It wasn't done on purpose. He said I was hopeless and a menace in the kitchen and tethered me to the bed leg as he made tea. I bellowed at him, but it didn't do any good. He sat down in front of me and ate, promising to leave me his bacon rind if I stopped grizzling. By wriggling I managed to untie my bonds and escape from my crouched position on the floor, only to be caught and tied again, this time to the garage doors, hands behind back style. It was impossible to smile innocently at passers-by. It's no wonder flannel and dishcloth fights were plentiful at the flat. Ben walked into a wall instead of through the door at the flat one day. A nasty bump came up on his head and he did feel groggy, love him. We both did the week before Christmas when the two of us got through a box of liqueur chocolates in roughly an hour. Ben made a steamed sponge pudding for tea, his specialty, but we didn't want it.

To be honest, that December Ben wasn't himself, healthwise. By Christmas he was ill. He tried to hide it from his family and me, but it was obvious. On Christmas Day he picked at his food whereas I wolfed mine down. Even though he was poorly, and I was worried about him, I did have a happy Christmas. It was our one Christmas together. We spent Christmas Eve with his family and I met his grandparents. As midnight struck, Laura brought in a large cardboard box of gifts, and I sat on the pouffe by my darling's knees and helped him open his presents. Early evening we had been alone to exchange our own presents. Ben himself chose the chunky knit cardigan he bought me. Everyone remarks how nice it is. It's snowy white with red and pink flowers embroidered down the front. I gave him mother-of-pearl cuff links and a panda. I suppose the panda case was soppy, but I wanted him to have warm pyjamas at night. When we left his folks in the early hours of Christmas morning it was snowing.

Ben called for me before lunch on Christmas Day. We drove to the Local where I kissed my man-friends and Mrs. Poynter under the mistletoe. Then on we went to his parents. The journey had me spellbound, because the sun shone on fields and trees, gardens and rooftops, but all were covered in a layer of snow. This was my first Christmas away from home. We ate a sumptuous meal, after which the men and his gentle little Mum dozed while Laura and I joined forces to tackle the washing up. Later we watched telly and played a marathon lasting game of Monopoly, which Ben had bought. He won naturally. I managed some tea, but Ben didn't. We had an hour by ourselves in the flat on Christmas night. I looked at him and did so love him, but he wasn't well. I wanted to help him get better. I bought him a bottle of Lucozade, but he didn't want nor like it. I could have clonked him with it.

Shortly after Christmas his tummy virus sent him home for some proper care and attention. His Mum took on the task and made sure he did live on soggy bread and milk. He had to replace the stomach lining, which he had wretchedly worn away. I don't think I saw him for a couple of weeks, because he said it was too far for me to go visiting. I don't suppose he felt like company anyway. His trousers hung baggy on him when I did see him again and he had two hollows instead of cheeks. Over a stone had been shed and my little pale-face looked a bag of bones, yet I wanted to cuddle and cuddle him non-stop. He was in need of fresh air and I put his arm through mine as we slowly walked across the Downs and along by the Sea Walls. He transferred my arm through his and I wriggled as close as I could get. Whenever we linked arms I put my hand in his pocket. I wasn't fishing for money or looking for holes. It was warm in there. Ben gave me a present, a corn trade diary so I didn't want a British Rail one from Dad that year. After that bout of illness his stomach seemed to play him up a lot. In the end his doctor sent him to hospital for X-rays together with a letter, which Ben steamed open to learn that it was a suspected ulcer. This was confirmed and thereafter he endured a fairly strict diet and bottles of pills.

Before he brought me home at night I plumped up his pillow and remade the bed, although he said there was no need for me to, because he would make it when he got in it. I put the hot water bottle between the sheets, and a glass of water on his bedside table, which was really a large cardboard box he had covered with pretty wrapping paper. Then I had a five-minute sit-down, the time it took me to undo the knots in his pyjama cord. It must have been tied loose enough for him to slide out of his pyjama bottoms in the mornings, or else he was some kind of magician. He is the only man I know who takes off his pyjamas leaving one arm and one leg turned inside out. Amazing! I always said I knew my place and in fact loved to sit at his feet and hug his legs to my cheek and smack them to get the face powder off afterwards. He didn't complain though if I did sit on his chair arm and cradle his head when he was sleepy. I felt so pleased too if he asked me to spell out words for him at odd times. I felt depended upon and of some use to him. Most men have a spelling weakness, even my brother-in-law whom we class as a genius.

A couple of days before 14th February he told me not to dare buy him a Valentine's Card, as he didn't believe in it. I had heard that said before by someone else! He said it was romantic nonsense and I was to save my money. I didn't put up a very good argument, which was a pity because I had already bought him one. I felt quite hurt, but there was no need to be. What made him change his mind I don't know, but he handed me one on the night of the 13th, sealed and strictly not to be tampered with until the following morning. I didn't want a telling off so next day, when he was out of the room, I put the card I had got for him under his pillow.

And then there was the time I walked out on Ben, something I don't think he ever could forgive and forget. It was the last week in February and I went to the flat one evening and found him in bed asleep. I haven't got a clue why I felt mad with him. He looked highly desirable when he was sleeping. Instead of climbing in with him, as practically everyone, including my boss, said I should have done, I banged around the flat as I washed up and put the crocks away. He didn't stir until I had finished. Too nicely timed. He opened his eyes, stretched and smiled "Hello Tosh". Poor thing! I let him have it. My tongue immediately ran away with me and lashed him. I've not forgotten my harsh words – you evidently need your sleep more than you need my company – and I flounced out of the flat. I stood at the bus-stop and let two buses go by before I faced up to the fact Ben wasn't going to come looking for me. He had told me once he would never run after me. His Mum used to say, so he said, "Never run after a girl or a bus. Another one will come along."

For two days I walked around in a dazed stupor, calling myself wicked dreadful names. What a moron. The third day the shock waves were hitting me so hard my hands had begun to shake. It was a Saturday. Throughout the day I trailed the streets of Bristol aimlessly, and bought what I was looking for in a tumbledown post office/knick knack shop near Christmas Steps. That evening I went to him. I won't ever forget the look on his face when he opened the door to me. For a second I read there despicable contempt for me. He made a cup of tea and we sat down in the armchairs opposite sides of the room and talked. He couldn't understand my actions of Wednesday night. I found it hard to explain, because I didn't fully comprehend myself. I said maybe I had acted that way as a result of pre-menstrual tension, and he had forgotten my Birthday, which had been on the Monday. My fault again, because I hadn't told him it was due. He thought it was in May not February. I gave him the present or peace offering I had bought that day, hoping it would symbolise what I was having difficulty in saying. It was what his Mum would call a dust collector, that is an ornament. It was two little china rabbits snuggling together in bed, and one could tell they loved each other by the contented smiles on their faces. I would hate to think those rabbits were on a rubbish dump now. They did bring us back together, because the next day Ben had a treat in store for me – fresh strawberries for tea. Foreign they were, and they must have cost the earth at that time of year. How he got hold of them on a Sunday I have no idea. When I saw him a couple of days later he said he was sorry he had missed my birthday, and there was something for me out in the 'fridge'. His fridge was the passage, same as ours at home, because it was freezing cold out there. There was the best present a girl could have – flowers. Fifteen red tulips stood in a row of milk bottles.

One evening I arrived at the flat and found Ben in great pain. His stomach was in uproar. I wanted to love and cosset him, but I kept quiet because he hated to be fussed over, particularly if he wasn't feeling grand. He was on the move the whole evening and kept getting up from the chair to walk round the garden. I didn't follow, as I sensed he wanted to be left alone. I bussed it home and worriedly asked Mum what could be wrong with him. She asked a question, which I answered, and there was the cause of his discomfort. I saw him the next day and my first words to him were "Spring Greens". My little love was better by then and relieved to hear Mum's diagnosis.

I found Ben one day peering at a lump that had suddenly appeared on his arm. It was pea-shaped and I could wiggle it around under his skin. He had looked up his complaint in a medical journal and informed me it was a sebaceous cyst. He knew the treatment required and carried it out without a wince, although I felt certain he would do more harm than good. He walloped his arm on the table edge, because he read that if whacked on a hard surface the cyst would disperse and by crikey it did too.

Ben occasionally suffered from catarrh, and the first time he brought me home from the Spa I informed him I often got bunged up, because there were a great many hairs up my nostrils preventing, so I thought, the passage of lots of fresh clean air to the lungs. Therefore, for the sake of us both, Ben started buying herb aroma airwicks. These were positioned about the room in gay abandonment, sometimes as many as six. There was one either side of the bed and in turn we would sit up and thrust a nose close to the wick, breathing in deeply with a sigh of "Aah, that's lovely". If the airwicks failed to unblock our nose holes, Ben crushed a fistful of pods of I'm not sure what in a cup, poured boiling water over the seeds and together we would sit under towels sniffing this concoction long and hard until stuffiness began to clear.

He had the audacity to buy bathroom scales so that he could keep tabs on my weight. I was pinioned to him and forced to step onto the wretched things. Half the time my weight rocketed sky-high, but after the first time I knew why. The bounder had his foot on the scales too.

Ben and I did like answering quizzes when they appeared in The People or News of the World. Nudes of the World Ben called it, on account of the many pin-ups adorning the pages. Every Sunday he would say he had bought the Nudes for me, because I got intoxicated reading the scandal contained therein. He was just as bad. If I had a Woman magazine on me, he would ask to read the problem page. In the love quizzes though Ben impudently gave me low marks and my total score, when totted up, made me out to be an icicle. To see his face as he gave me points! It was a picture of untold glee. He did it for a purpose. I had to prove to him that he was being unfair and that I did have one or two alluring attributes up my sleeve.

I wish I hadn't ruined every joke Ben told me. I was so slow to catch on. What was the simple one that had me puzzled for days, Boy Scouts, Girl Guides?

I could have crowned him on occasions, but it was more than I dare do. After shaving he would slap on aftershave, and I would sidle up to him saying, "Don't you smell beeooteeful" in the hopes of receiving a kiss. Kiss be blowed! I would get a few dabs of aftershave on the chin plus the word "Scrounger". Men! I bit Ben when I felt like it. I also liked to play with the hairs on his chest, curling them, blowing them, tying them together if I could, and tweaking them. He teased me after I introduced him to Des. He said he used to go out with her. I got quite indignant, as he said he even knew her middle name. He didn't know mine then, and when he did I was always Mary quite Contrary. It was days before I could check with Des as to what her middle name was. I clobbered Ben for telling an untruth and making me jealous of a past that never was. "I'm good aren't I?" I said to him once, because I managed to bring him a cup of tea without spilling any in the saucer. "Good for nothing" was his spitty reply, because I had forgotten the sugar again. He said I fished for compliments.

One Saturday afternoon Ben made me quite jumpy, misbehaving. He kept hiding from me at the flat, and would pop up in the most unexpected places. With four doors and a swish along curtain in the two rooms, I was clueless which one he would be coming through. It gave me the willies. We watched the Alfred Hitchcock thriller 'The Birds' one evening, which I found spooky. He took great delight in switching off the light at the end and hounding me. He said the birds would come and peck out my eyes in the middle of the night. The tyke knew I was scared of birds, budgies really, ever since Lin's perched on my head. That drove me crackers.

Ben took me horse-racing. I loved it. At Bath races I saw three Wimpey bosses spending their earnings. The Point to Points were held at Didmarton, Nege and Chewton Mendip. Ben would study the form and weigh up the odds. I went by nice eyes and colouring, as we watched the horses being walked round the paddock. I was only allowed to place two bob bets and I kept to the same bookie, because he would let me come to the front of his queue and be served first. It amused Ben and bucked me to death when I won eighteen shillings on a horse, which didn't stand an earthly chance. I wasn't aware what to expect and was quite shocked the first time I went to the toilet at a racecourse. Ben smiled when I whispered that I had had to sit on a hole in the ground. No worries, I soon got acquainted with this type of inconvenience. A hole was perfectly adequate for men.

(We had the Grand National a few Saturdays ago and Mum, Dad and I couldn't help but gallop in our chairs as we viewed the TV. The commentator's voice was hysterical. Bloss calls jockeys, drivers. We each had a hopeless system for picking the winner. Mum shut her eyes and stabbed herself with a pin before selecting a horse in the paper. Dad had a hunch a horse would win bearing a name remotely connected with Canada. I chose a 40-1 horse. Then if I won I would have big winnings. Yet we had nothing but fallers amongst us.)

One blustery Sunday afternoon Ben and I must have looked as mad as two March hares taking a walk across the Severn Bridge. The wind blew up our buttoned coats and nearly made kites of us. Ben said "Not blumming likely" when I asked if he would save me, should I be lifted over the side. As we got to the far side of the bridge, I pointed a finger and out came the word "Bullocks". I had caught sight of a field full, but Ben was tickled because he thought I had said something else.

Ben belonged to Bristol Walking Club years ago. He showed me the area that had been his training ground, around Halfpenny Bridge. The clubhouse, a caravan, was situated in a field at the end of a dirt track. This dirt track was our stop off place when we first started courting. Ben's silly car horn got in the way occasionally, as I sat on his knees and nearly broke them. However, we didn't disturb anyone's sleep, apart from the crickets, because he had been considerate in his choice of snogging location. There was a lovers' lane nearer home, Ironmould Lane, but I didn't want to poach on Terri and Rob's ground. Besides, I knew that on one occasion cops shone their car headlights and blinded Terri and Rob. Then, when the car window was tapped and Tritz wound it down, she got blinded again by torchlight. It was understandable she got indignant when the officer asked her "In any trouble Miss?" but she sweetened her smile and replied "Oh no" instead of "Course not". Insinuating young upstart, she called him as he walked away, and they then went back to enjoying themselves, doing what they were doing before being interrupted. Those were the days! Tritz and I so young in heart, interested and keen, eager to fulfil our dreams of womanhood with the ones we fancied most. Tritz was on to a winner, but I won't say I backed a loser.

The only time Tritz met Ben was at Sandie Cod's 21st birthday party. In bed that night I sat up with a jolt, suddenly remembering Sandie's present was still in my handbag. I had forgotten to give it to her. Ooh I had forty fits wondering how I would make my apologies. It's a good job the Cod family know I'm a crazy coot with an idiot brain.

In driving rain one Saturday afternoon Ben and I went to see a walking race near Gloucester. We stationed ourselves at the school gates to congratulate the first ones home. It made me wince to see them. Two brushed the tape, immediately went across to a drain and were violently sick. One collapsed in the gutter and rolled in agony amidst rushing water and his own vomit, nobody else's. The man Ben called Old Pop – he was in his 60s – came squelching in to the finish, wearing plimsoles with blood seeping under the tongues. He passed the finishing line, but umpires wouldn't let him stop walking at that point. He had to slow down gradually. Otherwise he would have had unbearable cramp. It's incredible that sport is classed as a pleasurable pursuit. Our Dave lives for his running, yet I have seen him frothing at the mouth after a race and doubled over gasping for breath. There was tea and biscuits before the trophy and awards presentation. A little boy who knew Ben asked him if he was married. Ben said he couldn't afford to be.

At Easter we walked from Iron Acton Common along the bank of the stream winding its way through fields to Nibble. We stopped at the weir and looked across to an old mansion set in a glade of pines. Its garden knew no boundaries. The only flower growing was hundreds and hundreds of daffodils in clusters, clumps and patches. They spread their pretty heads over grassy slopes right down to the water's edge. They were even springing up through cracks in the walkway crazy paving stones. Nearby on a hill Ben pointed to a wooded copse where he played as a child. We ambled happily onwards. Ben chanced to remark there were voles, which made me watchful where I planted my feet.

I was present the time Ben took it into his head to somersault into bed. He said that was the way he got into bed as a child, and wanted to see if he was still flexible. He was. One day, to prove to himself he had supple leg muscles, he vaulted clean over the bonnet of the car. I nearly passed out with fright, but I couldn't scold him because he was proud of himself. Then one Sunday, after we had walked round the lake at Tortworth, he realised he had lost his sunglasses on the way. Before I could stop him he sprinted away from me and returned ten minutes or so later puffing and panting, having run the same distance which had taken us a good hour to walk. He had found his specs too. He was chuffed and had every right to boast of his fitness. I washed him down when we got back to the flat. I washed his hair as well and got more of a soaking than he did, because I got soap in his eyes. Also, because he said I didn't have a woman's touch as I towel-dried his hair, he filled a bowl of water and grappled with me until my head was immersed. Freezing cold it was too. In future he preferred to get down on his knees and lower his head to the fan heater.

Summer approached rapidly. Ben and I planned to go to Cornwall for a week's holiday in June. A long time beforehand he worked out my monthly dates on the calendar, so that the week we chose wouldn't clash with a period. He didn't trust me and my workings out. When I mentioned to Lin and her Mum about going on holiday with Ben, Mrs. H teased and betted that I would buy a Woolworth's ring before I went. Lin and I were highly amused, and I chuckled as I repeated Mrs. H's funny remark to Ben. In all seriousness he asked, "Well, will you?" I stopped laughing, because he had stunned me by saying that. My thoughts ran riot. It would be like a honeymoon, sharing his bed, a double one not a single one, for a whole night, no, six or seven whole nights! Drat my hairy legs and rise and shine greasy face. I don't know why I blushed and felt hot, as I looked at him and said, "Yes, if you want me to". It was settled. I told Ben I hadn't stayed in an English hotel before, and asked if there would be a sink in the room for me to 'do' my legs in. "Of course" he said, but he didn't relish the idea of washing his face if I left any bristles stuck round the basin. I suppose I did spoil my image on occasions.

The following Saturday, without a word to Ben, I went into town and shopped in Woolies for a cheap 'gold' band, that is I roamed the store first checking to see that there was no-one in the place who knew me, before plucking up courage to edge close to the jewellery counter. I turned bright red, as I pointed to the first one I saw, coughed and whispered "That one please" to the assistant, who seemed to be looking a little strangely at me. I exchanged a few shillings for the ring and hurried away, furtively glancing this way and that to make sure spies or Lin's Mum hadn't witnessed my guilt-ridden act. Only on the bus going to Ben's did I try it on, and breathe a sigh of relief because it fitted, albeit slackly. I had to cast a look round the bus first though for a married lady, as I couldn't remember which hand or finger it had to be worn on. I didn't show Ben the ring, or tell him I had purchased one. It would have seemed forward of me to do so.

I think I've still got the ring. It was never worn. Our holiday in Cornwall didn't materialise. We were plagued by car trouble and streaming colds that week. Generous Pange was the one to give the sniffs and sneezes to Ben. However, we were happy. The weather was sunny so what more could we want.

On the Monday we spent most of our first day's holiday at Eastville. Some say it's a seedy part of Bristol. I wouldn't. Even if it isn't very clean, it has bags of colour amongst its run-down-ness. Ben left the car in a 'Repair and collect the same day' garage, and was told to call back at 3.00 pm. The winkers had gone kaput, the exhaust was coughing badly and a new tyre was needed. No doubt it did us good to walk miles, even though we got dusty and parched. There were so many lorries thundering by on the road that day to jar our nerve ends and stop us in mid-sentence. Noses were fumigated though, as we continued in a circle past the gasworks next door to the Rovers ground. We did sit in the park for half an hour.

At three o'clock we were back in the garage yard, only to be told "Another hour's work still to be done guv". Ben stayed chatting to the mechanic and I strolled off by myself. It certainly was a cosmopolitan area. Opposite the garage were three shops: an Italian barber's, a Chinese laundry, and an Indian grocer's. My eyes darted this way and that. I admired the attractive sari clad women who walked at a snail's pace, yet their foreign tongues jabbered incessantly. Most of them had pushchairs carrying luminous eyed moppets. I felt sorrow for the shabbily dressed tramp sitting on a rock amidst waste paper on the rubbish tip. I wanted to approach him, have a word and offer a couple of shillings for a bite to eat, but shamefully I was lacking in courage.

I pulled up sharp when a panda car stopped before a terrace house without a garden. Two policemen got out and knocked on the door. A white woman let them in. I waited on the corner pretending to look in a shop window, but discretely conning the house really. No one else was interested as far as I could see. The cops emerged after five minutes accompanied by two black men. No handcuffs were to be seen, but I think I elaborated to Ben that there had been.

I had heaps to tell Ben and made haste back to the garage, but he wasn't there nor was the car. I was clueless as to what direction the flat lay. I brushed past so many different races of people. I began to feel like an intruding stranger in Eastville and wanted desperately to hear an English voice again. Dopey twit. More and more people began sweeping along the pavements of the high street, because it was going-home time from their day's work. I wanted my Ben. Where was he? He must be looking for me, but how would he see me in the swarms? I stood in the gutter and distress soon ebbed when I heard a familiar beep beep. Up raced my knight in a shining Sprite. (Ben had cleaned the car in readiness for the holiday.) Unsympathetically, he said it was my own silly fault I had got lost and he had gone without me. (He hadn't though. He had been tearing up and down, combing the main street and scanning the crowds for my stupid nut, he said. Actually he called out "Oih Stupid" when he did catch sight of me.) I was suitably chastised for gadding about the side streets.

Tuesday we went to Chew Valley and Cheddar and had a fresh strawberry and cream tea after climbing the Gorge. I swore to Ben that it was nothing more than a mild touch of hay fever I had. I told a downright lie, because I've never had hay fever in my life. Ben believed me, thank goodness, and didn't pack me off home.

The next morning he picked me up at ten. We were going to Lynton and Lynmouth in Devon for the day. At half past twelve we were still in Bristol, in a spare parts office drinking our day's supply of thermos tea. The dynamo on the car failed and had to be replaced. The kind fix-it gents took the job on straightaway, but it was a lengthy business. I'm amazed that Ben and I didn't blow a head gasket. Ben eyed me warily and said he felt certain I was a jinx. Maybe I was at that. Better late than never, Ben drove off eventually towards our destination with quite a hole in his pocket.

We stopped on Exmoor where the high winds did blow. We ate our sandwiches and marvelled at a dog rounding up sheep in the Lorna Doone Valley. I replenished a dwindling stock of tissues up my sleeve and tried to ignore the fact that I had a streamer. I wanted Ben to do likewise. Lynton/Lynmouth was a delightful, pretty place. We went on the sheer cliff railway and, because the operator knew Ben, goodness knows how, we were allowed to stand on the footplate, rather than take our seats inside the compartment with the other passengers. I clung tightly to Ben and kept my eyes glued to his chin, not daring to let them drift a fraction upwards or downwards. We had strawberry jam and cream filled scones for tea that day.

I sent the office a postcard from Lynton. (It stayed Sellotaped to the filing cabinet in the office for centuries and the times ever I glanced that way and remembered the past. The same as I did with my picture of Lynmouth Ben bought me, which hangs on the bedroom wall. I couldn't bring myself to turn it face to the wall, nor take it down. I'm reminded of him when I go to my drawers and see a pebble, an airwick, Lynton railway tickets, and a bottle of Devon Violets with a pixie on the top, an egg-timer, and a heart shaped name tag. Ben bought me an assortment of little surprise gifts. He also won a whistle for me on the pier at Weston. And a skeleton.)

Thursday of our holiday week the car cruised without a hitch along the Wye Valley, and we puzzled over the ruins of Tintern Abbey before going on to Symonds Yat for a strawberry and cream tea. It was a beautiful day.

Friday Ben had a cold coming. By the weekend we were both tissuing and went back to work after our week's holiday with sore red noses. Cornwall would have been an unromantic wash-out for us couple of wet drips. I didn't even kiss Ben until the Wednesday evening when I couldn't stand the strain of going without any longer.

One Friday evening we had a tiff, my fault because I couldn't relax. We had the curtain pulled across the open door at the flat, and directly outside Mrs. S had the hosepipe fixed onto the outside wall tap. But it kept falling off. Hearing gushing water every few minutes, I imagined the flat being flooded and I couldn't lie comatose. I was all of a twitch. I got on Ben's nerves. He shouted once or twice at me, then went quiet, and was still huffy when he drove me home, early. He said we would have a rest from seeing one another the next day, a Saturday, and I felt sick when I got indoors.

I awoke in the morning to a fine sunny day. The sicky feeling lingered and I was muddled up. I loved Ben and couldn't fathom out what had happened to us. I knew the worse thing I could do was to mope around the house all day so I made sandwiches, a flask of tea, polished two apples, and with barely an audible goodbye to the family walked out of the back door. Heavy in heart and step, I caught a bus to the bus-station, and from there another one to Weston-Super-Mare, my favourite place for unwinding. I usually love the journey, which takes me away from the city. My eyes as usual flitted through the window at countryside I loved, but I was full of sighs and remembrances of happier times, as we passed by pubs, our pubs, where Ben and I had supped together.

I arrived at Weston. Being a summer's day, the beach was crowded. "Not for me" thought I, confronted with happy, untroubled faces, and I hurried out of their sight. I parked myself in the secluded spot where Rish and I have often sunbathed, on the rocks near the old fishermen's wharf. (I remember the time when Bob was on holiday in Spain and Rish was feeling miserable and lonesome. We took ourselves off to Weston for the day and gorged ourselves on the pier with chips, toffee apples, candyfloss, and she treated me to a Knickerbocker Glory in Fortes. We putted on the green, spent a bomb on the roll a penny slot machines and sunbathed on the rocks. It was a most enjoyable day, but she spoilt it by coming home and playing records, which Dave, Al and I thought were soppy, that reminded her of Bob and therefore made her miserable again.) I had rocks to the south, east and west of me. To the north lay the sea, the Bristol Channel that is. That was good. I was hidden from all eyes except those of the fishes. I had a lot of thinking to do, and if I got blubby there would be no one to see tear-drops. I loved Ben so much. How could I make him overlook my silly behaviour of the previous night?

I disrobed and put my two-piece on. Shorts, because I was unable to fit my backside into a bikini. I oiled myself, pulled my shoulder straps down, placed my sunglasses conveniently to hand, and lay back delicately. I juggled with my backbone until it fitted into a nice niche, shut my eyes and began floating off and sieving through my cluttered mind, as the sun's rays beat down unmercifully and turned me into a lobster beginning with nose.

Not many minutes had elapsed when a voice piped up "Cor Missy, you ain't 'alf sweatin". I drew myself up on my haunches, grabbed my chest as my bra top slipped and glared fiercely in the direction from whence the voice came. Not one grinning face was eyeing me, but two. I explained I wasn't sweating profusely, but had swamped myself in sun tan oil. They asked me if I was there for the day and when I replied yes, they said they were too. I didn't groan. Something about the two young shavers made me attentive. I was cheering up fast. Introductions were called for and that is how I met Mark and Graham.

Graham informed me he was fifteen and would shortly be leaving school, and when I asked him what occupation he intended taking up, he said he wanted either to be a policeman or work on the dodgems on Weston Pier like his brother did. My companions were both Weston born and bred and, on my life, neither of them could have been above twelve years old. This became apparent as the day wore on. Oh yes, they didn't stray far from my side the whole day. They had come to the rocks for a day's crabbing and I was invited to join them. They were experts and my two teachers taught me the art. Firstly, I had to get me a pile of limpets for bait. I was shown how to wade into shallow water, pick up rocks and prod loose with fingernails or pebbles the snail-like creatures that had sucked themselves to the rock face. I then had to tie a limpet carefully onto a length of cotton and let it hang down in the water until I had a bite. I didn't have much success, but my cronies gaily went on to fill up a bucket with crabs galore. They were highly delighted at the size of the crabs and poked and rummaged in the bucket, holding aloft clawing crustaceans for me to judge who had nabbed the biggest. I was told the greenish ones were poisonous. They all looked green to me. They also asked themselves why hadn't they brought any matches, because we could have cooked three to eat, shudder upon shudders. "Never mind boys" I said and shared my tea and sandwiches on condition they went for lollies afterwards, which they were only too happy to do. The lads' fame spread. Soon other little boys, having heard our squeals, came to watch enviously, then slipped away, badgered fathers for a few coppers and returned to our waters with their own crabbing lines, much to the contempt of Mark and Graham. I tried to have an afternoon kip, but it was impossible. A youngster had trouble securing his limpets and kept calling upon me to knot them tightly. Then for some unknown reason Graham began collecting seaweed, which he piled around me and ordered that I not let it be pinched.

He wanted it to dry in the sun he said, and when it had, he proceeded to pop the pods open. There were ants crawling all over it.

The boys began saying how good they were at swimming and diving, and I remarked that it was a pity they couldn't show me their prowess, whereupon Mark replied it could easily be arranged. His bike was chained to the railings and his home was only a mile away and he could go for two pairs of trunks. He ran off and was missing for half an hour whilst Graham and I sat contemplating life and popping our pods. When young Mark breathlessly appeared back on the scene, I was made keeper of their clothes, socks and shoes, and instructed to "Watch me" "No me". They bounded off into the water with hardly a gasp, and as I wrung out socks and emptied shoes, I did watch their antics and marvelled at their skill, as they dived off the old pier. They had no fear that avenging crabs would bite their toes. A water fight made them sore at one another, but not for long. They waved and I waved back, as the minutes ticked by.

Dusk was closing in and a chill wind had sprung up, making me notice how sluggishly grey the 'sea' actually was. I decided it was time to make a move for home. I packed up my belongings, buttoned my cardigan, scattered remaining crumbs for the gulls, armed myself with the boys' togs and, laden down with this and that, precariously balanced myself on each rock, gradually edging nearer to the boys flailing about in the water. I declined their "Come on in"; disbelieving the water was warm, because their aimed splashes told me otherwise. I said it was time for me to go home and wasn't it past their tea-time. "Not yet" back came the answer, "We'll go home in a minute". I'll bet one minute turned into many. And so with cheery ta-tas thrown at me, I bade farewell to my playmates. When I reached the steps leading to the promenade, I glanced back in the twilight and saw them as I still picture them. We had had a good day. I walked along the beach where only the donkeys chewing hay and their dung heaps remained. The crowds had simply evaporated.

Returning home on the bus I was feeling happier certainly, until a flabby woman, who told me she had been office cleaning, also said her corset was killing her and went on to show me where it was cutting into her thighs. Now why on earth did she want to go and do that for, because all that white meat bulging out of stocking tops wasn't a very becoming sight?

I arrived home in a better frame of mind than the one I had gone out in that morning. Before I had time to wash my burnt, grease-streaked and dirt-stained face, Ben knocked on the door – he always used his knuckles not the knocker. The postie had delivered a packet of photos to the flat that morning, and he thought I might like to see them. We were all right again.

Photos, which he gave me, stir my memory chain. I don't look at them very often. There is one taken at the home-made jalopy races we went to at Tetbury, which had to be abandoned because the heavens opened. What a downpour that was. We were muddy, dusty and saturated when we got to his Mum's. After tea, when we left to go to the flat, I wasn't only wearing his old tracksuit, but his spiked running shoes as well, and they didn't even slop off. His feet were a normal man's size. I guess mine are too. I had kittens when he slowed up as we approached the Local and he started licking his lips. The big tease relented and drove on when I whispered that the landlord wouldn't take kindly to me puncturing holes in his carpet. I have a photo of me on the banks of the lake at Tortworth. I remember, as Ben was about to take it, he stormed "Do your flies up woman". From where Ben stood he couldn't see what I could see. The bank sloped to the water's edge and sat in a nook on the slope, clearly visible to me, was a man and his son fishing, highly amused at Ben's utterance. I could have brained him. Photos of me baring a stark white midriff, although the rest of me was darkly tanned, I don't appreciate. They conjure up feelings of no wonder he left me, looking like that. I was a dead loss at taking Ben's photo. He has a house balanced on his head in one photo I took. Well, I've had one taken with a fountain shooting up out of mine.

We loved to spend a Sunday afternoon walking from Purton to Frampton-on-Severn or vice versa. The two places were linked together by a towpath, with the canal running along one side and mud-flats on the other. Beyond the flats lay the River Severn and Wales. In April Ben even discarded his shirt and caught the sun.

We had a constant companion on these walks. I called him Rufus, the tattiest, dirtiest, most unkempt looking dog I have ever clapped eyes on, the most lovable too. He was a sort of long-haired mongrel type Old English sheepdog. His coat was shaggy, matted and smelly. I couldn't see his eyes, but he could see us. Once though a big pink slide held the hair back from his eyes. Each time we parked outside the tea-rooms, he had us in focus and came gambolling across. He was such a slobber chops, dribbling affection. His tail, wagging uncontrollably, stung as it slapped across my legs. Ben called Rufus rude names and told me not to take any notice of him, but he kept on following us. At times he would loiter far behind, sniffing at everything along the bank and sprinting down into ditches to see what things of interest they held. He would then notice we were way ahead of him, and cease his lingering and come rushing after us in a headlong gallop. The chase was on and he would woof cheekily as if to say, "Aha, you can't get rid of me that easily". We nearly did twice. Once this rascal didn't look where he was going and fell in the water. He could swim though and was soon bounding and lolloping after us, only stopping to shake himself when he was abreast of Ben and me. He got himself well and truly ensnared in a bramble thicket too. He rescued himself after Ben flatly refused to go in after him, but he had thorny twigs tangled in the hair under his belly and couldn't run happily. I beseeched Ben to free him, but he said not on my nelly was he going near the beast. He did though. He held Rufus as I pulled the thorns from his coat. I can't help but think of Rufus now and wonder how he is, and if his waterworks are any better. Excitement made him cock his leg every few yards. He didn't seem to belong to anyone and I mentioned to Ben that no one would miss Rufus if we sort of kidnapped him, meaning he'd live at the flat on account of Mum and Dad hating dogs. He would be company. Ben hit the roof. He wasn't going to have his privacy ruined and sleep interrupted by a filthy hound. Nothing further was said. I'm sure Ben liked Rufus as much as I did. We had to rely on different tactics to lose Rufus when we wanted to go home. Once, as we drove by on the other side of the canal, I saw him looking anxiously around, wondering how his pals had disappeared.

The last two times we walked along the canal bank I didn't enjoy quite so much. The first time we saw a dead sheep's rump sticking up out of the water, and the second time a dead swan lay on a bed of its own bloody feathers in the ditch. Not a pretty sight. I never walked there with Ben again. Maybe it was for the best. The saying goes things come in threes, and I can't help wondering whether a dead body would have transpired on a further walk.

So many places bring back memories. One afternoon, as we drove through Cheddar, a woman opened her bedroom window and threw down a pail of slops right over us. Luckily we had the roof on, but we did get blinded for a minute as mucky water sloshed down the windscreen.

We hired a boat in quite choppy seas at Beer. I got confused with my left and right and steered us into difficulties. Ben told me to sit and not twitch a muscle while he took over complete manning of the vessel and brought us safely to shore.

At Seaton we went rock climbing. Where Ben went, I nearly always followed. Sure as sure though I would have killed myself, had I been as daring as him. Faced with the impossible Ben will try and find a way round it, and so it was he clambered over rocks a mountain goat would have thought twice about scaling. He promised not to take risks. I was a bad risk so I got left behind, that is I sat cross-legged on rocks. Chalk rocks were above, below and on both sides of me. In front surged the ocean, greeny blue and white-capped. The sun was sinking and had slashed burning red bolts and pink and yellow flames across the pallid sky. I gazed seawards and saw and heard nothing but the shrill argumentative cries of gulls, the steady roll of the sea and the crash of a wave as it hit forcibly and resoundingly against the cliff face. How tempestuously it threw water into the air. It felt like there was just me in the whole wide world. I was in a dreamy mood. My trance was broken when my agile Billy Goat came into view. While his breathing was being restored to normal, I walked to the beach and out into the sea and played a catch-me-if-you-can game with the waves.

We loved the seaside. Ben loved swimming. I asked him what his favourite stroke was once, and he replied with a naughty boy look on his face "Definitely the breast stroke". Mhmmm, I only ever saw him do the crawl.

The many day trips we had to Charmouth never let us down. The only clouds to appear were those when I made a hash of navigating. Ben said there was no damn need to turn the road map upside down, but as I could see it there was every need. It went the right way up for the homeward journey. I would get touchy when he sighed impatiently that I wasn't using my 'loaf', but all my bungles were overlooked as soon as we feasted our eyes upon hillsides blanketed with startlingly yellow gorse. Over the hills, drawing nearer, the coastline sparkled. Half dozen times in a day we went back and forth into the tingling water. Ben swam and I lay happily waiting to be bashed in the spot where big waves broke on shore. Or I knelt and butted the breakers, only to be tossed like a Useless Eustace further and gradually further up the beach. These were our happiest days, swimming and dozing, walking and talking. I loved Charmouth with its long stretch of sandy beach, its crumbling cliffs where landslides were plentiful (Ben and I caused a couple of minor ones), its fossils, and its cliff pathway bordering on lightly swaying cornfields. Ben didn't comment on my unsightly spiky legs the time when sea and sun made them poxy and tender, preventing me from cutting a dash with my razor.

We would come home as darkness began to fall. The practice we followed was to knock the sand out of our shoes before entering the flat, and then once inside my first task was to put the kettle on. We swilled burnt faces. A tin of new potatoes, tin of cherries and a defrosted sachet of peas were opened. Two slabs of cheese were cut. Brown bread was buttered. We ate like starving beggars, then slept like logs until the alarm went off at elevenish, if it was a Sunday night, or oneish if a Sunday morning.

I liked doing things for him. When he had itchy eyes I put drops in. When he got sunburnt I gently rubbed a soothing cream on his back, although the dodger ran away yelling, "Hands off me woman, you're too rough". When I slipped in town, and nearly dragged him down on top of me, I bloodied my knee. Immediately we got to the flat he ordered me to peel off my holey tights, then he massaged and creamed my stiff crinkle-cut knee, because I was incapable he said. I didn't mind my masterful master. He regularly cleaned my glasses, because he said the huff and rub over I gave them with my sleeve wasn't sufficient. A spot of washing up liquid went on each lens and was fingered thoroughly over the surface with a tissue. Muck was wiped off with another tissue. They were then rinsed under the tap and dried in a couple more tissues. Without him I have resorted to my slap-dash, sloppy ways and get many spots before the eyes.

I fought Ben once for putting groggy wasps he had bashed on the head with a newspaper down the drain, which was frothing and bubbling with soap-suds. He retaliated and said I was just as cruel, because I had taken a baby hedgehog away from its mother the week previously. I found it crossing the main road. (It's home was evidently close by Ben said.) I carried it home with me, fed it bread and milk and put it under the leaves of our rhubarb patch. But it didn't move far from our garden. Three days later I came home from work and found it dying on our front garden path. Whether a dog or cat mauled it, I don't know. It was covered in white tumours, besides crawling with maggots and ants. It couldn't eat nor drink. I wanted it to die quickly. I begged Dave, Alan and Dad to hit it with the garden spade, but it wasn't in them to do a mercy killing. I wanted Dave to drive me to a vet, but he said cobblers, it was no use. I had a snivel. I placed it on a bed of cotton wool and tissues in a seed box and locked it in the shed where no beasts of prey could reach it. I heard cats fighting that night out in the garden. I hate the row they make. My hedgehog was hanging on the next morning, but his breathing was ragged and he didn't last the day. Mum told me that evening on my return from work that he was in the dustbin. Dad had picked him up on the shovel and put him in there after he died. I swear I can smell him if I go out to the dustbin, but Dad says it's Jeyes Fluid. Whenever I accused Ben of cruelty he brought up the subject of my hedgehog and, if I hadn't taken it home with me, it might still be alive. That would shut me up. The truth often hurts.

Ben did have a bright suggestion for dealing with Dave and Al one day when they riled me near to snapping point. He said why didn't I offer to make their bunk beds and lay layer upon layer of newspaper in-between their blankets and sheets. He knew we would have plenty of stale papers, because Mum hoards them. The idea was appealing, but knowing the brothers it was a dead cert I would be punished without mercy for my wrongdoing, even if I did tell them Ben had invented the crackling.

He took me to his office one Saturday morning. Once upon a time it had been a bedroom in a Victorian house. There was a fireplace, but an electric fire had been installed in the grate. I was amazed to see a barrage of telephones across his desk. I knew my man overworked and told him so many times. For Pete's sake, I wasn't going out with an octopus! How was he expected to answer a dozen phones if they all rang together? Love him, he had a hundred funny little doodles on his blotter. He didn't phone me at work on a regular basis, but one time when I was expecting him to I answered a call with "Hello darling" and found it was one of my estate salesmen on the line.

The week before Ben's thirtieth birthday we had a terrible bust-up, not that we ever had a stormy, slanging match, but cutting words would be said in the heat of the moment. We had a week's holiday and it proved to be one of the rainiest on record. That didn't help matters. The day our holiday started we had a disagreement, which lasted the whole seven days. We tried to combat our miserable mood. We went golfing, crazy golf I should say, looked at the oldest tree in England, walked into an empty church where footsteps echoed and out again into a centuries old graveyard, explored the grounds of Blaise Castle and got bothered by horse-flies, climbed a tower in the Gloucestershire countryside – I meant to count how many steps, but forgot until I was nearly to the bottom, wandered aimlessly up and down Gloucester Road 'twenty' times that week. We lay in the same bed with no intimate closeness, watched any old rubbish on TV, read ancient newspapers. Ben went down the betting shop two or three times a day, mended my brolly, did any little thing to keep occupied. And way into the night, every night, we talked and got nowhere. Argued I suppose. Because of unflinching stubbornness, we made a gigantic mountain out of a molehill. In my living memory it was the most soul-destroying week. What was it he said, that I disillusioned him? On my return to work after the holiday I was told I looked ill. I felt as though I had been battered.

We weathered that storm somehow or other. Ben wanted us to have a break for a month. I lasted a day without him, before I sped to the flat begging him to take me back. It didn't occur to me it was belittling. We ironed ourselves out as best we could, but he wouldn't let me see him on his birthday, a Wednesday. On the following Friday, when I nervously arrived at the flat, he wasn't there and neither was the car outside. I hid my worry. I also hid his birthday card and present in the bread-bin. I tried the packet of cornflakes first, but they wouldn't fit in. However, I knew he made toast for breakfast. I walked down the road searching and found him at the petrol pumps. We didn't go back to the flat that evening, but drove to Weston. There was a detectable strain between us, but next day the air of gloom had lifted and my darling wanted me again. In the weeks that followed I did think he was glad to have me back.

One thing I couldn't help but notice. Following any tiff I would go to the flat and find everything done, even the washing up. I felt as though subconsciously he was trying to tell me he could do without me.

THE PARENTS DO A BUNK

September was perhaps a trying month for Ben in some respects. I had a lot on my plate. I became a Mum. I did try to let Ben come before anything else, but I had to rule the roost at home. Mum and Dad left us three kiddlywinks and went over to see Rish and Bob in Canada for a long, well deserved holiday. To tell the truth I was third in command, Al was second and Dave was very much in charge, wielding authority right left and centre as to how Al and I should behave in his lordly presence. Mhmm, the big joker of the family!

Mum was in a terrible fretful state the day they left England, mostly because of nerves about flying having never done it before. At breakfast on departure day she said in all seriousness, "Angela, Dad and I haven't made a Will, but share everything between you and no wrangling". She also made me promise to look after Al who was then, what, nineteen, until he got married. She honestly thought she would be a goner up in that plane. I think I, myself, had watered down milk on my cornflakes that morning. Dave rang my boss and told him I was awfully bilious the day they went, and I accompanied them to Gatwick Airport. I had forewarned the girls in the office I was going to be sick on the day in question. Dave drove us to the station to catch the train to London, and Mum didn't want to say cheerio to him. When we told her to hurry herself and "come along", she nearly took a 'No Parking' sign with her. At the airport check desk and weigh-in Mum was asked how much she weighed, but she couldn't answer because thinking of Ally had made her start crying. Dad made a guess and added excessive weight onto Mum, which made her indignant. Then Dad had to come back to me for his binoculars, which were round my neck, and apparently Mum's suspenders on her corset made the body metal detector bleep.

The plane was three hours late leaving and during that time Mum and Dad were sat in the departure lounge having chicken and ham sandwiches, lager, gin and brandy. I was stood on the observation platform, looking in at them through the glass windows, and the only food I had to eat was a stale sausage roll and a bruised apple, nothing to drink. I got leg ache through standing so long. I must admit when Mum and Dad did eventually take off and fly directly over my head it was an immense thrill. Watching the plane become a dot, thinking of them up in the clouds, at long last on their way, I went quite goosey as emotion engulfed me. I went berserk with my waving. I took my cardigan off and waved it frantically in the air until my arms felt loose and Mum and Dad were out of sight. I couldn't help beaming at the gathering and expect they thought I was a loony.

Rish and Bob gave Mum and Dad a wonderful time in Canada, but for them the highlight of course was seeing Marcus, their first grandchild. They said in their letters home they felt they were living in a dream world. I wrote back and said we would sue them for neglect if they decided not to return. They wouldn't have done that to me though.

Every night after work I found a hundred jobs awaiting me, what with housework, cooking, etc. Why oh why did Mum have two boy babies, and running and football/cricket fanatics in the process. Not that I minded greatly the muddy sports gear constantly in the wash-tub, it was the cheesy socks I didn't agree with. I don't think I would bat an eyelid if I saw a housewife doing her man's laundry with a pegged nose. I told Dave and Al to make a hanky last a week, because I wasn't partial to washing them either and left them soaking for as long as I could. Slimy. My hands turned wrinkly, as they seemed to live in water during that period. I wouldn't use Mum's boiler for fear of blowing us up. I preferred to rub the skin off my knucks. But the boys' undies and shirts were eye blinking clean and I didn't receive complaints on that score. Now ironing was a different matter. Such pernicketiness over shirts!

The time flew by, mostly I suppose because of the housewifely and motherly chores I was presented with each night. I wasn't put off, but I wasn't organised, as most nights I didn't climb into bed before midnight. I asked Des if I could telephone her at one in the morning, because it seemed the only time of day I was free for a chinwag. I know there was a morning I got up at 2am and watered Mum's potted plants whilst I thought of it, because I knew if I left it until proper getting-up time I would forget. Another morning at quarter to one I bade Ben a fond goodnight. Half an hour later I was hanging washing out on the line, bonking my head on dangling coconuts, after which I Bisselled the carpets.

I have a memory of Ben coming in for a cuppa when he brought me home one evening, and he put his feet up on the settee whilst I ironed shirts. I didn't want him to return to the flat and suggested he sleep in my bed and I could go in M/D's. I had to say it with brothers in the house. With that arrangement he said he would be lonely. Al and Ben chatted amicably that night, both whole-heartedly agreeing I was a dunderhead. Later on, after Ben had gone, Al shivering in his underpants had to spend ten minutes struggling to untie the knots in his arms and legs. Ben had put them in his jamas before popping them beneath the sheets. I was the one to be accused and cursed which was unkind to say the least. He said he would duff me up the following morning, but forgot to do so.

The brothers and I didn't do too many things wrong, but I'm afraid Dave busted the teapot, I burnt Mum's wooden rolling pin and Al shot wet tea-leaves all over the kitchen in the course of one day. My prayers got answered regards the bath blockage. It shifted itself. The boys were ever so good and only once did I have to sort them out and knock their blocks off. Al pinched Dave's peach and Dave was going to take Al outside and kill him, but it was okay in the end because the peach had a maggot in it.

I didn't dish up any burnt offerings. I didn't experiment hugely, but my specialities were cauliflower cheese and bacon and egg pie, simple dishes which disappeared in a flash. I made as well hundreds of cheese biscuits, which the boys ate like peanuts, but my chocolate krackolates were a failure. They simply would not set and remained a gooey, sticky mess. Al admitted that the two he took to work for his lunch break went in his waste-paper bin. One Sunday I excelled myself and for dinner we had roast chicken (cold left-overs next day), mountains of running beans and cold toad in the hole, no taters. That toad in the hole had been made the day before, but not eaten because it took ages to cook, hours longer than it should have done. I rescued it from the oven at 2.30pm because it was beginning to turn black on the edges. The inside was still runny so I tipped it out before the boys saw. Odd mixtures we ate, but it all went down the same way. I cooked a marvellous mixed grill for Dave at 20 to 7 one Saturday morning. He was off to a race meeting. An assortment of all sorts went into the pan. I had a plateful myself and then went back to bed, because I hadn't left Ben's until four that morning. We made do some tea-times. Al and I visited Nan one evening so it was a quick tea beforehand. Roes on toast for me and paste sandwiches for Al. Dave was on holiday that week and Nan showed us a postcard she had received from him addressed to Miss my-lady-love Bridges. She sent us home with half dozen new laid eggs in a stand-by teapot. This teapot she said had a good "sprout" on it. Oh, I also brought home ten shirts Nan had acquired which she thought would fit little Richard, Lin's brother.

There was an odd spell I went through when I came home from work one evening. I felt perfectly okay one minute and sickified the next. It was strange. I was all set to bake and had sieved flour into a basin. I then cut off a large dollop of butter to mix into the flour. I took one look at that butter and boy oh boy didn't I feel peculiar. I couldn't face it for five minutes. I soaked myself sweating with a fever, and my salivary glands worked overtime, because there was a puddle at my feet when I revived from sitting with my head betwixt my knees. Also, as I fell into the chair, my knobbly elb sent the bag of flour over the kitchen floor. I was in a lather and remember muttering to myself "I want Mum", but there was no one to hear my plaintive whimpers. In a matter of minutes though I was back to my dough pummeling and thinking to myself "You're an idiot Angela".

One night there were ructions in the kitchen when Dave and I decided to have an Italian dish for tea. It was one of those boil spaghetti and heat can affairs. I stabbed the tin with the opener immediately it came out of boiling water and the kitchen, Dave and I were liberally speckled, as tomato sauce shot into the air. The ceiling wasn't touched, thank goodness, because I don't know how we would have found time to do painting and decorating, but I'm afraid Mum's white net curtains developed a rash of red spots. A hairwash and bath were added to the evening's agenda. It was a rotten meal, because we sprinkled Parmesan cheese over it – it came in a little cellophane bag –

and there is only one cheese in this world I can't stomach, nor Dave, and that is Parmesan. It smells like sick.

We survived these little ups and downs. The boys swore at the time they were going to make a list of the countless things I did wrong, which would prove to Mum how hopeless I was. I couldn't retaliate by putting salt in their cups of tea, because I wouldn't have got my shoes cleaned. Dad left us a foot high pile of scrap paper notelets, which did come in handy. I didn't have the nerve to tell the baker off one Saturday, so I put the bread-bin outside the front door with a loaf and a note inside, which read "Could you please change this sliced loaf as it's doughy and looks chewed in places. My brothers refuse to eat it." I was crouched behind the door when the baker came and saw the note. I heard him mutter, "She's worse than her mother." Actually, our baker is a nice cheery lad. Once, instead of asking me if I wanted one loaf or two, he said "One lump or two?"

Al put himself in the dog-house during Mum and Dad's stay in Canada. I awoke one morning at 20 to 6 to hear grunts and groans coming from the landing. I investigated and found Ally boy worse for drink. He had been downstairs over the kitchen sink since 2.30am. The previous night he had gone to a fancy dress party, not as a drunk but as a Red Indian. And now here he was with feathers ruffled, bag-eyed, white-faced not red, and like a block of ice yet beads of sweat glistened in his hairline. His hair stood bolt upright in spikes and he looked absolutely ghastly. There was no recovery the next day. Looking worse for wear, he nursed our old blue enamel po hour after hour. I was disgruntled with him simply because he pushed aside my Sunday roast untouched. I can remember Al being near to tears that afternoon, as he sat miserably in the chair feeling extremely sorry for himself. Dave and I were both going out and he pleaded with us not to leave him. He said if we did he would tell our Mum when she came home. Ben sent me home with some fortifying pills for him.

There was another instance when Al was under the weather, but not for long. He fell off a tractor and bumped his napper. However, whisky was administered and he was soon right as rain apart from staggered steps. What he was doing on a tractor I never found out.

Al is a case. He slept in Mum and Dad's bed for a change whilst they were in Canada. He sleeps in mine if I go out Nan's for a weekend. It's probably because he's grown far too tall to fit into his own bunk bed where he's slept since he was a child.

One weekend that September I went into town and saw a cream dress and hot pants I liked and thought Ben would like, but the zip was broken on the pants. The assistant said the shop would mend it, so I paid a deposit and agreed to collect the outfit the following Saturday. The next weekend, however, I could not for the life of me remember which shop it was. I went in so many, but recognition didn't dawn. After hours of searching and swearing I wanted to sit down on the pavement and howl, but I wearily carried on my round of every single dress shop in town. Some I went in twice. I struck lucky near to closing time. The right shop was one I had been in once before that afternoon. I should never have bought the two-piece though, because I became very self-conscious when I donned it. Ben consented to take me to a works skittles match one evening, but I had to wear the dress (with a split up the middle right to the waist) and pants. Not having worn hot pants before, I did feel embarrassed and when I walked or sat anywhere I conveniently placed my cardigan over the slit until Ben got angry and yanked it off me.

The day before Blossom and Pop came home I made a packet sponge, for quickness, because Dad loves a sponge. I should have made one the cookery-book way. Mind you, it was pure and simple guesswork in our house, as Mum didn't have kitchen scales. Ben was the only person who didn't like my sponges. Well, what he did say was, I made a terrible sponge, but if I called it a cake instead, it was quite passable. This was simply due to the fact that my sponges were twice as big as they ought to have been. It was Mum's fault. In my teen years she imprinted on my brain that whatever amounts a recipe stated I should double all ingredients. Mum and Pop's home-coming sponge, combining two packets, was a complete flop. The two tins of mix in the oven collided; that is, the contents in the lower baking tin rose to huge proportions, hit the rung and the bottom of the tin above, before spilling out and running down inside the oven. I left them to get on with it, because they were still looking uncooked. When removed I locked the remains together with apricot jam, Dad's favourite, and left my solid efforts on the table for the parents' joyous return. It never got eaten, which didn't surprise me in the slightest, but I thought the birds might have been a bit more grateful.

The day Mum and Pop were due home I cleaned the toilet and bathroom at quarter to two in the morning. I wanted the place to be spick and span. Dave mowed the lawns in pouring rain the day before, only the second time in the whole of the month, and buggered up the mower. Also we took bags of jumble to a charity shop, which Mum has never forgiven us for, being the hoarder that she is. It was a spitty day for their return, but on my arrival from work I could see two beaming faces at the kitchen window. I handed Bloss my shopping bag and she took over mothership once again. (I had, on that very last day, run out of housekeeping money and borrowed from Dave and Al for bacon.)

Chatter didn't cease until bedtime. I sat beside Pop at the kitchen table after tea, because he had had a film developed in Canada and wanted to show me the photos. His head kept dropping and his eyes would not stay open, and within minutes he had nodded right off. Dave and Al dragged him to his feet and half carried him to the comfy armchair. Al went to bed about nine – culmination of extremely late nights taking their toll – but after half an hour he got up again and came downstairs, thinking he was missing out on things as Rish, Bob, Marcus and Canada nattering continued late into the evening. Marcus had thought the corn on Mum's foot was a Cheerio (breakfast cereal). Before bed I weighed myself and was pleased as punch to see I had lost half a stone in a month.

THE END OF US

October came. What did happen to Ben and me that month? It began badly. Ben had an abscess develop on a wisdom tooth and had to have it removed. That day, when he got back from the hospital, it began haemorrhaging and wouldn't stop. Mrs. S wasn't home and with tissues stuffed in his mouth, trying to plug up the hole, Ben, God knows how, managed to telephone for an ambulance, holding a bowl under his mouth at the same time. I sing the praises of the switchboard operator who had infinite patience to stay on the line as Ben tried to get his words out. She understood his need and sent men in uniform to take him away. He wouldn't go with them until he had locked up the flat. It was daubed in blood and he didn't want to put the wind up Mrs. S should she poke her head round the door for any reason. He was stitched and my Ben became swollen and lopsided for days and couldn't open his mouth wide. I could kiss him, but very gently on one cheek. I thought he would be bound to let me know when I could kiss him properly again.

Terri and Rob's wedding day came on the 9th October. We all thought the three sisters – the bridesmaids – had rotten colds, as there was a great deal of sniffing going on in the centre aisle of the church. Mum, Dad and I and the whole congregation had our minds put at rest as Mrs. Cod handed out tissues to Sandie, Sue and Jackie. Although being the bride's mother she didn't cry, but Tritz's three sisters were moved to tears. When one started, the rest dissolved. I wanted to blubber too, because Tritz looked so radiant – she was edged in white fur – and Rob so dashing. I did wish Ben could have been by my side, but he was at his Mum's making blood, as he had lost a huge amount.

That night I went to the Locarno ballroom with Lin, Barbie and Joan. I knew I would have become a right misery moo if I had gone home and watched telly after Terri's lovely wedding. I would have missed Ben and wanted to be with him. I had paid half my weekly pay packet to have my hair set in curls on top. I wanted to dress up, be a glamour puss, go out and have a good time and maybe I would receive a few appreciative looks from the opposite sex. I received one from a Scottish gentleman. Eric was his name and he was a civil servant. He had a warm, friendly disposition. I can remember things he said even now. He had a sister in Australia. He wrote poetry. He worked part-time in a garage. He gave me a fish pie recipe, his own concoction, and transported me miles away as he spoke with love of the highland croft situated on the bleak Scottish moors where his other sister lived. I was entranced, but came down to earth with a bump when he asked to see me again. I should have told him earlier about Ben. He accepted my apologies and asked if he could kiss me goodbye. I let him and guilt lingered for days.

The next day, a Sunday, I saw Ben at the flat. I hadn't seen him for a week and wanted to rabbit on at great length, but he didn't ask me anything. He didn't seem to want to know what I had been doing with myself and so I told him nothing. Not one word about my best friend's wedding.

Ben got better. One by one the stitches came out. I think he chewed up most of them with his food. I was able to kiss him on the mouth, but he seemed to want just light pecks. I never ever wanted to shrink away from him, and asked myself why did he draw away from me. Mum told me my breath didn't pong. I began thinking it was something I had done or said, or failed to do and say. I couldn't understand what had happened to us. I thought and thought. My mind went round in circles and my stomach churned over and over. A hundred times a day I tried to boost myself up. Things would come right I told myself, because they always had before. I kept my lips sealed and the hurt began festering inside. Ben was so silent too. Night after night I needed an emotional outlet and cried rivulets in my bed, yet I tried to be normal and cheerful when I saw Ben. It was no use. Things went from bad to worse. A kiss meant nothing. Romance, passion and warmth had flown out the window. I felt cold all the time. I had to speak up and ask him outright what was wrong. What was I afraid of? It would be a simple thing to do. It proved to be one of the hardest things I have ever done in my life.

We went to The Moon. We sat alone, not with our smashing friends, whom we hadn't seen for quite a long while. They must have sensed something was wrong. Things came out in a rush on both sides. Then talk subsided for a while. Ben moved to the fruit machine and inserted a handful of coins, but no jackpot fell on the floor to cast a glimmer of happiness. I had to keep blowing my nose. I had a stupid cold and had taken a sandwich to the pub – two tissues stuck together with a dollop of Vick. A Salvation Army man came into the bar and I bought a War Cry and attempted to do the crossword. I couldn't concentrate. My smarting eyes kept going to Ben, as he stood across the room with his unbending back to me. Only then did the fleeting thought pass through my mind and vanish, "What if Ben walked out of my life after tonight?" He came back and sat down and we tried another route round our problems. He hardly looked at me. When he did and saw my eyes filling up he muttered, "That won't get you anywhere." I said I had a cold, but I know that wasn't the sole cause for the overflow in my tear ducts.

We groped for any feasible reason, which could have caused our break in communication over the past weeks. Ben said I rarely cooked anything for him. That was true. I knew he loved crumble, but I never made him one. I knew he liked plain food. When Mum and Dad were in Canada, I took him some cold roast chicken for his sandwiches and a couple of un-rich chocolate cakes. (Dave ate six in one evening so they weren't poison.) He told me to take the lot back home, because he wouldn't eat it. I invited him to tea one evening while they were away and made a bacon and egg pie. I thought it would please him, but he said he liked his bacon and eggs separate and he didn't like pastry. He preferred scrambled eggs to my pie and went back to the flat to make some. At the time we didn't argue about such a silly thing, but there in The Moon it was a big thing. Why hadn't I, that tea-time at home, offered him an alternative to bacon and egg pie? I didn't know why. I said if he didn't like pastry how was it that a few days ago in the flat there had been a half-eaten tart his sister had made. I told him honestly, when I had seen that tart I could have done things to it in temper. I made him angry by saying that.

Petty home-truths came to light. Was it better they were dislodged from brains? He said he rarely got invited to my home and wasn't he good enough for me? I told him that was ridiculous. Also that as I tended to get the bus to the flat, instead of him calling for me, there wasn't much opportunity. Point taken on both sides.

He brought up again our holiday week row, when I had casually mentioned that next year I hoped to go to Canada with Dave for a visit. Upon reflection, that statement of mine may have been the beginning of the end. He thought by my saying what I did, I had no thoughts whatsoever of a future with him. Had I truly been given any indication that there was to be a future with him I asked? Now, I think I was wrong to say what I did. Ben didn't seem to want to fight. To fight for our preservation I fought a losing battle, but I didn't believe I had lost him that night. A solution would be, must be found, if not that day, then tomorrow. So he might have said he was disappointed in me, exasperated too I reckon, but didn't he love me as I loved him?

In the pub we didn't exactly row. We talked quietly with feeling. I felt his words were unkind and harsh, but did he, I wonder, think my tongue a whiplash too. People say I'm soft and get stamped on, but did I that night give as good as I got or not enough? Questions will forever remain unanswered. A silence can be a contented one or the exact opposite. Ben brought me home in a very unhappy silence that night. Talk about despair, I had never felt it to such intensity before. We still had everything to say to one another, yet couldn't bring ourselves to say anything more. I didn't have a proper goodbye from him. As I got out of the car that late October evening, his words to me were "Go in and get rid of your cold and we'll talk again. I'll phone you."

There was hope then and I lived with it through the weeks ahead. I carried a dead weight inside my heart. The telephones kept ringing in the office, but the call I desperately wanted never came. The sinking feeling became stabbingly acute. I regularly left the office for fairly long periods when I felt myself weakening. My hideaway was the loo where I sat, gasped and choked back sobs. They kept wanting to come in the daytime, but I tried not to let them. I let the ache out at night and weekends. Evenings I slumped in the chair saying nothing, but my ears were pinned back listening, forever listening for a familiar car to draw up, followed by a familiar knock on the door. None came. I would take a bath and by the time I had finished the water level had risen inches. Cliff Richard had his own show on the telly Saturday evenings and his closing song each week was 'Visions of You'. He would begin to sing and I would begin to cry. I tried to shield it from them, but the family got used to seeing my tear-stained face and jumping body I found difficult to keep in check. They ignored Drippy and let me carry on without sympathising too much. I knew, and they knew, it was better out than in. Food and a hot water bottle were my two comforts. How many hundreds of times had Ben said I was childish? Yet sometimes when he said it he smiled. He was a mere eight years older than me. No big deal.

Days turned into weeks. The sharp ache had become a dull one. At night I cried myself to sleep, either clinging tightly to my pillow or placing it on top of the bedclothes over my chest and tum, imagining it to be a dearly beloved body comforting and warming me. I pleaded with the Lord to let me lose my memory. I thought about catching pneumonia. Then, as I lay dying, I could ask for Ben and he would be sure to come. I would, of course, make a complete recovery and we would live happily ever after.

I made an effort the Sunday Blob's Mum and Freddie came to tea. I put make-up on, tidied myself and went downstairs when they arrived. Hello wasn't so difficult to say. They asked how I was and I said all right. Mum said later she could have kicked herself for intervening, because she followed my "all right" with "She isn't really." That started me off and I bolted for the stairs. Time and time again I did it. Zap, I would go out of control. I was the lowest I had been that afternoon. I cried for ages and when I was spent I sat on the bed staring out of the window. An hour, maybe two, went by. The sun shone spangles through the trees as the wind, wild and free, shook leaves to the ground only to toss them into the air the next second. The afternoon drew to a close. Dad came up to see me with a cup of tea. I unlocked the door and let him into my darkening room. He squeezed my hand and told me to keep my pecker up. I sobbed my heart out to dear Pops. I must have worried him. My whole body was torn apart in wretched convulsions as Dad held me and I struggled to ask him why had Ben left me. My poor Dad didn't know the answer.

Letters I wrote to Rish in November and December were smudgy, because I even cried whilst writing to her. Mum would find me at it in bed. She didn't beg, but she wanted me to go to Ben and talk. I wouldn't though. I longed to do so. Pride didn't stop me. So many other things did. The main reason being, I thought he wouldn't properly listen to me or hear me out. I began a letter to him a week after we finished, but put it aside.

The weekend after Ben and I parted we were due to go to June and Phil's for supper. Debbie and Robert were invited as well. It would have been the first time Ben had met them and I would have been so proud of him. He wouldn't particularly have wanted to go, because they were two young married couples, but he would have, I think. It transpired I let June know (in a letter) too late about our breakup and, on the Saturday we were expected, a starving Debbie wasn't allowed to start on the food until nearly midnight, when June was finally convinced Ben and I wouldn't be coming.

I began wandering again. Daft I know, but I even sat on the Downs at night. I was lonely. I missed everything in my life connected to him. I missed his presence most. I missed going to the flat, no longer seeing the regular Bingo players sat on the bus, nor the old man with the sad face shuffling aimlessly up and down Zetland Road in his tattered shoes. He wore no cap on his head, or scarf that I could see, and some nights it was bitterly cold. All winds and weathers he trailed the gutter and patrolled shop doorways searching for dog-ends.

Another month crept by and then one Sunday afternoon I went to Weston. It was the best time to go, in the winter. I wrestled with my puzzled mind as I walked on the sands. The sea breezes did me good and helped to unbefuddle my brain. I noticed things. There were sprouts and carrots in the swirling 'sea'. The tide must have brought them in, or the donkeys perhaps had left them behind. I always look back. I did that day from the bus-station and I'll thumb my nose at anyone who disagrees, but Weston 'sea' was silver in the twilight. I came home more at peace with myself and finished off Ben's letter. The burden was eased if not lifted. He replied, after which another letter passed between us. We both did some soul-searching. Ben gave me answers to some questions, answers I desperately needed even if they weren't the ones I wanted to hear. I picked up the pieces slowly but surely, and threaded myself together as best I could.

In December I saw him a couple of times at the Spa, the place where he entered my life. It proved harder to face than I thought it would, and I got very depressed. So low was I one Saturday evening, I wept in the cloakroom and my friends couldn't wring a smile out of me. Des brought me home and as soon as I got indoors I broke down again. Al found me with tears streaming down my cheeks in the bathroom. My baby brother he may be, but he was a comfort to me. Both brothers were just before Christmas when I was feeling decidedly morose. They sang Carols outside my bedroom door most mornings to raise a smile. I decided to stop going to the Spa for a while, because it upset me to the core of my being seeing Ben there with other girls, and knowing he didn't want anything to do with me. I spent lots of weekends with Nan and gradually restored my mind on an even keel, because it certainly had been knocked off balance.

Christmas Eve came and on my return home from work I found a card from Lloyd, dear Lloyd from The Moon. It contained a lovely sincere message. I was so touched I cried my eyes out. As I was doing so the back door opened and in walked Nan (Dave had gone to fetch her in the car) carrying a coal bucket full of presents. She was crying her eyes out too, because she had been with Aunt Olly all day. Nan knew Aunt Olly was dying. I sent Lloyd a New Year's Card c/o The Moon.

PAULS I AND II

I'm sure Paul 'I' was sent to me in my hour of need. Christmas Eve began and my heart was breaking up inside, because I didn't have Ben in my life. I was in a much happier frame of mind come evening's end. I went with Des and Pru to Ashton Court Country Club, entering under an assumed name. I posed as another friend of Des, using her membership card. Des and Pru were paid up members. The evening started out flat. Seemingly, it was nothing but couples at Ashton Court, with no spare men to be had, that is with the exception of Cecil who came up to my armpits. We had a dance during which a vision came to me of lifting him up for a Christmas kiss at midnight so it was ta-ta pretty pronto. Des was going to commit hari-kari, Pru's frown got deeper and I felt like screaming loud and long as we watched the loving couples dance. I'm glad we didn't drown our sorrows in drink. Along came Paul. He was tall and handsome with Danish blood running through his veins. Des and Pru knew him slightly. He danced with Des and she asked him to dance with me, because I had suicidal tendencies. He did and that was the beginning of a new and lovely three-month courtship. One of the first questions I asked him was "What birth sign do you come under?" Thank God he didn't reply "Leo". Both Ben and Martin before him were Leos. Mum said I must ask this question to every single fellah I fancy in the future and, should they reply Leo, her advice to me is run like hell. To escape possible heartache I suppose she means.

Paul is fondly remembered. How many men came and went that year, some ships passing in the night, others staying for a while. Paul 'I' was the first boyfriend I had after Ben and on reflection the best of the bunch.

Paul 'I' did shift work, but I still saw a fair bit of him. During the week we went either to the cinema or for a drink in one of the many pubs in the town centre. I was also treated to the odd meal out, and Sunday mornings had me turning over a new leaf. I would get up bright and early to go ice-skating with him. We loved those mornings. But then Paul hurt his foot at work and could only hobble so we had to give up rink gliding. Talking of his foot reminds me of Boot. Boot was Paul's dog. When I queried why Boot, Paul joked that he often got it. I know he was joking. Paul loved jokes. He told me some extremely naughty ones, but they all made me laugh.

I remember one evening in particular. It was lashing down with rain. Paul's car was off the road and we didn't have a brolly. We found shelter in quite a grotty pub in the heart of Bristol. That night though it became the best place in the world to sit, drink, talk, laugh and hold hands, I expect because there were candles on the table. It was the time of the electricity workers' strike. I recall that I had a huge pimple on my forehead. I had tried to camouflage it, but Paul noticed and told me not to pick it. I already had. We left the pub and got soaked to the skin, but we were full of smiles and chuckles. We saw a student march. They looked like the Druids. They chanted as they walked slowly round the centre, many of them wearing dark cloaks in the relentless drizzle. Each one held a long candle, because the black out had affected street lighting. Paul steered me to an undercover hideaway and within seconds of us being there he had to chase away a Peeping Tom, quite an elderly gentleman he was too.

I was such a strange occity still. The bruises I had acquired when Ben left me were very much in existence; scared shitless I was of getting hurt again. I wanted Paul to be lustful. He was. I wanted him to want me, but couldn't cope when he did. He tried to understand. He said I was fragile and so easy to break, but far from easy to mend. (Sheer poetry to my ears.) Peggy at work liked him the best of all my boyfriends. Whenever he phoned the office she conversed with him. She thought he sounded an extremely pleasant fellow. At a bus-stop one evening there was a man stood behind us with a little girl in his arms. She asked her Daddy if we were married, as Paul and I kissed goodnight. Her father replied most definitely we were.

I do admit to two-timing Paul 'I', but not for long because it was asking for trouble. The girls thought I was mad to let it worry me, but it did. The thing was I didn't see Paul 'I' on a Saturday evening. That was the night he went out with his mates for a pint. I would go dancing with the girls. One Saturday I met Paul 'II'. He was instantly likable. Whereas Paul 'I' was fair haired and brown eyed, Paul 'II' was black haired and blue eyed. Paul 'II' was a sweater man, but the casual look suited him. He was a theatre attendant in a Bristol hospital. With a twinkle in his eye he told me "Oh yes, I've seen it all." Years back he had been a men's hairdresser. At his flat we drank beer and ate peanuts. He was an avid coin collector and I showed him ones Dad had found in the garden. Also the medallion Granfer had found in the street just before he died, with the Lord's Prayer in minute print on it. Nan gave it to me. We studied the coins and tried to match them in the books he had on the subject of coinery.

One evening Paul was in the kitchen making coffee and I picked up a couple of hairpins off the carpet. I thought I had better tread warily, because I did find him attractive. He was furry. That is, he had a black pelt of hair on his shoulders, which was most eye-catching.

I think the main reason I stopped seeing Paul 'II' was because of his flat. Things tended to get a bit out of hand there. My Paul 'I' lived at home with his parents and his hanky-panky in the car, at the pictures or in shop doorways I could deal with. Another thing too, Paul 'II' took me to a Pizzeria one evening. The next day I was eating there again with Paul 'I', served by the same amused waiter. I felt I was getting into deep water. The waiter didn't rumble me. One thing I didn't have to worry about was calling them by each other's name. Paul 'II' wanted me to change my mind, which was nice of him, but I didn't. We parted the best of friends.

I carried on dating Paul 'I'. He wanted to make further progress in our relationship and this got me into a blind panic. I began to feel trapped. I hadn't gotten over Ben sufficiently to get myself deeply involved with another man. Regrettably, I had to make a break. I didn't really want to, but felt I had to. Coming home on the bus, when the deed was done, I found myself singing silently "Run Rabbit, Run Rabbit, Run, Run, Run". I've sung it a few times since.

I hope that sweet, lovable, happy-go-lucky, kind hearted, dependable man has been blessed with some of life's riches. He had normal desires and instincts and I'm mightily sorry I couldn't bring myself to participate. It would have been exquisite I'm sure. He was a good friend. I'm thankful he came along when he did.

It is remarkable. Months went by and I saw neither hide nor hair of either Paul. I went to the Spa one Saturday with Des and Pru. It wasn't a good night. We left early to go on to Ashton Court. As I left the Spa Paul 'II' was entering. Half an hour later I was walking into Ashton Court as Patricia – I had taken over her membership card – and who should be leaving but Paul 'I'. I did have a "Hello, how are you?" from both of them before they vanished.

Another fellow appeared on the scene quite quickly, but oh-dearie-me, we weren't suited, not one little bit. Robin (such a drip) was an accountant. He wasn't bad looking. That was why I sidled up and made eyes at him, but wished I hadn't later. He didn't offer to buy me a drink at the Spa, although we danced the night away. He didn't like the sea, didn't eat much, didn't have a car, and he carried a brolly which made him look a pompous ass, because he tapped it on the ground as we walked. A bowler would have been most becoming on him. Oh, and he was short. He did let me share his taxi home from the Spa and a date was arranged for the following Tuesday. I met him too blumming early if you ask me. 6.30pm he had said.

It was a terrible stormy evening and the centre of Bristol was plunged into darkness with yet another power cut. We walked along splooshing through every puddle, as we couldn't see them. His stupid brolly didn't stop the rain from beating us on all sides and the wind whipped and chilled us. He wouldn't take me to see 'Love Story' as it wasn't his cup of tea. (Paul 'I' had taken me to see it and lent me his hanky.) Instead we went to the Kings to see seedy sex films entitled 'I want you now' and 'If you don't play the game, get out of my bed'. We had cheap seats right down the front, which was bad on the eyes. I knew he wouldn't offer to buy me an ice cream. Luckily, a black out came halfway through the second film and we got turfed out of the cinema. I felt certain he would ask for a refund, but he didn't. We went in a pub and by candle-light he talked for a solid hour over one drink about horticulture, soil and the potted plants in his greenhouse. He used nothing but Latin names. It was his hobby, a passionate one. Blinding me with science he was. I answered no to his questions when I should have said yes and vice versa. I tried hard to look interested. He droned on and on, that people shouldn't be allowed to have children because of over-population in this country. Innocently, I retorted that I would have to emigrate to have the six I wanted. I'm glad my bus came straightaway. I certainly didn't want any canoodling with him. I think he realised we had nothing in common. He said, as Treasurer, he had an awful lot of horticultural committee meetings to attend the following week, but he might see me again at The Spa. I nearly let him have "Not if I see you first mate". He was a tight-fisted bugger, as mingy as they come.

I saw him once afterwards at Ashton Court. He began to introduce his friend to me, but had forgotten my name. I introduced him to Des as Dobbin. He was such a let down in the male stakes, I gave up men for a while, excluding brother Al that is.

Al accompanied me on Monday evenings to dancing class. The school was in Clifton and on the way we passed Ben's office. I always looked up to the lighted window, but never saw his outline. The dancing instructor called me Ange and he said Al had good rhythm. Ferdinand often partnered me. I loathed the reggae reggae. I could do the knee bends okay, but my bottom movements went haywire. I got flummoxed with my exaggerated hip swivelling and consequently lost the beat. The instructor said the way I was doing it, I would do myself an injury if I wasn't careful. His comment made me go scarlet. The waltz I found most difficult. Instead of doing three basic steps, I did about ten. I had to dance with a poncey young twirp who made it his business to take away every last gramme of confidence I possessed. As he swung me, my nails ripped across his cheek giving him a white weal, which served him right.

Al and I gave up dancing when Teach said he would put us in for our bronze medal. Our nerve cracked. Anyways, it was totally wrong, dancing a smooch at the end of the lesson with my brother. Mum, whose favourite TV prog is 'Come Dancing', said she would kill Al and me when we stopped going to "proper" dancing class. She changed her mind and vowed instead never to speak to us again. Her word was kept for five minutes.

Dave went to a dancing school at Bath not long ago, but two lessons were enough for him. He muddled through with the help of the woman instructor, who had to take him into a little corner by himself because he was so hopeless. Hopeless was Dave's word to describe himself, so I'm not being unkind. He bludgeoned her tootsies. Al asked if there were any nice bits of crumpet there to partner him and Dave replied "Cor, not half", but they couldn't have been inviting enough to get him going every week.

IDLE TIME

Des, Pru and I went to Ashton Court most weeks until April when our membership ran out. We enjoyed going there on a weekday straight from work. After a snack tea we watched the film that was showing, then had a drink and women's talk and often stayed for the cabaret. Girlfriends' company was, to be perfectly honest, preferable to men's, as no effort involved. There was a funny incident whilst we were watching a James Bond film at Ashton Court. During a madcap car chase a voice said over the intercom "Emergency, will the owner of car registration number so and so, come immediately to reception as it is running away." Up jumped a chap and tore across the screen with whistles and cheers from the cinema audience spurring him on.

My girlfriends helped me get over losing Ben. They were so trustworthy. Throughout last year we enjoyed much together. There were shows in the Colston Hall. Jack Jones definitely turned Pru, Des and me on. I agree with Mum, he does have come to bed eyes. Nan thinks he is sexicle, but as to all the loves in his life she can't figure out what he's got that other men haven't. She says he's made the same after all. Mattie at work thought he was Tom Jones son! She is a crackpot as they must be roughly the same age, Tom and Jack. Lin and I got tickets to see Cliff Richard at the Colston Hall, because we find him extremely edible. Lin says she likes to see him wriggle, not wiggle. Unfortunately, I forgot my specs and had to squint at him. He has got a minuscule tiny bottom. We were late home after the show, as he did extra time God Bless Him. Lin nearly bent our taxi driver in half for saying

Cliff was bent, simply because he isn't married. I told that ignoramus driver Cliff was merely waiting for me (or Lin) to come along. One can live in hope, can't one? Him or Prince Charles would suit me fine. On arrival home Lin found her brother, little Richard, still up, waiting patiently, although very tired, for Lin to bring Cliff home for a cup of coffee. This had been Lin's excuse earlier in the evening. Richard had kicked up a song and dance, because he wanted to go to the show, and had only allowed Lin to leave the house when she said she would bring Cliff home to meet him. It doesn't pay to mislead the young. He squawked far more in the long run. When Richard gets going neither love nor money will shut him up. Well sometimes money will. Temper it is. Red hair you see.

Last year I went to the Hippodrome with Lin, her Mum, dozens of people from the Ford Estate who belonged to the Community Centre, and kids galore, to see Parrot Face in Panto. We had big trouble during the performance. A little boy in our row cried out "Wee wees Mum". His Mum, one of our lot, produced a lemonade bottle. Empty I hasten to add. Poor little snip had an awful job trying not to splash people's shoes and nearly ended up with an addition to his private, but Mum was at hand to give a pull and uncork him.

A night to remember springs to mind. It wasn't so long ago I went with Des and Pru to see Shirley Bassey sing in concert. I think it's disgusting, but admit she is the one woman who can send shivers running up and down my spine. My friends reacted similarly. At the end of the show I surveyed the hall to see not just a handful of people, but everyone rise to their feet and clap their hands red raw. I couldn't have spoken a word to anyone, because the drawbridge had been raised in my throat. The three of us were much too elated to go home so we went for coffee and a natter.

I learnt Des's office had been taken over by gherkin growers. They were all at it. The surroundings, apparently, were good for stimulation. Two bosses had introduced them into the office. I hope Rolls Royce won't go bust, because if they do an awful lot of gherkins will have to be uprooted besides people. They are a funny lot in Des's office. A man once brought in a yellow marrow for all to see. Gargantuan it was. He wheeled it in in a wheelbarrow. He asked Des if she wanted to smooth it, but to mind herself, as it was prickly.

I got home about oneish following the Shirley Bassey concert and was in the bathroom when I heard a commotion outside and milk bottles clinking. "Oh oh" I thought, "Al had gone out on a stag night and this must be him now, wait for the singing to start." But there was no singing. Key fumbling went on in the lock. After an age the door opened and Ally came in like a pistol shot and thudded into the passage wall. I kept quiet at the top of the stairs draped respectably in a towel. A voice said "Will you be all right?" and I heard a mumbled "Yeah" in reply. The door closed and there was dead silence. I narrowed my eyes and could see in the shadows Al trying to mount the stairs on all fours. Suddenly the front door opened again and the key was thrown in. It closed and there was silence once more. Al made it with an extreme effort to the top stair, which was praiseworthy in his condition, then slumped with head down between his knees.

Oh my goodness. I had seen him in similar plight, but never so ill as he was at that moment in time. I couldn't do a thing with him for ages, other than hold on to his lapels to prevent him toppling downstairs. I put the landing light on with my nose. He had dirt caking his face, suit and hands, which he doesn't remember anything about to this day. He held on to the banister rail while I flew to get the blue enamel po (kept from childhood for emergencies). This I thrust under his nose with one hand whilst gripping his jacket with the other.

Our Mum had to wake up, didn't she, and come out to see what was going on and then, ahem, our Dad. Justifiably, he wiped the floor with Al, because it wasn't the first time he had arrived home at dead of night incapably sozzled. I took bets it wouldn't be the last, even though Al feebly vowed it would, and that he had learnt his lesson. We still couldn't budge him from that top stair. Poor Al. I could have wept for him. "Don't tell me off Dad" he kept wailing, followed by a stream of mumbo jumbo, before we plainly heard him say "You silly bugger Alan, you silly sod" and that isn't like him at all. Al isn't the cusser of the family. I suppose I am, or Mum. After repenting his sins, it was pleas to Blossom to go and get the doctor because he was dying. I think Al was near to tears and Dad stopped going on at him when he cried, "I'm sorry, I'm sorry, I do feel bad, I want our Dave". And our Dave? Oh yes, he woke up, came out on the landing to see what the fuss was all about, patted Al's head, said "You'll be all right me old son" then went back to bed shutting the door on us.

We managed to wrap Al's arms round our shoulders and drag him into the bathroom, but that set him in motion for further heaving and retching and my hand got in the way. The dolt had had a couple of whiskeys after excess pints of beer and this curdled with his tea. Toad in the Hole it was. I remember it well. Mum excelled. She made one for the four of us using no less than 24 sausages. I told her she was an impossible oddity and she only beamed. Dad made black coffee. I really thought Al had had his chips after one sip.

I didn't want to leave him, but come three o'clock I was beginning to feel rather tired and groggy myself, so was told to hop it and scoot off to bed. I went down to the kitchen to wash my sticky sicky hands. Next minute waves washed over me and I collapsed across the draining board. It only took a matter of seconds for me to come round and I stayed there for a while, resting my head on cold steel, feeling a trifle sick myself, and thinking "Oh dear, Ally's got the po." However, Mum came to investigate, because I hadn't answered her, and helped carry me off to bed. I hadn't even tasted liquor! I couldn't go to sleep though, not until all went quiet and I guessed Mum and Dad had shifted Al out of the bathroom and shoved him up his bunk bed steps.

He was violently sick in the night. It flew out his mouth and over the side of the bunk bed, splattering Dave on its descent. Dave never forgave him. The terrible smell in their room lingered and lingered although aftershave, perfume and deodorant were liberally squirted on the carpet stain.

The following morning Dave had the cheek to oversleep. I set off for work leaving the others in bed, but during the day my peepers went from open to half shut to one shut and when I got home I went zzzzzz as soon as I had had my tea. Not before Al had greeted me with a hangdog grin though, and enquired if I had phoned his office to tell them he was ill. The bleary-eyed varmint hadn't got up until Dad had gone to work. Frightened to face him he was.

There was another time he was so perfectly blotto when he came home in the early hours, he mistook bedrooms and went and flopped right across Mum and Dad. Brothers! It's nothing unusual to hear Al come upstairs at three in the morning singing or humming gaily. It's when there isn't any humming I think something is up, and contemplate hurrying for the po in case he is in dire need.

The last holiday he had was on tour with twenty-six cricketers in Shropshire. On their first night in the hotel a chap had eight pints of water poured over his head in the bar, because they couldn't waste good beer. Another night a fellow wearing pyjama bottoms and nothing else was parading through the corridors holding aloft a tray of drinks, pretending to be room service. A mate opened a door to see what all the noise was about, undid the poor chappie's pyjama cord and slammed the door in his face. There he stood starkers and before he could see to himself who should come along but the Manager on patrol. I don't reckon Ally boy told the whole truth and nothing but the truth after that incident. They just must have slept in hedgerows for the rest of the week.

Our Dave hasn't caused much trouble in the booze line. He swam in it last year on holiday with his running pals, and a sleepy Yorkshire village admitted at the end of their stay it would never be the same again, but I think the yokels probably liked the boys for their jolly pranks. They must have been thought of with some affection, because they were invited into the back room of the pub with the locals when the bars stopped serving. A mate of Dave's woke up one morning, after the night before, wondering what he had done with his specs. A thorough search was conducted and they were found stewed in the teapot with the dregs. He was the one who spent a night snoring beneath the stars, propped against a haystack. When he did meander down the cobbled main street next morning, about 5am, he was covered in dew drops, which had soaked through to his bone marrow, and he was singing his heart out. They enjoyed that holiday, living on beer and beans.

Once Dave got beaten up after a night out. He came in looking like death with torn skin plastered over his face. As he ran upstairs on his way to be sick, he winked at my dumbstruck open-mouthed face. He was delirious when we steered and put him to bed, as he tapped Alan on the head and woke him, laughing all the while.

Chaps are all the same. One friend of David Jay's was so insensible last Christmas he gorged a large bite out of half pound of butter, thinking it was marzipan. He did recover.

I learnt only last Saturday not to jump to conclusions. I got up at 3.30am to spend a penny and saw the light on downstairs. I thought "Aye aye then". I went halfway down, peered over the banister, and through the open kitchen door saw a pair of long legs sat at the table. I sighed and automatically concluded Al had gone and done it again. I knew he had been out on the razzle. I called out to him "You all right Al?" I fully expected a green face to appear round the door. Instead a cheery red smiling one said "'Lo Pange, I'm hungry". There he was demolishing a cold chop and fish fingers, always peckish that brother of mine.

Last Saturday, no, no, no, Sunday morning, 5.30am, he was cruising home along the Bath Road after a lengthy date (a particularly good one he said) when who should he see, our Dad just come off of night shift. Dad tut-tutted when Al stopped to offer him a lift. Al admitted he felt a bit sheepish.

I was sat in the deckchair half an hour ago when Pops passed by with the mower and showered me with grass cuttings, aiming to snip my toe-nails methinks. Oh well, it would save Mum a job. I wouldn't mind him taking my little toe off to tell the God's honest truth, but it would be a waste of a freshly applied carnation pad. I've got a couple of demon corns griping. Dave's remedy was to put cornflakes in my shoes. That's as bad as Lin saying potatoes in new shoes will stretch them.

My back feels as rough as sandpaper at the moment. I put lashings of spot cream on it and ended up with toasted breadcrumbs. I've had to see the Doc again regarding my back. That's why I was trying to get rid of spots before I saw him. He said my trouble is largely due to walking, standing and sitting incorrectly, bad posture and a slouch in other words. Huh, tell 'em that at work and they would have me balancing a book on my head throughout each and every day, screaming at me as well to stick my posterior in. How would I manage taking dictation?

My hunch is still with me. I've always been round shouldered. The first time I took Terri over Aunty Vi's in my early teens, Aunty Vi said light-heartedly "Straighten up my girl" and I went waah, boo hoo, making a dafty spectacle of myself. When my system had been wrung dry of tears, I sat in a corner of the room sulking. Poor Tritz, what she has to put up with! She made an awful lot of small talk that afternoon to make up for the both of us. I don't know, braced and flat-footed as a youngster, shoulders nearly meeting as a teenager, now at the ripe old age of twenty-three I'm acnefied and dub-less.

Before going to a 'do' last Saturday, I moaningly asked Mum if my spots showed. I wanted her to say they didn't, which she did, but she also added I looked like I had been dunked in a flour sack and I had far too much cake make-up on and blacking round my eyes. In fact she called me a tart! I'm spreading as well. Others are noticing my widening beams. I get so cross with myself. I've just given in to my superior buds. I longed for beetroot so had a sandwich. White bread too, instead of Dad's wholemeal. Yesterday was the same. I wolfed down one of Al's kidleys off his plate. We two love giblets, especially gnawing on a chicken neck. Skin too, preferably crispy. I bet our ancestors were cannibals.

Of course my feet will always be a let-down. However, I've become mod in my shoe sense. I usually go for the dainty look and more often than not plump for black ones, because the colour is slimming. But the other day I got with it and bought a pair of clodhoppers in black, pink and purple suede. They make me into a six-foot lady, but I've got used to my buddies calling me Giant Gorum. (Giant Gorum was the Fair that came to Bristol each summer when we were tiddlers. We liked the Dagenham Girl Pipers best. One year I climbed onto a horse backwards.) Now these shoes of mine, in the shop I tried them on, paid up and was leaving with my purchase when the assistant rushed up to say would madam mind trying on a different pair of the same shoes, because she had sold me one six and a half and one seven and a half shoe. I hadn't been able to tell they were oddsies. The mistake was soon rectified and there are no prizes for guessing which size I came home with. Horrible it was, the first time I put them on after wearing flatties, because when I went to the toilet I didn't think I was ever going to reach the seat. Talk about going down and down and down. It gave my stomach quite a lurch. I had to check where the seat was exactly, then realised it was my five-inch heels making me misjudge my place of rest.

I do get trouble with shoes. Shopping with Mum the other day, after receiving my usual telling off from the dentist for going mad with my toothbrush, I saw a pair of sandals I liked. Needless to say my size wasn't available, but the young chappie serving said he would order me a size eight. Mum piped up, didn't I think I should have a size nine to be on the safe side

(I could have bopped her, but a frosty look sufficed) and he grinned and said if the eights didn't fit me, he would give me a pair of shoe boxes to wear. No need for sarc from the cheeky basket was there. I plucked up courage to go into the shop the following week, to work my way into eights come what may, but on enquiry the dolt informed me he had been told the largest size made in that particular sandal was a six. "Sod it " I felt like saying. I had a few minutes earlier stood on the back of a Dr Scholl's outside the shop, making the owner-occupier nearly sink to the pavement. I did hate my feet that day.

Mum's are worse though. I went downstairs today to find her clumping around the kitchen in Dave's suede Desert brown boots. Size 12s. She didn't want any more mickey-taking about her hammer toe and bunions protruding through her own shoe leather.

Five year old Ian from next door has just come knocking asking, as he invariably does, if Alan would like to come out and play with him. Al usually obliges with a ball game, even though there is fifteen years difference in their age. (Ian has brothers Dave and Al's age, but they won't play with him.)

Ian came into tea the other day. He is such a polite, well-mannered little boy. He had his meal, and then sat at the table eating an apple, after which he stepped down, went over to the pedal bin in the kitchen, and threw in the apple core. He followed this up with "Thanks Mrs. Burborough" and went into the living room to watch television. Mum stepped across to retrieve the apple core. It was lying on top of her pile of dusters. Mum is the only woman I know who has made a home for her dusters in a kitchen waste disposal bin. She would throw garbage in the washing machine if we had one.

WHAT ELSE?
ODDS AND ENDS

The girls and I met practically every Thursday evening last year. Often we went for a meal. Pru, Des and I love curry. It hates me and creates havoc with my skin. The smell lingers for days. Besides clinging to clothes, it emits through every pore I swear, and Dave and Al won't come near me the day after I've eaten a curry. (Be thankful Pange, for small mercies.) They say I'm rank. In our favourite Indian restaurant the loo is strung together. To my mind the sink looks cleaner and more comfortable. However, the food is excellent.

If we didn't eat on a Thursday night we drank, usually at The Hawthorns, the reps' hotel. There are the quiet bars and the noisy bars, and because of our age we preferred the former. When time was called we made our way to the coffee lounge and here we certainly did spend hours over a coffee in a glass, with that delicious layer of cream floating on the top. We rabbited on and only suspected it was time to leave when the cleaners appeared with hoovers, and the lights in the place were doused one by one.

Some Thursdays were strictly for the birds and we made it a girls' parlour evening and talked the night away in Pru's bed-sit. This is what we did a week ago. Pru had a new carpet and lino she wanted to show off to us. Before meeting her I had half an hour to spare so, being well wrapped up against the elements, I roamed the Downs. It was a blowy evening, but not too cold once I began striding. I started out on my walk quite near to the roadside, but after a while found I had ventured into the middle of the green and there wasn't a soul to be seen, only splotches looming up in the darkness and, between hilly tumps, distant car lights. Upon realising I was far from the traffic, an idiotic panicky fear gripped me, even moreso when I thought a tree moved, but I angrily curbed this sensation and stalked on, grinning as I came alongside my waving tree. Pru picked me up in the car and back we drove to her bed-sit to thaw out. Des joined us. Pru did make us chuckle. She had a story to tell. The previous day she had been at her current's flat when a wall cupboard fell down on his head. He staggered under the weight, but only suffered mild concussion. He turned the air blue with strong language, because all his crocks fell out and smashed to smithereens. Also a bag of sugar and a bowl of freshly poured dripping tumbled to the floor. What a gritty, scrunchy, ploppy mess. Bill's main concern was for the new shirt on his back. Fat had flipped out and squirted him as the bowl went on its crashing descent. Pru laughed until she got orders to clear up. She didn't mind hugely. Clear up is better than clear out if he's nice.

Occasionally we went bowling. I almost disliked going with the girls. Upon handing in their shoes, they were given red and black bowling shoes to wear. I was given orange Aertex ones from the men's range of footwear. Not because my feet needed air holes like men's, but they wouldn't fit into the largest size of women's shoe provided for the sport. What if Uncle Les was to go bowling? I presume he would have to wear women's, because he has got such a tiny foot. It's two sizes smaller than mine. The last time the girls and I went bowling, it must be months ago now, we had a duff alley. The pins wouldn't come to rest and kept sticking in mid air, as they were being lowered. Not only that. Barbie's ball ran halfway down the alley and stopped. We knew it wasn't permissible to walk down the alleyway, so we summoned the young chap who worked there, and asked him if he could get our ball back. As if on a tight-rope, he walked down the ridge at the side of the alley where the balls rumble along. He came abreast of the ball and balancing like a pro, leaned over and picked it up. We clapped him and thanked him as he handed it to us. He whispered that he had to go home and change his trousers. Before we could look the other way, he showed us his backside. Where the cleft in his bottom was, the seam had come unstitched three to four inches. And by crikey, he didn't have any pants on! That's what happens for being so obliging. We told Barb to swing the ball harder, which she did, but she sent it rolling the wrong way and scattered people stood at our rear.

Bowling had to stop the day Des went into hospital. She had been born with curly toes and due to them becoming painful to walk on, an operation was performed to straighten them out. The nursing staff wouldn't attend to her bunions at the same time, because she was too young. Pru and I went to visit her in T for Toe Ward after she came round from the anaesthetic. Poor Des! Never had we seen anything like it. It made my knee go slack and jumpy to look at her toes. Her feet were swathed in bandages. The visible toes were yellow, with iodine I suppose, but certain ones, we couldn't see too well, had steel skewers poking out of them. The comical thing was the two women in beds opposite Des couldn't bear the sight of these skewers, so the nurse had screwed corks onto them. We left a scowling Des at 8.15pm. The nurses were bringing round the bedpans, which was the thing Des hated most about being in hospital.

I'm glad Des had two cheerful Charleys in with her. Apparently, one barrel of a woman wore nylon purple pants that clung uncomfortably and, as she couldn't move her arms, she would waddle round to the next bed and politely ask her dutiful neighbour to 'uncling' them for her and pull them out of her crevice. (Mum calls cravats, crevices.) The one other woman in the ward was a dear old lady, no trouble to anyone, so frail and poorly. The nurses made her cry each morning, because they hurt her bedsores and this upset Des and the other two ladies so much they cried along with her. There was one unfortunate creature in the ward next door who had a tampered brain, and she kept calling out that the Russians were coming.

Des was corked for weeks after leaving hospital and walked valiantly round on her heels without the aid of a clinical clothes-horse. I grimaced when I saw her. She had to be careful not to get the skewers rusty. One kept working its way out and Des had to keep pushing it back in. She did take the bandages off to see for herself what had been done, but upon discovering "two lumps of raw meat" she hastily recovered them. She thought she would need therapy to learn toe wiggling again, but her own mode of exercise soon got them working properly, and she could do far more with them than she had ever done before. Oh, she did once have a tickly stitch so she got hold of an end and nearly pulled the lot out in a great long strand.

Des does tend to do things she shouldn't. She's a lot like me. She climbed into someone else's Mini once, thinking it was her own. She clamped the seat belt on and was ready to start up the engine when click went her brain. "I haven't got red upholstery," thought Des and she left the car as if it was full of wasps.

Another time Des was waiting at a bus-stop one morning and noticed a police panda car parked on the other side of the main road. The cops in it seemed to be beckoning to her. She crossed the road taking her life in her hands and the car window was wound down. "Do you want me?" enquired Des, wondering what on earth could be wrong. The smiling reply was "Not you love, the gaffer standing behind you. He's just coming." (One of those stifling, hot under the collar moments.) She has had a few, has Des, but the most blushing experience must have been the time her brolly handle hooked itself round a woman's suspender in Woolworths.

Last year I went to a couple of orgies, but they were for women only. They were really Pippa Dee Parties where women tried on frilly undies that they fancied buying. There were Tupperware parties as well, which, I suppose, are for the wedded woman, but I got a nice sandwich box for myself. There was one cosmetic party too where I bought an ice cool cologne stick to sweep across my forehead in moments of stress.

What else did I engage myself in with girlfriends? Lin and I never did get round to having a sauna. We booked up for one, but my cycle prevented me from going and we haven't bothered since. I recall attending a German Food Fayre with Des and Pru. We sampled pumpernickel bread, sauerkraut and rubbery cheese.

Des, Pru and Barb, it's safe to say, will not forget a certain evening at the Hawthorns Hotel. I won't either, but I'd like to. After work we had gone out for a drink. We weren't big drinkers and had our normal quota, two a-piece. We had gone in Des's Mini. She was going to give us a lift home afterwards. Come elevenish we made our exit and oh bugger, no car, spirited away, stolen. It was such a shock to the system. Back we trooped into the foyer of the Hawthorns, and Des explained our predicament at reception and asked if she could telephone the police, and thereafter her Dad. We leant against the desk, disbelieving our (Des's I should say) misfortune. Suddenly, I remembered my shopping bag had been in the car containing not much else other than a cardigan, an Easter Egg from one of my bosses and, oh Lor, my page a day diary!

I don't know what came over me, but I turned to the girls and said, "I'll just go and sit over there, I feel a bit funny." I started to weave my way through the jumble of tables and chairs in the fairly crowded lounge. I suppose I had a 'quiet' seat in view, but next minute I blacked out, smashed into tables and chairs and by all accounts dented a marble pillar. Poor Des on the telephone to her Dad by this time, not only sorrowfully told him her car had been nicked, but also squeaked "and Angela has this instant knocked herself unconscious". Some stupid woman, the barmaid I think, tried to prise my eyes open before they were good and ready. And I felt wet – water had been splashed over my face. When I tentatively flicked my eyelids upwards, it was to see a sea of faces peering down at me, so I shut them again. I heard a voice mutter, "Drink!" the cheeky beggar.

I was quite relieved when the ambulance men arrived and carted me off on a stretcher. Barb and Pru refused point blank to make their own way to the hospital. They would not be swayed from clambering aboard the ambulance and accompanying me to the casualty department.

I left with them a few hours later, none the worse for wear apart from scrambled brains. Des did get her car back, but it was empty. I wonder what became of my diary? Gave someone a laugh no doubt.

I saw my buddy Tritz a lot last year. On Rob's skittle nights I kept her company. We chattered, watched telly, looked at old photos and reminisced, played records – Tritz on her death-bed would like Andy Williams to be there to croon her farewell. I don't know if Andy is in preference to Rob. I doubt it. (I'll never forget I was with her when the moon men landed in '69.). I nearly drowned her in the bathroom one evening, washing her hair, and when Rob came home he nearly did himself a mischief in a skid. The trouble is at Tritz's I don't stop eating. The last time we polished off a box of chocolate fingers during the early part of the evening. For supper we had three pieces of toast and marmalade each, with three cups of coffee. Rob brought us home fish and chips, which we ate with bread and butter. Of course I had had my tea before going to Terri's, macaroni cheese. It's no wonder I'm monstrous, but harsh all the same why Tritz remains a Slim Jim.

Terence still calls me Ern. Going back a couple of Saturdays, I was forcing my way through Woolworths crowds when a voice rang out loud and clear across the store, "Ernie". There was no need for people to look curiously all around them. I knew it had to be for me. We took an unplanned break from shopping, linked arms and went off for a curranty bun. I was surprised Tritz had spotted me. She has got awful bad eyesight. Time and time again she has let a bus go by, because she can't see the number distinctly as it approaches, only to be told when it's gone it was the one she wanted. We were window shopping one evening and her head nearly went through the glass of C & A's shop front, simply because she hadn't realised it was so near as she peered closely at price tags. Her sight is improving though as she's getting older. Strange that.

Terri and I unfailingly treat each other to a Birthday meal, sometimes weeks after the event if it crops up in a money slump period. We went to a grill house this year and had a lovely meal, but coffee took forever to come and we became irate because we had last buses to catch. I remember in a spasm of outrage thumping the table top and the sauce bottle jumped into the air and landed on the floor in bits. We got immediate attention then, if not service, and would you believe I ended up apologising to the waitress instead of her saying sorry to us. Tritz thought the episode quite hilarious.

I visited Debbie quite often too. Her twins are four now. They grow more adorable and more alike each time I see them. June and I usually go to Debbie's together, and the boys get terribly excited if they know we are coming. Debbie reckons their blood pressure soars. I can well remember the time when they were tiny tots and how they charged around the front room so full of beans. Adam ran right into his potty and then out to the kitchen with wet feet. Probably on arrival June and I had boobed and called Adam, Scott and vice versa. They call us nitwits if we blunder. Their bikes get wheeled into the front room. If they don't ride them, they become mechanics and lie under the seats twiddling with make-believe engines. Needless to say, we get the brum brum noises. Their broom horses, their guns, footballs are all brought into the living room and above the din we three girls manage to catch up on news. The twins' bedtime comes and they consent to climb the stairs only if June and I accompany them. They have a terrific bed bounce and romp, after which Mum reads one story although they demand a dozen.

We retreat to the living room, but for the next hour it is as if they are in the same room as us. They call down "Angela and June, will you please come up and read us a story". A great many pleases are heard then pitter-patter and it becomes obvious the twins have left their beds and are on top of the landing shouting down to us. Little voices get more and more agitated, because they are being ignored. Finally, it's "Oih, you down there, come up here this minute and read us a story". Debbie fumes and bawls at them. June and I laugh at them, but we carry on talking. Suddenly Debbie flies to the living room door, flings it open to reveal two pink, shining faces belonging to the twins. They are armed with their story books, and inform us they have come down to us for another story, as we haven't gone up to them. Debbie points a finger up the stairs and admonishes "Go to bed immediately". Looks speak for themselves as four tiny feet go stamp stamp stamp. We hear an indignant voice say, "Mummy is a bogger". Then "Mummy is a grilla". "Eek" Debbie says and a lot more besides. She has doubtless had a trying day.

Once when June and I arrived we found the twins standing in different corners of the room (should have been faces to the wall), because they had eaten nearly all of six bananas and a bite out of eight tomatoes when her back was turned. Debbie allowed them out of their respective corners and Adam asked her to guess what he was going to buy her when he grew big. We thought he would say chocs or flowers, something like that. But what came out was "A pair of daps", and off he went grinning cheekily.

They have started play school now. The last time we visited, Debbie asked them to tell us the name of their new playmate. A duet of "Foo Foo" sang out. "Uh?" June and I thought, but they weren't mucking about. He's Chinese. They were sent off to bed that night and wouldn't settle down to sleep. Half an hour after going to bed Scott appeared at the sitting room door wanting his teddy. Debbie hunted for it. Adam too sauntered in looking for Scott. Threatened smacks, "No ice creams tomorrow" and "I'll tell your father" did the trick and off they went grumbling upstairs. That evening Debbie stuck false eyelashes on June and me, the first time we had tried them. I thought we looked scarey.

I did baby-sit one Friday night not so long ago. After Mum and Dad went out the twins chattered endlessly, ate oranges, stuck Green Shield stamps in my shoes, on my bag and brolly and over their bikes (Debbie lost out on a gift that night) and played a robust game of football in the living room, both of them chanting "I am Georgie Best". They proudly showed me their photograph, which had appeared the week before in the evening paper. Debbie had taken them into the Evening Post office one day, because Scottie was desperate to go to the toilet, and a newsman spotted them. He was so enraptured he took a shot of them with one on a typewriter and one answering the phone.

Come bedtime they tried to pull a fast one. Up the stairs they went and scampered into Debbie and Rob's room. They climbed into the big double bed and told me that I had to sleep in the middle of them. I put my foot down and ushered them off to their own bedroom. Here we played animals after a bounce on the bed. I declined an invitation to join them in somersaults. They hid in turn in the wardrobe and came out making appropriate animal noises, e.g. hissers, mooers, hee-hawers, snorters, tu-whit tu-whooers, etc. I hope Debbie's walls are thick. Reading a story, stories I should say, was a bit difficult because the boys have single beds and they quarrelled as to whose quilt I should sit on. I therefore scooped one onto my lap and joined the other on his bed for story telling. Scott was adamant I should get under the covers with him. Before shut-eye they decided they had better go to the bathroom. Adam scooted off and Scott set off in hot pursuit and slipped on the mat. His eyes filled with tears and a little sob came out "I want my Mummy". Inwardly I panicked. Outwardly I stayed calm and picked him up. I thought action stations, quick say something so out came "Let's go and see what Adam is up to". Master Adam was scrubbing the toilet. At least he hadn't put a toilet roll down the lav, which I knew had been done on previous occasions. Eventually, they did stay put in their beds. Scott asked me for a goodnight kiss. Adam said he was too old to kiss. Past it at four years old! I stood, should have sat down, on the bottom stair as they talked down to me. In such an adult voice it was "Leave the landing light on otherwise we'll cry". They said they would bring me a cup of tea in the morning and the biscuit barrel, which they did do. They also said I could have Weetabix for breakfast if I wanted. They probably would. Silence descended about ten o'clock, rather a late night for them.

I watched telly until it closed down and started to read the paper. At quarter to one full of alarm I flew up the stairs. Both the twins were sat up in bed crying pitifully. One had had a bad dream and woken the other one up. They were rather grumpy, but knew me so that was a relief. Scott settled back down, but Adam wanted a glass of water. I hurried downstairs and came back with two half-full glasses. They were both sleeping peacefully by then and weren't to be disturbed. I sat on the bed for nearly half an hour after all whimpers had subsided, nearly having a fit every time a cough spluttered and a wriggle writhed under the bedclothes. I got cramp sitting so still. I eased my shoes off and peered closely at each sleeping bundle. I wished they were mine. Breathing was heavy. They were sound. Scott had discarded his teddy. I stepped carefully over three slippers. We had hunted high and low, but one of Adam's disappeared into thin air during the course of the evening, the toilet perhaps. I tippy-toed downstairs and sat in silence, straining my ears to breaking point, expecting further yells which thankfully didn't come.

Rob and Debbie came home around two and we talked until three. The twins woke at ten to eight and one second after they did, we did. I heard little voices demanding to know where I was and could they come in to see me. They aren't adept at dressing themselves and needed a helping hand. Eleven o'clock we assembled at the car. Rob was going to drive me home, but he condescended to let Debbie take the wheel, saying "God have mercy on us". I had had prior warning from the twins that Daddy would get huffy with Mummy if she drove.

MUSINGS

In 1972 both Lin and Barbie met their intended. Lin is a dark horse. A month ago she went into town so-say to buy a dress and came back with an engagement ring. Lin and Ted are to wed next July. Lin made me laugh last week. Flo next door had a new cooker delivered and Lin nabbed the very large cardboard box it came in. She thought it would be ideal to store her engagement presents in. As she is so short, she had to stand on a stool and lean over to lay stuff on the bottom. Hup and over she went, head first into the box. She didn't hurt herself, because she landed on towels. She wriggled about inside until the box keeled over. Lin's bottom drawer is filling up nicely since she got engaged. My complete bottom drawer consists of an apron and two egg timers. Lin gave me one, Ben the other. For two years I have had four brand new nightdresses stashed away in the cupboard. They're quite revealing and sexy and I thought I would save them for when I get married, in a hundred years time the way I go about things.

Barb met her Russell at the Spa early in April and love has grown. He is very good to her and won't stand for any nonsense. I met her in town last Saturday and over coffee Barb told me Russell had brought her a surprise present a few days previous. In the car he had handed her a brown paper parcel and eagerly she opened it expecting and hoping for perfume, because she had been dropping hints right left and centre. She found not perfume, but lots of newspaper containing lettuces he had dug up from the allotment. "Not rubbish", said Russell. "Do you more good than chocolates" – Barb is dieting. Most thoughtful of him I call it. Barb called it and him something else entirely. She loves him really and does as he bids. When I left her Saturday she was going in the bus station loo to put a pin in her hearing aid. It had been acting up that morning and was a bit crackly. She said it needed a new battery. She used to speak "Hello, hello, hello" into it to see if she could hear, but Russell said that was idiotic, because it certainly wasn't going to answer her. Now, on his advice, she locks herself in the Ladies and speaks "Rhubarb, rhubarb, rhubarb" into it.

We had had a giggle in town that morning. As we began to walk through Littlewoods store, a man wearing a white coat came towards us carrying a tray of tomatoes (unripe luckily). One fell off the tray and precisely the second he stooped to pick it up my foot accidentally kicked it almost the length of the store. Barb did laugh, but I didn't until the man did. He didn't hit me. As he scurried after it he said what a good centre forward I would make.

Barb went through a trying time with her Mum on the first occasion she took Russell home. They weren't expected. As she walked into the sitting room, with Russell about to follow, she came upon her Mum with girdle round her knees, struggling to get out of it. Barbie's Mum gaped and went all of a doodah. Barb whirled round and like a tornado pushed a stunned Russell backwards through the door. She slammed the door shut, gave a nervous chuckle and made up a story to do with the room being a tip and propelled him into the kitchen. Russell saw not a thing, but must have wondered what caused Barb's rather peculiar behaviour. He didn't know her then like we do, but he's learning. Who makes a cup of tea three times before she gets it right? Barbie. The first time unthinkingly she poured tea into the milk jug. Easily done. The second time she put a sandwich to her mouth and most of the salmon fell out into the cup of tea. Even the third time a dunked biscuit broke off and sank to the bottom, disintegrating, but we all do that. Digestives are the worst. By the way, Russell had tea at Barb's that first time she took him home. After eating, Barb's Dad handed Russell the paper to read and out fell her Mum's roll-on.

Barb flexed her muscles on the sports field last week in a Smelting Works football match. Barb and the girls played in striped pyjamas against the men who wore nightgowns and balloons. The ladies won 11-4. They could have done slightly better, but Barb capped an own goal, much to boyfriend

Russell's displeasure. He bopped her with a black pudding in the car that evening as punishment. He's bonkers about black pudding. He wrapped one up once in greetings paper and gave it to Barb's Mum for Mother's Day.

Talking of football matches, Tritz and I graced the field earlier this year for the first and last time. We turned out for a Wimpeys match, women versus women, watched by the men. I don't know what I was doing as Captain of our eleven (the Knickerbocker Glories), because I think I touched the ball once and that was with my hand. Terri was roped in to play for us, as we were a man short, and by gum proved she has got potential. I did train the night before the match. I had five minutes kick around the garden with Big Al, until the ball went in the stream. I won't say who was to blame, but Ally stalked off grumbling, "I'll never play with you again".

The evening of the match found us full of nerves, changing into our attire in a furniture van. Our colours were those of the Bumble Bee. Vain hussies we were, as most of us kept our tights on, to make our legs look nicer. Peggy kept her girdle on, tucking the suspenders inside her shorts. We swooped onto the pitch, which hadn't even been shortened, and proceeded to warm up. Then it was time for the off. I tossed a coin with Vinegar Bottle, she's so sour and waspish, and soon it was legs eleven all over the show. Tritz was the man of the match undoubtedly. She ran rings round our opponents and her nifty footwork, dribbling, and shin attacks, etc outwitted them all, and her own side too. We, the rest of us, shilly-shallied with the ball, but gave up running after one minute's play and walked the course letting Tritz get on with it, and that is what she surely did. One, two, three, four goals she scored, not once heading the ball with her nose like our Al does. And every time she banged one in, she would jump high as the goal post and scream "Yippee Ern". We let the other side get one goal. They even sported an extra player. Tritz was heralded a star in the making. Terrible really that she won the match for us. She doesn't even work for the firm. It ruined our health though, young and old alike. I was wheezy for days after, and Peggy and Mattie complained of muscles and bones they didn't know they had. It took Terri a mere five minutes after the match to recuperate. Beer agrees with her.

I would like to be good at sports like Dave and Al. Once, years ago, I played table tennis in Aunty Vi's living room, and Great Aunty Flossie thought I had the makings of a champion much to the sarcastic amusement of Dave, Al and cousin David Jay. I didn't think I was that good, because the balls bounced everywhere but on the table. However, she did keep saying "Brilliant shot, brilliant" even if I missed the ball, although she laughed fit to bust at my every slam. When I played last year with Ben he took immense pleasure in thrashing me. I aimed for him in the end.

Now Pops is an all-rounder. Any sport he will watch on the telly, boxing being his main love. He boxed as a young man, until Gran got fed up with bloody noses and shirts and threatened to throw him out, so he gave up biffing. I can't understand it. Pops is gentle as a lamb, but when boxing is on the box he sits on the pouffe, leaning forward intently, shushing the whole household, yet shouting "Go on 'Enry" or "Go on Cass" himself. Gradually he works his way nearer and nearer to the TV set, until his nose is a couple of inches from the screen. He will fall off the pouf one of these days when excitement gets the better of him. It's the same if boxing is on the radio, his ear is right alongside and he's offering shouts of encouragement.

I can hear Dave chanting "England, England". He's downstairs on his tod watching the Saturday afternoon football on telly. Oh now it's a rendering of 'You'll never walk alone'. It's making me wince. He is so off-key. One second he is down in the depths with a 'Wandrin Star' voice, next it is shrill and wavering in a poor imitation of Maria Callas. I can't take much more. He is just ruining 'Abide with me'. I would make him a sandwich if I had an ounce of chalk dust. He reckons he has been given hormone pills actually for one of his recurring racing injuries. He spoke in a high-pitched voice after swallowing the first one and Al felt his dubs to see if they'd grown.

He's something of a celebrity, as he is always being called upon to give speeches at functions and talks on the radio re his running club, Westbury Harriers. The other day in a practice run he took ten seconds to say his speech. He said we were distracting him because Mum coughed once. He went upstairs to play Gordon Lightfoot LPs (his favourite singer), as Gord would be sure to give him inspiration. I type up his speeches. He'll make additions like, "Marcus Harding (our two year old Canadian nephew) and Gord Lightfoot, two up and coming young athletes", and when rehearsing before the family he does Edward Heath laughs where he hopes for ripples from the audience. When he was due to appear in a radio interview he told us beforehand he would sing on air one of Gord's songs and dedicate it to

Master Marcus Harding, Canada's future Prime Minister. And sing Gord's songs before an audience he certainly did, not then but at his twenty-first party. It was all deadly serious with several pre-performance run-throughs leading up to the big night. At the party it was a full blast of 'In the early morning rain' and 'Sundown', nice go-ey songs. ('If you could read my mind' everyone joined in. That song is very well known.) Dave sang, the Weed sisters backed him, and there were chaps on two guitars and one on the bongos. On Dave's lovely worded card Al had written "Happy Birthday Moron". As Mum had chosen and bought it she was cross. On my last Birthday Card from Dave and Al it read "With love from Al, the boy, and Dave, the man". Only last week Dave's photo was splashed across the front page of the Green Un, as he ran through the tape. He's brilliant. The week before too, there he was in the newspaper clad in old vest, Long Johns and cloth cap for a sponsored charity run. He looked funnier than that the other night. Al also. They went to a pyjama party wearing bedgowns and moth-eaten blue and white Wee Willy Winky hats with bobbles. Al had a hot water bottle tied round his middle with pyjama cord and Dave carried the blue enamel po – Mum said "Don't forget to bring it back" – and a tooth-brush. They drove off looking like that.

The football match was one fun time at Wimpeys. I can also remember others. Looking back the wasp incident was hilarious. On a summer's day a wasp was buzzing round Miranda who tried to clobber it with a ruler without success. Peggy said she would get rid of it and armed with a file she started scuttling around the room, lashing out at the buzzer. When it settled near the open window she gave a mighty swipe and out it went. Not only the wasp, but as well an important document flew out of the file, carried on through the air and came to rest on the canteen roof. You can imagine the nervous chuckles. It wasn't until the afternoon a man from the yard got a ladder and climbed up to retrieve it. The thing was, that day the lift wasn't working and anybody walking downstairs could look through the glass and clearly see this document, with its visible legal markings, lying a few feet away on the roof-top. The girls were on tenterhooks all morning, fearful that Mr. P's eyes would pop out in disbelief as he strode downstairs, but lady luck smiled on us because he must have been blind as a bat that day.

Wimpeys isn't such a bad place. The people are nice. Now take Horace. If we, that is Henry (Peggy's husband), Peggy and myself give him a lift after work he sits in the back of the car behind me, holds my hair in a pony-tail and cries "Giddy-up Petal" all the way home. I don't mind that. It's the "Whoa there" outside the gate which I find unpleasant. Peggy and I had the giggles last night. Horace drove us home for a change and, as we were driving along, the pair of us (one in the front, one in the back) were trying to do him up, that is, clip his seat belt on. In the darkness it was practically impossible to fit the harness. We nearly strangled his waistline, a large one, and tickled him to death.

Patrick is a firm favourite of mine, but it's a wonder he's friendly because I was quite rude to him when he joined Wimpeys. What happened was, one lunchtime, a month or so ago, a man stopped his car and offered me a lift. Stranger thought I. Not on your giddy aunt. "No thank you" I sternly replied and, with my nose in the air, snooty pants sallied on. Ho hum, he was at the tea urn that same afternoon. A Wimpeyite like me, but a newcomer I hadn't seen before. If I remember rightly, the next day I was stood on the corner of our road (reading my Stars in the Woman magazine) waiting for a lift from Peggy and Henry, when who should come along but him again. "Would you like a lift?" "No thank you very much" passed between us once more. I did smile that time. I thought to myself "Drat, not making much headway here, are you girl" but third time was lucky. He's a nice chap. Only today he gave me a lift back to work from Lin's, a distance of what, one hundred yards! Trust! I came out with the wrong thing. He asked why I hadn't had the flu prevention nasal spray at work this morning. Knowing how easily I faint, I said "If it had been a sugar lump I wouldn't have minded, and besides I've got a pimple up my nose". It would have been positively painful to have a whiffer stuck up there, but he told me it was a sniffer not a whiffer. What a damnably attractive man he is.

Pity he wasn't with the firm for the annual 'do' a month ago. Due to Mattie's match-making, I got lumbered with a fellow from the drawing office who I wasn't keen on. I suppose it wasn't a bad dinner and dance. Wimpey females were given the afternoon off to have their hair done. Frederick in the Village did me. Whilst waiting my turn, I mentioned the annual 'do' to the woman sat on my left whom I knew slightly, and commented it was okay for a free nosh and booze-up. The woman on my right turned out to be the Regional Manager's missus. I recognised her that evening.

It's a shame Susan has been ill for a long time. Her place until recently was taken by temp Daphne who came for a week and stayed for nearly a year. When Daphne got married she changed her name from Star to Stone and nearly lived at Cream Cottage situated in Pudding Pie Lane. Daphne told me to beware of the glib tongued young men who say "The pleasure's mine, the baby's yours". The week after Daphne left Wimpeys she telephoned Peggy at work and said, "Wave to me". We all did. She was stood in the window of Oxo across the yard from us. Mattie also has left now and I'm thinking about it. Mattie's going-away present from the firm was a rocking chair. She remarked it was the next best thing to a horse.

There was a day not long ago I disgraced myself in front of Daphne and Mattie. About midday I glanced at my watch and mentioned that Mum was at the hospital having her lipoma looked at by a specialist. Conversation turned to hospitals and minor ops. Mattie said she had had a fatty lump removed from her neck, and Daphne gave details concerning her thyroid operation. Nothing ever so gory, but being a prize nit I came over queer all of a sudden and told them to hush. They did, but too late. I do remember saying "I'll just put my head down on the typewriter for a minute" which I did, and then darkness rapidly fell.

Thank goodness I didn't flop out of my chair onto the floor, because a boss would have had to be summoned to remove my carcass, and I might have shown stuff I shouldn't have. I nearly did, but Haggis saw me begin to tilt, flashed from her seat, sprinted round or over desks, I'm not sure which, although knowing her it would have been over with a cry of tally-ho as well, and managed to catch me by the scruff of my neck.

They had a devil's job trying to revive me and it took an age before I came back from nowhere. The first thing I recall was ciggy smoke clinging to Mattie's jumper, as I was leaning on her bosom, then faint voices in the distance telling me to wake up, but the blackness wouldn't go. I've been told I went an icky yellow colour and I know I had the shakes and pins and needles pricking. What a mess I was in too. Saturated! The women had had a fine time throwing water over me. Daphne with her hanky mop, taking care of my forehead and wrists had given me black eyes where mascara had run. Mattie grappling with my abundance of hair had squeezed water down my neck making rivulets run in all directions across my back. Besides this I was like a sweat bath. Knickers, tops of legs stuck together, even though they were adamant they had not soaked me there, and under arms were wringing wet, making me not nice to be near the rest of the day. The office was in chaos, as they had quickly opened the windows to give me revival air and a hurricane had blown in and swept and swirled reams of paper off the desks. Afterwards I felt shivery and in need of the loo so chuckling, and holding onto my fuzzy-wuzzy head, I made it out there, not in a straight line, and cuddled the radiator.

Such stupidity. Listening to talk I go out like a light, yet seeing things, like Des's skewered toes, I'm perfectly okay. While I was 'resting' on the keyboard, typing with my nose, Mattie turned to Daphne and said, "Thank goodness she isn't having a baby, she wouldn't be able to help herself". It shows I wouldn't make a nurse. I could cope with tending the sick and mopping up blood I think, but my downfall would be attending lectures. I wasn't one to faint in my teens when certain girls are inclined to. I used to envy Lin who sat down at the back of the school hall during morning assembly, because she suffered fainting fits, whilst I had to stand to attention. It seems though I'm now growing into a weakling. Daphne consoled me by saying it had happened to her twice, once at midnight mass and once on top of the Eiffel Tower.

The comical thing was, before I snuffed it, Mattie had made Miranda a cup of coffee and left it on her desk. Miranda was then called up on the phone – and through the wall – for shorthand and went into Mr. P's office. I flake out in her absence, Daphne rushes up, grabs Miranda's cup, out she whizzed clippity clop in her stilettos to the Ladies, tips coffee down the toilet, no time to flush, fills the beaker with water, comes back and flings it at me. Oh, she also dipped her hanky in water and swabbed me all over with it. She said later she didn't think it was a particularly clean one. In the meantime Miranda rushed back into the office, gasping for coffee sips while Mr. P was answering a phone call, and what is she met with, no coffee but a sprawling me out for the count. It was like the Keystone Cops and I missed it. Peggy and Mr. Ede did too, because they were both on holiday (but not together). I admit to having had stitchy pains in the following hour, but I know why that was. I laughed excessively. I should have been ashamed for causing a ruckus, but the women enjoyed the excitement and it brightened up their day. Luckily no one else knew of my clown's act, except Mr. P and he did ask me later if I was all right.

It was Mum's fault. If I hadn't thought of her being looked at in the hospital, I would have stayed upright at my work bench. She was ashamed to learn of my turbulence and I got a wigging, although it tickled Pops and the two mobsters of the family. Mum always thought I could be relied on in an emergency. Now it doesn't seem that I can be. As it was, the hospital told Mum she could please herself whether she keeps her lipoma, or have it sawn off.

Just before Christmas too, I slumped down a wall in the corridor at work. I was last to leave the building at 5.30pm and had to revive under my own steam. It quite frightened me. I didn't cry until I got home. There was nothing to cry about then. I was perfectly fine and completely recovered. A touch of exhaustion I expect it was. We always get a rush on at Christmas.

I should give my finger a mention here. Last Friday I asked if I could go home from work at 4.30pm, but Mr. Ede said no, I had to stay without a murmur. He was in a depressed mood and tickling him under the chin hadn't brought him round like it usually did. I had developed a 'gungy' finger. Two weeks previous I had transplanted my cactus after sixteen years of it choking in the same pot. The following week I had to dig it up again, because I had forgotten to put broken bits of tile at the bottom for drainage – I had thrown away what had been in the other pot thinking to myself, what dopey twit put that in there. Dad put me wise. Well, to get back to the point in hand, a cactus needle must have embedded itself right by a fingernail. I didn't know it was there, not at all, until it formed a yellow head.

I was in expert hands though. Peggy's husband, Henry, prised and squeezed the thorn out, and he is County Chief of the St John's Ambulance Brigade. (One might be wondering how he came to be in our office on Friday afternoon, when he is top brass in the Civil Service at Flowers Hill – stupid name that, because there aren't any flowers on the hill, only Government buildings and Saw Mills where many moons ago we got sawdust for Sooty's hutch. But I digress. Well, as Henry finishes at 4pm on a Friday, Peggy invites him round to our office for an hour and a half, so that he can put our files away before taking us home. It's a cheek on our part, but he's good as gold, even if he places them back to front and upside down in the cabinets. He is clever at sneaking into our building and his reflexes are pretty damn quick, because at a cough from Peggy he ducks down beneath our glass windows as Mr. P's precise dominant footsteps go echoing by in the corridor. One day Mr. P will have Hush Puppies on and we'll be snookered.) Henry did blink in amazement, as he studied my swollen finger for the best way to tackle the operation. He said, "I don't suppose you've got a needle?" "Oh yes" says I, and produce a dirty great big legal document needle from out of my drawers, treble the size and thickness of a darner. There should be a hole in the ceiling where I took off, as he plunged the dagger in and a yellow threadworm reared up through my skin. I pulled through that major op with finger intact.

My big toe also gave me cause for concern the other evening. Before putting a foot in the hand basin for a wash, I inspected one of my big toes. For days it had been sore and nipping and I couldn't fathom out why. I found it to be red and puffy and when I touched it I jumped a mile, as it wept yellow pussy liquid. I hopped quick as a flash downstairs shouting "Ugh, Muh, ugh Muh". Pops thought maybe it was an ingrowing toe-nail. Mum thought it was her fault for prodding too deeply with the scissors when she cut them. Daphne at work said I ought to put a kinky advert in the paper "Husband wanted, must be willing to cut wife's toe-nails, and preferably more experienced in the art than mother is". She shouldn't mock the afflicted. I can't help having bone hard toe-nails. Anyways, my big toe hasn't dropped off, and there isn't a sign of lockjaw, although Mum was adamant I should go for a tetanus jab, which I said tripe to.

Mind you, I do endanger myself. I ran the bath water the other day, undressed in the bedroom and was all set to scuttle into the bathroom when Al came upstairs. I draped a towel about my physique, grabbed my razor, and made a dash straight into the closed door, dropping the razor onto my hand. "Tarnation" said I, but stepped on into the bath. Ooh, the flow of blood spurting out of my hand! Before many minutes I was sat in tomato juice water. There was nothing for it but to get out quick before my legs turned to jelly. I hissed round the door to Al and explained my predicament, and could he go downstairs and get me an extra large plaster without letting

Mum know, because she would feel faintified and tell me off. Necessity called for a plaster and I would have to put up with the itchy rash it gave me. Al rushed away and got one with Mum none the wiser. He pushed it under the bathroom door. I stuck it on the cut and got back into rust coloured tepid water. I sat for a few seconds, thought to myself "I feel queer" and got back out again. I opened the door, told Al to hang on to me as I was going to faint, and a roaring rushed to my noddle as he helped me into the bedroom. "Let me get Mum" he said. "Don't you blumming dare" I said. When I regained my walking legs sufficiently, I climbed into the bath for the third time and got back out one more time. The water was cold and I couldn't bear the colour of it.

It's obvious I don't get on with baths. At Easter when Nan was staying with us I rose early and went straightway for a bath, a steam one. The water was near to boiling and I had forgotten to open the window and I felt myself being overcome. I jumped out pretty sharpish, knotted a towel round my wet body, got to the bedroom and flopped in a dead faint across our half-asleep Nan. She fumbled for her smelling bottle in her bag at the side of the bed and revived me. When I came to I dried myself properly (Nan and the bedclothes were more damp than me), Mum brought me breakfast in bed, and then I had another successful bash at taking a bath.

Last Saturday I had a narrow escape in town. I was embarrassed rather than hurt. I had been nonchalantly looking at Birthday cards in a crowded shop when suddenly I was struck from above. A huge card saying 'I love you' in a whacking big box fell off the top shelf and hit me on the nut. It was most unexpected. I literally staggered under the blow. Wind must have gusted through the shop. Fancy getting thumped when I've done nothing to deserve it!

A BUNCH OF DATES

I don't know what has happened to my romantic inclinations at present. They are pretty well extinct. I can't afford oysters to pep me up. For something to do, I will concoct a dossier on last year's bunch of dates. You never know, talking about them may revive male yearning in me. Let me think now.

After Robin Dobbin and I dismissed each other as nothing outstanding, Adrian travelled into my arms. He was a super-duper man and I loved snuggling up to him for a whole two months. Cockney Adrian was a rep, a good one I would imagine. He was so amiable. Over the Easter holiday I couldn't see him, because he had to rig out little Indonesian men in fire fighting uniforms. They only spoke pidgin English and presented him with a few problems as to their measurements. He and his brother had bought a nice three bedroomed house where they lived and fended for themselves. Adrian did, however, want a couple of girls to share the house and look after them. He didn't qualify for an au pair. I had first offer, but turned it down, because I had a rough idea what my duties would entail. He was honest with me right from the start. I knew he had a baby girl who was the apple of his eye. He wasn't married though, never had been so he said.

Adrian had an endearing way about him. The first time he invited me back to his house, it was put to me that we could go and watch telly and he would get supper for me. However, when we got there we found ourselves locked out. Brother Harry's doing. He was a forgetful sort and had gone to bed and bolted the doors. Stones and abuse thrown at the window-pane eventually woke him. They usually got on well together, except for the time when Adrian was away for a couple of days and on his return he found Harry had drunk his whisky and smashed his beer mug through a mishap in the sink. I learnt they had an older brother in London who went to panty parties. The mind boggles.

Adrian regularly telephoned me at work. The women said I blushed every time he did. That was because Daphne started humming the Wedding March and I thought he might hear this background music.

I did meet Vince, a lonely bachelor, whilst I was dating Adrian. I wouldn't two-time and clamped down on the attraction elements that welled up inside me. Vince told me to tell Adrian he was a nuisance, which I thought was a smashing compliment. He gave me a barley sugar to remember him by. Adrian has got a couple of things to remember me by: a rabbit face oven glove and a tin opener. These were house-warming presents I gave him the night we parted. The night I said finis I went home, got in the bath and cried, wallowing in self-pity. I wanted the bath water to rise a few feet and drown me. I wanted to stay with him yet wouldn't and didn't fully understand why. I was wanted yet couldn't respond fully and gave up a great lovable guy who thought highly of me.

Chris was also a peach, although at first I gave him no chance to prove it. The night I met him at the Spa he asked me to dance four times before I finally decided to stay put with him. I learnt he lived in Gloucestershire. True, it was a long way away, but on reflection this fact kept our relationship going for a couple of months. I saw him only every other weekend and therefore it was impossible for us to flourish and form a deep attachment. He was again just what I wanted. No strings attached to our infrequent dating. When we did see one another we were indeed sweethearts, craving to eat the other up, because two weeks apart seemed like two months. All over each other we were like a rash. He must have been at least ten years older than me, which was to my liking. He had a driving school. He was at one time a chemical man and I don't know why he gave it up, as he loved the work.

Chris told me snippets in relation to his pupils. One woman told him her daughter was on the pill and she couldn't help worrying. He told her not to worry and that the girl was right to take precautions. As a matter of courtesy, rather than interest, he kept the conversation flowing because the woman seemed anxious to talk. He asked if the daughter was thinking of getting married in the near future and then found out she was thirteen! Another woman pupil told him she couldn't communicate with her husband and had begun talking to her hamster. It paid her more attention than her husband did. (A bit kinky that.)

My dates with Chris were all good ones. He was nice to be with. I remember our first date. I could choose where to go and plumped for Tiffanys. We had a meal and he said he had bits of me in his ice cream, Angelica. Nutty it was too, because I had a taste, although he didn't want any of my apple pie. In the dance hall he had to leave me to go and get petrol. I slept with him that night – we sat in a dark, secluded recess off the dance floor and he fell asleep on my shoulder so I joined him. We probably both had our mouths lolling open.

Every date we went on I was treated to a meal. Dunlops was our favourite restaurant. A man with a gorgeous voice sang Jim Reeves songs, plus they had a marvellous selection of goodies on the sweet trolley. After our meal we headed to the Mecca and ignored the fact we were the oldest couple there amongst the teeny-boppers and danced off the fat we had just put on.

On our third date we parked by the river for our romancing. I asked him outright, because I thought it was high time I knew, and said, "I forgot to ask you before, but are you married?" He smiled slowly and said, "No, are you?" I deserved that. He was a mystery man though. Mhmmm, methinks he could have been spliced. Something deep down inside niggled. Being Joe Blunt I asked him if he had ever loved and lost anybody. He nodded, that was all. He didn't talk about it and I didn't press him, because a sad look had settled on his face. Chris was a perfect gentleman in that he walked me from the car to the front door after a date, in case of prowlers in our privet hedge he said.

Then one Sunday he didn't appear for our date. I waited and waited in our usual place outside the Hippodrome, but to no avail. I was sore to think he had stood me up, but this initial reaction soon disappeared and I blamed myself. I am sure I should have turned up on the Saturday, instead of the Sunday, because all our previous dates had been on Saturdays. I had more than likely misheard the day he said. We had no way of contacting each other and I didn't see him again. It was a shame we ended like we did, probably both of us blaming the other for the brush-off.

Donald was a funny little chap with a bushy beard and horn-rimmed spectacles. He had a lovely pair of eyes underneath. In his spare time he played the guitar in a group and was also learning the Double Bass, which must have been an awful lot taller than him. Mum said I shouldn't go by height, but I imagined people looking and laughing, as we walked along holding hands, and saying "There goes the long and the short of it". I liked him, but wished his feet were bigger than mine. He was an electrician, but he still managed to blow up his washing machine. He had a flat and quite soon I was invited there for an egg-flip, and a touch of the udder, as Dave and Al crudely remarked. He did as a matter of fact brew his own beer, but I was wary about sampling it in case it was power packed.

Summer had come when I met him and I had begun a tan, not successfully. I burnt like crazy. Donald understood when I politely told him not to dare touch me or I would screech. We didn't last long. He was a well educated man and quite wise. He did tell me never to think I can outwit or outsmart a man.

He brought me home one evening and mutually we decided to call a halt. He was pleasant about it and said, although he liked my company, for his own peace of mind he had better revert to going out with girls who let him have his own way. Fair enough explanation. I therefore didn't have to bother with mine relating to his height and feet. I got out of the car and waved him goodbye. As I did so a thought came to me and instinctively I started to run after the car shouting, "Stop!" My legs worked furiously, but I didn't have a hope in hell of catching the car. Donald didn't hear my yells, but I no doubt woke up the whole street. I came indoors near to tears and frightened Mum, because she thought Donald had taken liberties. It was nothing like that, much worse, my beautiful cardigan, Ben's Christmas present to me, I had left on the back seat of Donald's car and we had finished with one another.

I didn't sleep that night, and the next day at work felt so upset as the bounder didn't phone. By 5.15pm my mind was made up. I was going Donald hunting. I didn't have his address and didn't have much to go on. I knew he lived in a terraced house somewhere in the Kellaway Avenue, Coldharbour Road and Cranbrook Road area. Also there were what I called Rhododendron bushes in the garden. I had told the girls in the office what had happened, because they had guessed something was wrong by my long face. Miranda was a gem. We toured round in her car in sweltering heat (a hot summer's day and the heater was on, although it was switched off) looking for Donald's estate car and the house. My memory served me shocking. I sent Miranda home for her tea. She came back after only a minute saying she had seen an estate car parked in a side road and it could be the one. It was definitely worth a try. Into her car I got again and we raced to the scene of the car. False alarm. Wrong one.

I patrolled on alone, trying to recall Donald's whereabouts. Kellaway Avenue, Coldharbour Road and Cranbrook Road are three of the longest streets in Bristol, with hundreds of side roads attached and all full up with identical terraced houses. I knocked on two doors. I didn't wait for the first one to be opened, because I heard children's voices inside. The other one I wish I had ignored. I did feel foolish when the woman who came to answer the door said "We don't have Rhododendrons in the garden. They're Hydrangeas". (Wrong plant, wrong season, which I wasn't to know.) I began to get footsore and my frown was deepening, but I struck lucky the third door I knocked upon. "Promising" I thought when a fellah answered. He was French and spoke little English. "Donald upstairs?" meant nothing to him. I didn't know Donald's surname. I had forgotten his kitchen was upstairs, but his sitting room was downstairs. I was about to turn away in despair when a familiar bushy-bearded face poked round the passage door. It was him. The bleating on the doorstep had woken him from a nap. He knew what I had come for, of course, and had intended bringing me the cardigan that evening. I think he would have done, but patience wasn't my strong point. I simply couldn't wait to get my cardigan back.

I told a fib and said a friend was waiting for me, because I didn't want to hang around. It was scorching and there I was carrying two cardigans. I could have hugged one, so pleased I was to see it. I got myself hopelessly lost. I walked miles in the wrong direction. I knew this when I got on a bus going out of Bristol. The conductor turfed me off and pointed to the other side of the road, saying "Over there for you milady". For safe keeping Ben's cardigan stays in the wardrobe for now and evermore, "til it rots," Peggy said.

Tony and I didn't click. Not a conquest. He was far too clever for me. He brought me home at the termination of our first date and we agreed we wouldn't go out together again. After this joint decision was made we proceeded to talk, sat in the car, until nearly three in the morning. It was "Tell Aunty Ange all" and I unlatched my vocal cords on Uncle Tony. He had recently suffered a broken engagement and wasn't ready for any kind of involvement. We were two of a kind, possessing the same heart ailment. I almost hated him though a month later when I saw him talking to Ben at the Spa and realised they were friends. I wished I hadn't opened my mouth to him, the traitor.

Maybe I got more out of one-night stands than I did from dating. I met a batch of rather interesting mortals last year. I'll get shot of Gregory first. He was a pretty kettle of fish who would have led me up the garden path as sure as I'm Fanny Adams.

The night I met him began badly. In the powder room of the Spa I got in a pickle with my mascara brush. Somehow or other it got tangled up in my hair and the more I tugged, the more my hair turned black. After appealing to God Almighty to release me from my plight he did, leaving me with a black streak in my freshly laundered, and therefore fair, locks. I combed and combed which only served to give me many black streaks and a comb that looked as though it had never been washed.

The streaky look must suit me, because that night Gregory came along to give me a night's wooing, plus a bit more than I bargained for. His approach was polite and most favourable. He touched my arm and said "Excuse me, but I believe I know you from the year 1966." For starters that pepped me up no end with the present year being 1972, as I thought I couldn't have aged greatly since I was sixteen if he recognised me. He went on to say that he had been at college the same time as me and we travelled on the same bus. Actually, I had seen him previously at the Spa and knew these facts, but he said he hadn't seen me there before. At college he studied to be an engineer, but decided he wasn't fiddly-minded enough and became a policeman instead. I was interested, because I found him interesting. He had spent two years in South Africa as a policeman and had had a boy batman 'do' for him, but had returned and joined our force. A well-travelled, well-spoken and well-experienced man of twenty-five he was. My goodness, but that was a death defying ride home in his beaten up old van! The passenger seat was broken beyond repair. It wasn't fitted to the floor. A gaping hole in it made my eyes widen, as there was a nasty looking spring emerging from it. Tentatively I lowered my bottom over the hole and said "Whoops" as the spring jabbed up my backside in a weak attempt at giving me a thrill. I arranged myself as best I could and rode home sitting on this movable, holey seat. Oh too, my knee got bashed rather a lot by an extremely long gear stick as we journeyed home. His home not mine. I had no say in the matter because, as I didn't have to get up for work on Sunday, there was no earthly reason why I shouldn't go back to his place for a coffee. No qualms overtook me. I had long nails. His parents would be in bed if I needed them (they must take flipping sleeping pills) and I was within running distance of our house if I had to bolt, which I didn't do, because I saw things through to the bitter end. As I, yes I made instant because I don't know how to make proper coffee, and wiped up mugs and saucers lying on the draining board for the purpose, Gregory rummaged through his record collection. He told me he was hoping to get a flat soon. No bones about it, I received a command not an invitation that when he got it I must go and spend a night with him. Fellows can get right on my wick, but at the same time one can't help feeling flattered.

Apart from the fact he was a bit too adventurous, he was quite nice; not that good-looking, but he had something I couldn't quite put my finger on. Charisma possibly. It's funny how we develop. All those years ago we went to the same college but never spoke, not even a "hello", or a smile of acknowledgement. He said he wished he had sat by me on the bus then and got to know me, but I told him he would have found me a mouse, frightened to say boo to a goose, whereas I can remember he was immensely popular at college.

Although I made a perfect cup of coffee, I didn't get to drink it beyond the froth. It wasn't fair, because he knew exactly where the light switch was. I didn't know where the devil he had gone for a split second. My pathetic enquiry was soon stifled when he loomed up out of the darkness and fell across the settee. I was on there too, cornered. Five minutes later he decided he preferred the floor, and cushions and I were deposited roughly down there alongside him. I thought I wouldn't see the light of day again and wondered where his truncheon was. I quite enjoyed a romp until the tussle got a little out of hand for my liking. I forgot for a moment he was a policeman and whispered, not unkindly, "Please do get off me or I shall have to put the boot in". I made him tired, gave him a cuddle and the cups to wash up, as I supervised. Then he walked me home.

Next morning I woke up to find I had blue lips and it wasn't because I was cold. I was bruised with bites. They were fat and navy blue in places. I was perturbed. Dad was disgusted and Mum did nothing but chuckle every time she looked at me. She wouldn't have been any good to call as a witness so, out of the goodness of my heart, I didn't bring a case to have the barbaric barbarian thrown out of the police force for committing atrocities on me. I had to explain my blue lips to Lin. As it turned out she knew Gregory from coming in the shop. In her opinion he is a big head. I expect he wonders why she grins knowingly at him over the counter now.

Months later I saw him again at the Spa. His greeting was to poke me in the belly.

Bart was a tunnelling expert. I called him cobber on account of the Australian twang in his speech. He had just finished a job in Bristol the evening I met him at the Mecca. He had gone to the dance hall with the boss's son Roy and an elderly work associate, who parked himself in a corner and spent the evening snoring his head off. Bart talked about himself, his work, his hobbies and a bit later his wife, children and home. He had knocked two cottages into one on the outskirts of London. Life had been good to him he said. He walked me to Pru's van. Roy escorted Pru. We stood two by two on opposite sides of the van to pay our respects. Bart thanked me for a pleasant evening and I returned the compliment. It was all right for him to kiss me I suppose.

Alex was a twenty-nine year old married man with two children. Why these wives let their menfolk out of their sight beats me. He was a smelter so we had a common link. He told me not to have anything to do with him, yet he said he had singled me out from the crowd, which doubled my head size. Married men can only hurt single girls he said. I was fascinated so went home for coffee. It was a real home with a kitten in a cardboard box and toys on the floor. He admitted he lived with his wife, but they went their separate ways, so he said. She was a barmaid and often stayed overnight with the kids at the pub where she worked. That was where she was that night, but I acted gingerly until I was sure the house was empty.

He seemed honest and likable, young but old. I saw his family crest. They had been white slave traders in the past. He had been in prison at an early age for forgery. He got nabbed because somebody grassed on him (and the punchy friend he was with at the Spa). He said he liked it in prison, particularly working in the gardens. He was inside for six months. He didn't strike me as a crooked type, but I was a bit of a greenhorn. He admitted he came from a rough family and bad neighbourhood. In his time he had worked on banana boats. His wife, he said, had changed him for the better and it was thanks to her he became educated. He only ever worries about his kids. He brought me home in the wee small hours, but still we carried on chatting in the car. We watched one of our neighbours roll down the road sozzled. I got to bed as the dawn broke and the birds began to sing. Nan was staying with us. She stirred, as I climbed in beside her, and said "What time do you call this Mary Jane?" I'm always Mary Jane when she thinks I have gone off the rails.

Elmer was an American living in England. He was the mascot for a Rugby team. He accompanied the team on their weekend jaunts. They had had a match the Saturday I met him and the players were in jubilant high spirits, because they had won. Team members had flocked to the Spa and drank the bars dry. Elmer wasn't drunk though. He was happy and smiley, but he said he was never anything different and this I could believe going by his lively face. His job was buying and selling antiques (Pop said he was one at thirty-five) and he was also an Historian. He told me he was soon going to Memphis for six months on business.

I met him late in the evening and, by the time the Spa was ready to close its doors at 1am, Elmer and I still had a heap of things we wanted to natter about, so I consented to go back to his hotel room, a thing I had never done before in my life. However, I felt safe. Straightaway, as soon as we got there, he pointed to his suitcase and said, "That's my address". I looked at the label and it said Mr. & Mrs. "My trouble is I'm too honest" Elmer said. I had guessed anyways that he was married. He was too nice not to have been snapped up. I told him it didn't make any difference, because he wasn't going to do anything he would have regrets about and be ashamed of later. We had lots of interesting talk centring on people, oh and war. I found out he digs his elderly neighbours' garden and like me he can't kill spiders. He wasn't

Romeoish, too tender-hearted for that. He cares about the universe and all who populate it. Two sweet things I remember him saying. One was that his wife would like me and the other was that Mum and Dad must be nice folks. I couldn't help laughing at him. He danced a rumba round the room, as I applauded with soft claps so as not to disturb sleepers in adjoining rooms. When he asked if I cared to join him we ended up struggling to walk the floor with his feet balanced on mine. He was no lightweight neither.

Before we left his room he cleaned his teeth and ate a bit of toothpaste, because he liked the taste. He got me a taxi, wished me all the luck in the world, gave me a pound for the fare which was more than adequate, and waited on the hotel steps waving until I had gone out of sight. A little fling he had had, but he was a tonic to me. I stopped thinking all the nice men had departed from the world. He asked for my name, address and phone number, and said that if he were ever in Bristol again he would like to go for a walk across the Downs and hold my hand, because I was a swell friend. He had winning ways. Elmer's outward appearance was one of a big solid dependable man. I looked inside and found an affectionate boy with love in his heart for the whole wide world. So different to Nick!

What is there to say regarding Nick but fume and fume again? He was a detestable male. I met him and my faith and trust in mankind evaporated into thin air. Nick should bloody well be put in the nick for the rest of his days, the sod. However, when I met him I didn't think he was a louse, far from it. He was pleasant, a lot of fun, acted keen and we did seem to hit it off. He wasn't a yobbo, quite intelligent in fact. I knew a fair bit about him within half an hour. We danced close-up and personal. He was loving and said nice things. He suggested a drink, went and got them and told me to sit guarding them while he sped to the Gents. He didn't touch his drink before he went. I sat minding them, wedged beside a crowd of football supporters.

When ten minutes had elapsed and he hadn't returned I was beginning to feel a lemon. Funny looks were coming my way. After fifteen minutes the fidgets got the better of me so, armed with the drinks, I set out to hunt him down, stopping first by my girlfriends to tell them of my predicament. I made my way to the Gents and hovered outside. I couldn't pluck up courage to ask an entrant if he could let me know if there was a sick man inside.

Nick had certainly not been blotto when I was with him, but I had become worried and was at a loss what to think.

I turned to go back towards the dance floor when, who should appear before me but him, hand in hand with some other girl. You could have knocked me down with a feather. I acted rash. I thrust his drink into his hand saying, "Here's your drink, I hope it chokes you", tightened my lips and stalked off carrying my own. What I should have done is sloshed both drinks in his face. My regret is that I had requested a fruit juice instead of a double brandy and Babycham.

He looked to be taking that other girl into one of the bars for a drink and, who knows, he could have been ready to play the same dirty trick on her. I can't make out his immature behaviour. Why the hell hadn't he said thank you (very much) on the dance floor and walked away. Why go to the expense and trouble of queuing to buy me a drink, and one for himself, which was left with me untouched, and then doing a vanishing act. He spoilt, wasted rather, an hour of my evening. I felt an idiot, but as the girls said it could have happened to anyone. I was most put out when I got back to them, but soon laughed because I could see the funny side as well as them. I might have been banned from the Spa if I had baptised him I suppose, but wish I had taken the risk. It put me off beards. Tricky Nicky is a case I shall never be able to fathom out.

I did meet another Robin, but he wasn't much improvement on the first. He brought me home from the Spa one Saturday night, parked the car and in no time at all the windows had steamed up. He leant over me and I thought he was going to wind the window down. Instead he pressed a knob and down I went, except for my legs. They shot up in the air. The bounder had reclining seats and I nearly broke my back. It should have been a romantic moment, but I got the giggles. Well, I had to cool his zeal somehow. I don't like such goings-on when I have only just met the guy. I wanted to growl "Control yourself heathen" but made do with "Get orf me". In a way I can thank Ally-boy for rescuing me. A car full of Ally and his mates drove up and stopped in front of us. Al got out and I turned to Robin Hood (he said if I cared to look I would see for myself he didn't have a red breast, but I said I wasn't a peeping Tom and believed him to be a Hood instead) and said sweetly "That's my brother. He's 6'4"." Robin began to simmer down then.

He did walk me to the door, but that was because he wanted to straighten himself out and tuck in his shirt tails.

Then there was the magnetic man whose name I don't recollect. He was a real Bryan Ferry look-alike, a here today, gone tomorrow man, in Bristol for one night only. He barely smiled, but when he did, wow. He enthralled me. He had been, what he called, bumming around for three years and had seen a great deal of the world. He had been a lumberjack in Canada. New York he hated, South Africa he loved. The sights he had seen in India had left their mark. Because he had saved a tribal African from drowning, he had to accept the reward offered, to bed down with the fellow's wife, whom he didn't find at all attractive – she had a bone in her nose – but it would have been insulting to refuse. He therefore went through the motions. He said I was too young to hear about such things. I must have been smitten, because I remember he only allowed himself to come close when we danced to Andy Williams record "Home Lovin' Man" and boy, was he snuggly. Plus his aftershave was divine.

This solitary man and I talked for a little while outside the house. He was going to try and settle in England and hoped to become an athletics coach. Probably, because I was virtually a complete stranger, and someone he wouldn't ever see again, he did tell me why he had taken to roaming. He left the shores of England after he found his fiancée in bed with a friend of his. Understandably, forgiveness didn't come easily to him. Three years later he still had a chip on his shoulder. I could see it. He must have thought me priest-like, the fact he unbent a little. Looking back, I wonder now if he spun me a yarn, whether his story telling was truth or fiction. I kind of like to think he was a man of mystery, someone who had lived life to the full. Yes, well, he was very easy on the eye. Downright delectable I kid you not.

There have been quite a number of let-downs of course. A bloated, pot-bellied old fellow laughed every time I opened my mouth. He really threw back his head and haw-haw-hawed. I had to disengage myself when he did it in a waltz. He was slimy, a real slug, and I'm rather glad his stomach protruded, because I didn't want to get close and certainly not cheek to cheek. He was a messer, as Nan would say.

I met Simon at the Spa. I wish I hadn't. He was all right, but he might not have been. He was a thirty-two year old bachelor, so he said, who had come to the Spa with a friend whom I didn't like. He was blunt and belligerent, this friend. He thought I acted phoney and I told him I couldn't care less what he thought. They were both golfing instructors from Surrey. Apparently, Simon is some sort of champion and travels a great deal for tournaments. They were staying at Chepstow and taking part in one.

Anyway, blithering idiot that I am left with them to go to a "bit of a party" at Chepstow. I must need my head read. I did tell him I wanted to be home in the early hours of the morning – church tomorrow (liar) – no later than two, but I did agree to three when pressed. Maybe I went with him as I didn't want to rely on Pru for a lift, the second time that week, and also because two exes were at the Spa. I did ask outright what Simon's intentions were and he said a few drinks, a lot of talk and some laughs.

We arrived at Chepstow. The grounds were magnificent and the hotel itself was a delightful old country mansion. However, it was silent as the grave and in darkness when we rolled up. No party, no open bar, not even a cup of coffee. Simon's friend went off to his room and I ended up in Simon's for a cup of tea. Each room had a teasmade. It was rather a fight for my life. That wasn't overly scary, because I kept my head and he eventually took no for an answer. Strange as it may seem, as soon as he removed his glasses he didn't seem attractive any more. He looked kind of sinister. What did make me extremely nervous was that when he realised he wasn't going to nobble me, he said to wake him up at five, better still six o'clock, and he would run me home. Well I thought I had better let him have a little sleep. Not me though, oh no. I was in a frightened state of exhaustion, but collapse, not me.

The seconds ticked slowly by. I couldn't stand it any longer. I switched the bathroom light on, looked at my watch and it said 4.15. I altered it to 5.15. I shook him awake and said I wanted to go home. He was angry I could tell. He made a racket dressing and was obviously having a temper tantrum (he had stripped to his vest and pants – nothing startles me nowadays). He was sighing loudly and didn't say much except that he hadn't wanted to leave right then. He said he had been drinking and if he were stopped on the way he wouldn't pass the breathalyser. If I had left him till six he would have been okay. God above, he had been to the toilet four times in about three hours! There couldn't have been any booze left in him. You can bet he wouldn't have wanted to stir at five, six or seven o'clock if I had left him. I don't always take things lying down. Sometimes hackles go up and I bristle. We had a fraught, deathly quiet journey back to Bristol at top speed. I was scared he would dump me at the roadside, or over the Severn Bridge, but he took me as far as the Centre, gave me a pound and told me to get a taxi home. I did get six bob out of him so I mustn't grumble. It isn't worth taking risks though. I trusted him and up to a point my judgment was sound. He tried, but didn't take advantage. I wished I'd spent the afternoon cutting up chilli peppers. That would have frustrated passion. I must say though I'm thankful to have gotten home unscathed and in future I'll be more careful. Oh yes I will.

I met another crazy character at the Mecca. He was a beautiful skimmy dancer although he was a rugged sort of bloke. He owned a string of betting shops. He had a twinkly face, even if it was pitted, and I didn't mind being called a sod (it made me laugh) for playing hard to get and refusing to take his marriage proposal seriously. I mean to say, I had only known him for five minutes. Drink had affected his logic.

TAXI DRIVERS
AND OTHER IMBECILES

A taxi driver I aim to punch on the nose next time I see him and hope for his sake I don't. I never forget a face. A few weeks ago I was in his taxi homeward bound following a hopeless night at a dance. We chattered for a while. I was sat in the back and could see that his eyes in the driving mirror looked kind of kindly. He asked where I had spent the evening. I told him and mentioned how awful the pop group was, who had been playing at the dance. He said his friend was the drummer. Enough said. I shut my trap and pretended to snooze. We stopped by the lamp post outside our house. He turned round in his seat and Good Lord! He was fabulous, but now I hate him. I asked what did I owe him. He replied, "Eight and sixpence and can I see you one night?" I said "Pardon" and he repeated himself. I said "Eh?" and he asked a third time for a date. I then said "What did you say?" and again he came out with his request. I was taken aback, because it came out of the blue and I could only splutter, "Are you sure Mr. er hem?" He said he was. He couldn't give a definite night he would be free, but he asked for my works phone number. I came into the house singing. It had been a cheap ride too as usually I pay in the region of eleven bob.

For three weeks now I have been waiting for a telephone call. I don't any longer jump when the office phone rings. I know I did tell him my number was 7333 and it should have been 76333, but he could have looked up Wimpeys in the directory if he had really and truly wanted to. It makes me evil. It makes my blood boil. Why on earth did he ask to see me, fill me with hopes and desires, when truth be told he had no intention of doing so. It was a cruddy thing to do. He had better watch out though if there is a next time he is my taxi driver. He'll get nothing out of me except a lot of lip and no tip.

Never again will I be courteous in a taxi queue neither. Some people do have an infernal cheek. There I was the other Saturday night on the Centre, stood minding my own business, quite near to the front of a mile long queue, when a respectable looking chap and his girlfriend standing at the back called out "Anyone going to Bris?" I nodded and he said did I mind if they shared my taxi and we could split the cost. "Not at all" says I, and they joined me. That is they stood as one, kissing and fondling in front of me. After an embarrassing wait our taxi drew up. They got in and slammed the door in my face without so much as a thank you. Struck dumb I was, and the taxi had gone before I came to my senses, otherwise I may have kicked it. Bloody nerve.

I'm not that bright regarding taxis. After a hen party recently, eight of us ordered taxis to pick us up outside the Victoria Rooms. I was going home alone and, because the driver who turned up looked a sweet old gent, I got in the front with him. Do you think my friends would allow it? Not they. They wouldn't let him budge until they had dragged me out, seated me in the back and locked me in. They said, "You never know". As if an old geezer would have gone for my knee! He was only interested in my ankles. He said I had a shapely pair when he opened the car door for me later. He was polite at all times and called me dear. I have met one driver who has a holder for a rolling pin next to his gear stick, in case he has to cope with undesirables.

The last taxi driver I have been with caused blood to flood my face. I was sharing a taxi with Lin and Dinah and he said he would tell them something about me when I disembarked, because he had had me before. Of course I wanted to know what he was going to say and badgered him to tell me to my face. He wouldn't though. I wondered if I'd fluffed in his taxi. I said I bet it was to do with my Bristol accent and he went into guffaws and said he thought I was going to say my Bristols. I coloured up and mumbled they weren't worth a mention. I was glad to get out of his taxi and leave Lin and Di shaking in mirth behind. They said after, what he did say about me wasn't too bad so that was all right, but they wouldn't elaborate for fear of hurting my feelings. Yes, well, I remain puzzled. I shall peer into cab drivers' windows in the future and scrutinise them before climbing in.

The other day Barb thought the taxi man had overcharged her and said so. He said he hadn't. She handed him a penny tip, because she didn't have any change other than a two bob piece and she didn't think he warranted that. He said he didn't want her penny so she said that was fine and whipped it back off him. She told him it would come in handy.

Once at a taxi rank I saw a woman pick up a man. She stopped in her car and enquired of him how to get to such and such a place. He gave her explicit directions. She thanked him and asked if she could give him a lift! He thanked her for her kind offer and away they sped to I wonder where. Now that took some nerve.

I shouldn't go by looks. The friendliest bod up the Spa has a coconut head. An awful lot of electricity runs through his hair making it stand on end. He is a labourer, a rough and ready sort of chap, but he gives me winged feet. I don't know how, but I do all the proper dance steps with him. I have to keep asking him what the dances are called. His feet lead me perfectly with a fine twirl at the end of each one. He has, I swear, not a miserable streak in him.

There are always the dross "Let's be having you" types and I unfurl my nails ready to spike 'em one if they don't pay heed to my "Not tonight Josephine".

The first offer of a dance I accepted one evening was from a man who was there with his daughter. I felt most ancient and could only think he had picked on me because he mistook me for middle-aged. Ego deflater he was. Then the girls said the half German/half English chap I had been dancing with looked nice. From their distance no doubt he did, but close up I had seen his fang tooth.

I left the Spa the other day and had a contraceptive pamphlet thrust at me yet Des and Pru weren't accosted by literature touts. I felt a Jezebel. I must have been the chosen one because I wore dark tights. It was the first pair I had ever bought. My normal purchase is flesh tone or American Tan. My nice boss approved and wanted to know if I wore midnight blue undies too. He said nothing speeded up the flow of his adrenalin more than dark stockings and midnight blue underwear.

The girls and I suffer many off nights at the Spa, meeting chaps who don't measure up one little bit. Nobody wants to talk amicably. No one comes up to expectations. That is apart from last night when conversation between a fellah and myself reached an all-time high. I accepted his offer to dance and on the floor his initial question was "Will you marry me?" First time ever a chap has come straight to the point, no humming and hawing. Only trouble is he couldn't possibly have meant it. Anyways, he was a long distance lorry driver. Had he been a short distance one, coming home every night, I might have considered it. He would have been quite nice had he not been a Welsh twit, so I left him, rejoined my friends and a bit later teemed up with Jerry. He was as Irish as they come and it took ten minutes of his repeated question "Do you come here often?" before I cottoned on to what he was saying. The music was loud so that, besides his accent, affected my hearing. Actually, he did have a loud voice himself, because whilst at the bar I cringed within when he shouted, instead of whispered, that he was going for a wee. I stayed with him though, as I enjoyed listening to him talking about the potato farm back home, which his brother ran. His own period of study at Cork University I was least interested in.

We left the dance early and went on to the Irish Club in Bristol, travelling not in comfort but style and I loved it. His car was a vintage 37 year old topless model, all front and no behind. We did get stared at by others on the road. The Irish certainly do let their hair down on Saturday night shindigs. The lusty singing nearly took the roof off the old church hall in which Bristol's Irish Club met. I was in raptures watching the Irish jigs, also the brawl that developed between a couple of beer swilling and sodden men. Not one punch landed, because they were incapable of hitting bang on target and they wouldn't put their tankards down. These unruly drunks were thrown out amidst tremendous cheers and jeers for disturbing the peace. A shenanigan Jerry called it, which sounded Irish. The last I saw of them they had patched up their differences and were helping each other along. They kept thumping into walls as they lollopped down the stonework corridor. Those people could sing with such heartfelt feeling. I saw an old gaffer cry into his beer as the multitude sobbed aloud "When Irish Eyes are Smiling". Come 1am the merry-makers had had their lot and were asked to leave quietly. Some hopes! With breaths reeking of booze, crowds of shamrocks spilled out from the hall, either singing as they stumbled homewards or tooting car horns as they wished the centre of Bristol "Top o' the mornin to ya".

Into the Vintage Jerry and I clambered and chugged back to the flat, which he shared with five other chaps. This time people looked at the car, as we rattled along, because we had smoke belching out of the radiator hole. We had dried up. The flat wasn't far away, praise be, and we got there without conking out. A couple I had been introduced to at the Irish Club arrived the same time as us. What a place that was. It was impossible to move without tripping over something. We walked into the kitchen and there stood the weirdest couple. A bald headed checker and his lady love who stayed most nights. She had tears streaming down her cheeks, but she was chopping up onions. Her boyfriend was swilling bottles. Hundreds of empties were scattered all around the room and others were filled with ditch-water looking gunge. There were siphons and pipettes leading here there and everywhere with murky brown liquid fizzing, plopping, spluttering and gurgling its way out of one flagon into another. He was in the process of making his own beer, a complicated method if ever I saw one. The sitting room we entered next, and that is the only thing one could do in there, sit. There were two settees, a divan, two armchairs, all with tears and stuffing coming out of them, six hard backed chairs round a table and three more loungers. A threadbare carpet covered the floor. A heater, bookcase and a massive colour television also occupied the room. Coffee was served. One fellah had cheese on toast, the beer maker had goulash, and Jerry indulged in hunks of bread, blocks of cheese, half a jar of pickle and two whole Spanish onions, sliced. This proceeded to give him the burps because he ate too fast, although he said it was the hiccups. We watched a silly late night movie where a woman sang a love song to another woman and then the same goings-on went on between two men. This potty film with sub-titles dragged on and on and on, as Jerry munched on and on and on. I got ants in my pants caused by boredom. I told Jerry I had to be off so downstairs we trooped with a bucket of water. He filled up the still steaming beauty and with a lot of backchat from her we roared away into the night.

We were nearly home when somebody flagged us down to say the rear lights weren't on. A fuse had blown. I was blowing one as well within five minutes. Jerry didn't have a screwdriver so with make-do tools he proceeded to take things apart and reassemble them again until he got flickers in her rear. My ardour had cooled dramatically after spending a goosey half hour hunched in the car. Nose drips had formed icicles I swear. Outside the house I thought to myself if he comes near me with those oily hands and onion breath I'll hit him, so I didn't give him the chance. I gave him a quick peck on the cheek and thanks for a lovely evening (well, it had been different), jumped over the car door rather than look for the handle and dapped inside the house before he could say Jack Robinson. He was a sweet lamb really, but we weren't suited. I loved his car. Des knew a Jerry Handle once. What were his parents thinking of.

Other nights we miss out altogether and consider ourselves the dregs left to stew in our own juice along with the few remaining cast-offs in the dance hall. It is supposed to be the pairing up pen, but rather unflattering to be passed over by each and every one of the bulls, rams and hogs. When this happens, as it often does (too often sad to say), we make a blue exit bemoaning our funny faces and vowing to dig up our Bristol roots. We have even gone so far as threatening to walk along to the Suspension Bridge, where we would link hands and jump. At least we would go with a big splash, all four of us. We figure if we leave this world, the next one we enter can't be half as bad.

Pru met a pleasant enough chap at the Spa. After several dances they went into the bar. Unfortunately, someone knocked Pru's arm and spilled drink down her, but the kind fellow she was with came to her aid. He produced a hanky from his pocket, a woman's hanky with lace edging. One of his wife's in fact, because his own hadn't been ironed. At least he was truthful, not like the chap Lin met before her Ted. They had danced the night away in the Mecca ballroom and Lin readily accepted his offer of a lift home. Fastened on the back seat of his car was a baby carriage and when Lin pointed to it and queried "Yours?" he said it belonged to his baby sister.

BLUSTERING NORMAN

Then there was Norman. I liked him at first, but after a few months' courtship I didn't really like him at all. However, looking back we had some nice dates. I can remember our meeting at the Spa. I liked him instantly. He was all there with the patter and just had to be a rep with his gift of the gab. We sort of clicked I suppose, and his words were he could "go a bundle on me" – funny saying that. He wasn't what I'd call handsome, but had a pleasant face. (He looked like Rish's old school chum Duffy, the one who used to say, "Come tiddle my toe"). He was 6'4" and big with it. He looked solid though, not flabby; sixteen stone something, but he wouldn't determine his poundage. He had lost weight, because at one time he weighed seventeen stone. He was twenty-five and lived with his folks near the Happy Landings pub. He loved his job, loved selling and said he could be quite ruthless and a bastard at times. Yet he was a big softie with me, and full of compliments. Norman said after our first date I was in a bubble and he would like to prick it and lift me out, utter tripe, but still a sweet thing to say. I didn't particularly want a boyfriend, but he dangled a carrot in front of my nose by saying he would take me for a Chinese meal, a day trip to Ilfracombe, an evening drive to Weston, and we would pay a visit to his sauna club. Curiosity forced me to ask whether it was a mixed one.

We met at the Spa and it was there he made a marvellous suggestion, which I was only too ready to accept. Off we went to Portishead via the Suspension Bridge where he handed a bob to the toll keeper and had it given back to him. Not a word was spoken beyond thank you, but apparently they knew one another. Norman gives him tins of coffee, his firm's brand, and uses the bridge for free. There were few cars on the road at that time of night. Well it was about 1.30am and it was a heavenly drive with the radio romanticising, and the two of us chattering as though we had known each other for years. We parked by the swimming pool, and there wasn't a car, or a soul in sight. Out we got. Norman collected a walking stick from the boot for my use if I needed it. He didn't have a gammy leg, but used it to uncover things as he walked, and he could do manoeuvres with it. We linked arms and toddled off like two old fogeys to discover night beauty. I tapped up the cliff steps and then we walked on spongy grass across the headland. There weren't any boulders to fall over or pot-holes to fall into. And there we were at the top of the cliffs with the sea beating below on the jagged rocks. He chuckled when I politely asked, "You aren't a murderer, are you?" because one can't be too careful nowadays. He said not on Saturdays or Sundays so I was safe.

From our vantage point we could see the curve of silvery water where it met glistening pebbles and over the bay Clevedon pier was winking at us. Not far from where we stood was the white Portishead lighthouse shining its light across a dappled sea. Beyond we could see the bright yellow lights of Clevedon, lamp posts I expect, because most of the houses had to be in darkness at that time of night. And to please me even more, the wind screamed and whipped us. I felt glory of glories. It was beautiful and intoxicating. I loved seeing such a place at dead of night. We walked a little ways along the cliff tops away from the lights, but as we couldn't see a darn thing beyond our noses we turned back.

We sat in the car devoid of cobwebs and exhilarated by wind and sea. Oh, when he put the stick back in the boot he gave me a present, a sample pink packet of what Mum calls Mine-strone soup. Every date which followed I was given a packet of soup. He never missed. That first night he also had two dozen eggs on the back seat and I enquired if they too had "fallen off the back of a lorry". He smiled and told me not to be ridiculous, because if that had been the case they would all be broken, wouldn't they, but I'm not so dumb.

He thought about taking me to a transport cafe for coffee, but he decided against it. When I asked why, he said the last time he went to this particular cafe he had had to put two fellows outside. Threw them out to be precise. They had poked fun because he had walked in wearing a suit. He said that at the outset he had ignored their ill-humoured quips, but when one picked up a sausage and flung it, hitting Norman's face, he retaliated by giving them his undivided attention. He picked them up by the scruff of their necks, plonked them outside on the pavement and went back to his own bangers and mash. I said I had nails, which could come to his aid should the same thing happen again, but instead we came home for a cuppa.

I'm a daft 'apeth. I was put off a bit, only because I lost my sense of humour. He came into the kitchen to watch me make tea, ruffling his hair on my pants and dancing bra hanging on the kitchen line – I told Mum off next morning. He saw what I thought were Mum's teeth in a cup. (In fact they were Dad's.) He suggested putting a cigarette between them, but he saw my shocked, rather disgusted countenance. (Mum hates ciggies – she said the next morning that Norman's ciggy smoke had drifted from the living room upstairs to their bedroom, passing through two doors!) He said, if not a cigarette, how about the cooked rasher of bacon lying on a plate on the kitchen table. I don't know what was wrong with me. I didn't think it was at all funny and I went quite hoity-toity with him, but he had a fit of the giggles. Thinking about it now, it would have been quite chucklesome for Mum and Dad to have come down the following morning and found a bacon slice between the set of teeth. They laughed anyways when I mentioned it to them, but Mum was quite indignant to think I had told Norman that the teeth were hers. She enlightened me that she has only got a few false ones on a plate, not a whole mouthful, and hers are a much better colour than Dad's, and I had to tell Norman this the next time I saw him.

Anyways, after Norman made his suggestion I became half annoyed with him, yet I still liked him. However, I was a little on guard, because I suspected what was coming, how about a further date? I wanted to tell him yes. I also wanted to say no for some peculiar reason. He suggested Tuesday as our next date, but I told him I was engaged with another man that night (Lin and I were going to see 'our' delectable man Clifford Rich in concert). Wednesday he said was his best free night, but I told a fib for that evening and said I was going to see Nan, whereas I actually wanted to wash my hair. Thursday was out of the question, as it was my girls' night out and his boys' night out. Friday he was away working. Saturday was Rugby and he played for a Welsh team. That Sunday evening he was going to Taunton, his birthplace, to visit his aged Gran who was poorly, and to meet his uncle for a pint. Monday evening he had a works meeting. I told him I wasn't going to snuff it or leave the country that week and I would still be here the one after, but charming fellow said it would be too long to wait.

He wouldn't leave until I agreed to a definite date and I was on tenterhooks expecting Mum or Dad to bang down, because he had a bad smoker's cough. It was 4.00am when I finally booted him out and then I had a broken tossed sleep. He was a nice young man, a friendly sort and a gent, not smothersome as some are, but I told him I wasn't a settled person and usually after a couple of dates I scooted with the wind in my sails. He seemed to understand. He told me he wouldn't cut my grass meaning, I suppose, that I was a free agent to do what I wanted and with whom. So a pact was made, to remain pardners until we fizzled out. One thing perturbed me. When he first conversed with me, Norman formed the opinion I was either very intelligent or simple. Dave and Al shrieked with laughter when I told them. The day after I met Norman, as is wont to happen, I had forgotten what he looked like.

He didn't turn up for our first date. I was that cross and vowed I would tell him to go take a run and jump if I ever saw him again. However, he did call and I was as nice as pie to him. I did expect him to apologise though, but he didn't. On second thoughts I was glad he didn't, because I would have said, "That's alright" if he had. I told him I had enjoyed his soup. He said he detected hints and he would see what he could do, most unintentional on my part. He showered me with soups thereafter, and several jars of coffee as well. Nescafe, although I told him I preferred Maxwell House. I was his convenience girlfriend, so he said, as it took him three minutes in the car from his house to our house.

In the beginning I enjoyed our dates. Norman took me to nice places. We often went to his club for drinks. It was an underground club consisting of a maze of passages leading to the sauna rooms. At the bar I met a handful of members, friends of Norman. Two were even bigger than him! I liked them immensely. There were those with cultured and polished voices whilst others lacked such refinement and possessed an earthy quality, like Frank, the plumber, but they were friends and equals one and all. That was one thing about Norman, he was pretty good with people and made them feel important. Norman introduced me to Southern Comfort at his club. He said it was power packed and matches would be struck in my tum. I don't know about that. It nearly blew my head off. One evening we watched a horror film in the club cinema. Norman dozed, but even so I kept lunging for his arm. We were sat in padded rocking chairs. All the seats were rockers, all twenty of them. We were sat in the back row. There were only two. Guess what, the film was run entirely for our benefit! There wasn't anyone else in the cinema.

My taste buds worked overtime with Norman. We had a favourite Chinese restaurant. We always had the same meal with bits of this and that on our rice beds: pork, chicken, prawns, different veg besides bean shoots and my favourite water chestnuts and a Chinese fried egg with a stand-up yolk placed on the top. Most droolsome. Norman and I would empty the soya sauce bottle over our plates.

One Saturday evening we had a meal with a couple of Norman's friends, Len and Andrea, but unfortunately Norman had to complain that the steaks were tough as old boots. They were a nice couple. Len was Norman's old Spa-ing partner before he married Andrea, and Norman referred to him as "my friend Everard". The stories I learnt. They led girls a merry dance in those days, introducing themselves convincingly as anything from undertakers to muck-spreaders, even dancing instructors proceeded by demonstration (finger) steps on believing girls' outstretched palms! Andrea met Len at the Spa. That night he was a brain surgeon. Being a district nurse she was able to lead him up the garden path and the tables were well and truly turned. You see, Andrea knew what he said was codswallop, because in the first instance she had felt his hands. He was a bricklayer. Norman and Len tried their luck years ago with Des and Barbie. No go. The girls saw right through them when they said they were explosive experts and sent them packing.

Our nicest dates were those spent in cosy, popular country pubs set in the heart of Somerset. We usually ate ploughman's lunches in these places, even if it was evening, with our port and stout. One night we ate hot buttered rolls, cheese and pickled onions and I saw Norman in action, regarding his selling technique. That is, he tested how the land lay. He slyly pumped the two young serving wenches as to what products were used in the kitchen. It wasn't his brand, but you can bet your life it is now. After we left the pub he said he supposed I wanted to go for a walk and I nodded vigorously. So 11.30pm found us huddled together walking beside Chew Valley Lake. I think we injured a duck. Norman skimmed a pebble far out across the water and a sudden squawking filled the night air. We immediately turned back to the car, for fear of being attacked by beaks. We sucked a mint each before kissing goodnight. It got to be a habit with us.

Norman had a hole in his back. He had recently been in hospital to have a cyst removed. He was naughty one evening whilst in hospital............. Norman and a bed mate pitched a ton of Smarties at a sleeping patient lying opposite them. They were aiming for his open mouth. Poor chap's bed was littered when he awoke next morning.

With his job Norman attended several conferences, often in London, which meant dinner on his expense account and drinks in Soho beforehand. I queried "and what else besides?" once, and he replied, "Don't be flippant Info." He rechristened me Info. His first question every date, after an initial greeting of "Hello sailor", was "Got any information for me?" He had it in mind to plant me as a spy in one of his arch rival firms and offered to supply me with a trilby, off white trench coat, dark glasses and a brief-case.

Norman had numerous names for me. One afternoon he came knocking on the door enquiring, "Does Enid Blyton live here?" (That was because I told him I wrote lengthy letters to Rish in Canada every week.) I was in the bath at the time, but informed him later that I would rather be called Dickens, so Dickens it was. That day he handed Dad a bulky envelope to give me, which Dad in turn pushed under the bathroom door when Norman had gone. I guessed what it was, my packet of soup, Scotch Broth, which he had forgotten to give me on our previous date. A message was written on it addressed to his little lady. I was indeed little stood alongside him. Oh, he gave me a whisk too, because I complained his soup went lumpy when I heated it.

Our dates would end up on Runway Number Nine in the moonlight. The rogue took me plane spotting where there were no longer any planes to be seen – the old Bristol Airport which had been shut down for donkey's years. There were quite a few other parked cars besides ours though. I believe a girl from Ford Road got stuck down a manhole there trying to elude a boyfriend.

Unfortunately, Norman had faults that bugged me; the same faults I could ignore or tolerate in other people. He would invite himself in for a cup of coffee instead of waiting to be asked. He also walked across our lawn instead of taking the path and was always at the front door before me, often with muddy shoes. I got irritated too, because he threw toffee wrappers out of the car window as we drove along. I was hard on him I suppose. He was a huge man, but I found him boyish. Mum, Dad and Nan quite liked him.

On Christmas Eve Norman drove me round Bristol looking for drunks. We counted three and a half. One led on his back comatose, another being hauled along in the middle of two friends, the third was a bundle of human flesh slumped across a chap's shoulders and the half drunk was sat on the kerb by the Town map with his head down through his knees. We came home and Norman insisted on playing cricket with our balloons with him the batsman, me the bowler and Mum the stump. Mum left us eventually with Norman calling after her he'd be up later to tuck her in and tell Dad to look the other way. It was my turn to be teased then. He swore I had my mini panties on when his hand slipped to my rump and he twanged the elastic against my skin.

I did find out though that Norman not only gave me a load of flannel, but also told one or two out and out porkies. I told him if he went into a confessional box he wouldn't come out in a month of Sundays. I therefore went right off him. Now, sometimes, I refer to him unkindly as Horrible Big Fat Norman and the girls know exactly who I'm talking about. They never liked him. He did too give me a box of chocolates at Christmas, a big box I grant you, but they were his firm's own make and he got them for nothing I bet. I bought him a bottle of the world's best aftershave. Who says so? I say so. At that price it must be. Hai Karate became Kama Sutra when I asked for it.

Therefore, as we were getting on each other's nerves, there was nothing for it but to end our relationship, probably both breathing a sigh of relief to be shot of one another. Norman went out with the old year and now it's January 1973.

TIME TO MOVE ON

And now I no longer dream of Ben. For a long long time I dozed and idled a great many spare moments thinking of him, sometimes smiling to myself at a 'warm' and pleasant memory and other times trying not to be bitter and begrudge him happiness. Once I dreamt that Ben and I did get back together again. We came across one another in a dirt tunnel. Everyone in the world was living under the ground at the time. We set up home together in our own burrow and it was quite nice. Twice in the last year he has brought me home from the Spa. The first time he switched on the car radio and the song being sung was 'The Second Time Around'. It didn't apply to us. The second time we went back to his new flat for a coffee. I noticed the Birthday Cushion Card and Christmas Cushion Card I had given him were both fixed to the wall. I'm glad he liked the pictures on them. I also saw, however, that the words of love on them had been neatly blocked out. Whilst he was in the kitchen I glanced round the room and was quite stunned to see my photo – the roses grow on you one – was on the sideboard. There was another photo too of a pretty girl.

It was nice to catch up on news of old acquaintances, although I was sad to hear that Alfie had died, and the landlord's wife at The Moon. Winston still runs the pub, Ben told me, and continues to fill up the lounge with fine displays of flowers, which he grows and arranges himself for the pleasure of patrons. Ben told me that several times when he has been in the pub Lloyd has casually swaggered up to him, waved my New Year's Card under his nose and said in his ear, "Do you know whose handwriting this is?" Ben knew of course. Unforgivably, Lloyd did it when Ben was there with another girl, but I do forgive him. Ben remarked that after we split up his only true friend remaining at The Moon was Mr. Poynter's Labrador. He couldn't talk. But I know that isn't really true. His friends, who became my friends, care about him.

He asked me what I had been doing with myself and courtesy forced me to reply a bit of this, that and the other. It didn't sound right somehow. Now he has a girlfriend who gives him salad with flower tomatoes. He's changed. Gone is the old sports car. Now he has a flashy hard top. Gone the old bed-sit. Now it's a luxury flat in Clifton where the bed folds into the wall. He even looks different. Des and Pru have noticed the change in his appearance, not just me. He is so smart. He's quite friendly with Pru now. I'm not sure how friendly though. The last time he brought me home, as I got out of the car he said "Goodbye Trouble". Oh well, allow yourself one last sigh Pange and be done with it.

Now quick, change the subject, think of Nanny Rosebud, this past year I have spent many weekends with Nan. We sit by firelight and Nan tells me eye-popping tales concerning country folk. For starters there is Bobby the Bear, Happy Legs and Mr. Glasshouse. Aunt Beat, Aunt Carrie, Aunt Kate, Nelly and Pansy live in the same road. (The last two share Herbert.) Nan's beloved neighbour Aunt Tidville died soon after Aunt Olly and now Nan has Lulu living next door to her on the one side. Nan said people got no right to call Lulu the mad 'oman just because she stays in men's baggy, striped pyjamas all day long. She puts her boots on and goes out to the ice cream van dressed like that. She's way past ninety with hardly any hair left on her scalp, only odd tufty bits here and there. There is the sad decrepit old man who told Nan he is the most miserable man on earth (and Nan knows why, because years back he gave his own daughter a baby and drove her down the asylum). Yes, Nan and I ignore the telly. I tell her my troubles and she tells me about life. We attack the sherry bottle and get through a plate of polony sandwiches while we're about it. We have gone to bed quite tiddly at times with hiccups.

On one visit not long ago Nan opened her sideboard cupboard to reveal bottles of stout, sherry, egg flip, brandy, phosphorene tonic wine, cherry and apricot wines, plus, do you know how many boxes of Ritz biscuits? Fifteen!

Ritz biscuits are one of her life preservers. The two other things, which she says keeps her going, are her fire and the brandy bottle. She is quite partial to brandy snaps too. The one thing Nan doesn't like, in relation to where she lives now, is that she can hear the church bells on a Sunday morning. Nan has an aversion to church bells for some reason.

One Sunday morning Nan put her skirt on inside out and didn't know until I noticed it at lunchtime. I only did then, because when Nan poked the fire I saw a money spider on her Long Johns. "He can definitely stay on my britches" (breeches) Nan said, and he did. If I stay overnight at Nan's we take the thermos to bed with us for an early morning cuppa. She keeps a large cold magnet in the bed to stave off cramp. Mum told her to. Last time I was there Nan had a bad turn, when she saw me come back from the loo in the middle of the night, and needed the wet flannel on her forehead. Her heart was racing. She murmured that she wouldn't make old bones. (She's eighty.) Earlier she had been whacking Flying Daddy Long Legs with her Long Johns. Poundage goes on at Nan's. I've counted eight taters on my plate before now. Nan will not hear of me dieting. She eats mouse helpings herself. She says I was a big young-un and therefore I had to turn out to be a big strapping girl. Nan has a luxuriant head of hair she keeps looking neat and tidy under a hair net. She went without one once, but it didn't suit her. She won't go to the hairdresser. Aunt Rose's daughter-in-law gives her a home perm every so often but Nan, when she feels weighed down with hair, grabs handfuls and hacks away, either throwing her tresses on the fire or putting them out for the birds to line their nests with.

Darling Nan, she went to a Church fete a couple of months ago, and bought a jar of shrimps. She kept them upright in her bag so as not to spill the vinegar. When she got home she admonished, "You fool Alice". She had been looking forward to having them for tea, but couldn't because they were candy ones. Poor Nan can't see brilliantly. She's got cataracts. She gets the kiddies knocking on her door for sweets so the shrimps didn't last long.

Nan does miss Aunt Olly. Part of her day is now spent sat in the window of her little bungalow watching the world go by, quite a quiet world out in the country. Her hands constantly doubles over then unfolds the hem of her pinny. She has a sleep most afternoons in the armchair. I wondered why, when sat there, she would periodically glance behind her into the longways mirror. If she does that she can see clearly what and who is in the road outside. I'm ever so fond of Aunt Rose, Granfer's sister, who comes down to sit with Nan nearly every evening. She says she's fine company – falls asleep in the chair she does. She occasionally brings with her little Eleanor, her great-granddaughter of seven, who sits on the floor and is such a chatterbox. She says to Nan about eight o'clock, "Isn't it time we had a cup of tea?" She is a sweet pretty child and hates it when Nan isn't home. She refuses to believe that Nan has come in with us for a short stay, or gone to Aunty Vi's or Aunty Gwen's. Aunt Rose has to take her down and hammer on Nan's door. Only when Nan doesn't answer will Eleanor realise it's true and return home crying. Aunt Rose greets me, Dave and Al with a cheery "Hello my cockers". I can't help but smile. Nan and Aunt Rose are firm believers that should a dog howl for a long period of time, or kids pass by kicking cans, it means there is going to be a death in the locality.

Last Christmas pensioners were given a £10 bonus and whereas others said they would spend theirs on goodies: food, coal, whisky, etc, Nan said adamantly it would go towards burying her. That Christmas in our house Nan opened a surprise present from Dave. We watched as she unravelled layer upon layer of tissue paper. First she thought it was a bone, then a curler, and then a date stone. At last she uncovered a tiny battery. She had remarked earlier that there wasn't much power left in her. She turned to Dave and smiling at him called him a bleeder. When she left she was calling us all good young uns. The day she went home Dave came into the bedroom at 7.30am to say cheerio to his "sweetheart" and to kiss her. He came in again two minutes later for "a last look at my darling". He had put a going away present in her bag, which he did tell me to warn her about – an overly ripe, squashy, smelly nana. Her last quip the night before was, when watching a telly prog to do with cannabis, "I've never taken cannon balls". We laughed and she changed her mind and thought it was instead cannibals. Al put a pair of his red silky football shorts on Nan, but she whipped them off quickly when Dad went for his camera. She did consent to her photo being taken with Dave, sat together on the settee, and the instant before Dad flashed Dave put a big furry joke spider on her head.

Nan's best friend is Nelson. He is eighty-six years young and rides his bike daily, even as far afield as Bath, which is a fair distance from Farmborough.

His eyesight is excellent, because I have witnessed him threading cotton through a needle with the smallest eye. He is also a champion darts player in the Butcher's Arms team, and will knock skittles down as well if they're a man short. He raves about the goodness in whisky same as Nan does about brandy. Nan knew his wife. Nelson smokes a pipe and his wife did. It used to be clay ones. They didn't get muddled up whose was who, because Nelson has always had a very long stemmed one. Nan often buys him an ounce of 'bacco for being such a gem. At the Post Office they let him sign Alice Mary Bridges in Nan's pension book, to enable him to collect her money, because she can't walk far now. He'll come round with a turnip for her, and when the street isn't looking he will run in with a bucket of coal, which he gets free from pit.

Nan is a dab hand in the coal shed herself. She wields a hammer as cleverly as a miner and his pickaxe. I get frightened for her eyes and mine, but no fear is in Nan. I'm her assistant. I load up the buckets and carry them indoors.

Nelson has never worn a tie in his life, not even on his wedding day. His shirt is buttoned up to the neck though.

Nan has been told to bang on the wall if ever she needs him. She had to bump for him the other day and he came dapping in straightaway enquiring "What's up Alice?" and emptied the bucket when Nan was sick. He made her a cuppa and wouldn't let her get up from the sofa for the rest of the day. Early morning he comes in to check on her. He worries if the curtains remain drawn at 9am and taps the bedroom window calling out "Alice, be alright?" until she lets him know all's well. It's comforting that he keeps an eye on her. Uncle Jim was hanging Nan's toilet roll on the wall the other day and the minute Nelson heard hammering he came hurrying in, full of anxiety, questioning, "Be you alright Alice?"

Last week Nelson told Nan he dreamt he was getting married again. He didn't say to whom. Nan gets teased regularly as to whether Nelson has proposed. The warden of the old people's homes has got her name down to be bridesmaid. Nan says to us Nelson is her dearest friend and companion, but she wouldn't want him "that way". Nobody can take the place of Granfer Bridges, or Father as Nan refers to him. It shows that Nelson has a soft spot for Nan. He told Mum last Wednesday that he was trying to persuade

Nan to go to Jersey with him for two weeks holiday, and he said it with a twinkle in his eye. Nan says he is forever asking her to go for a ride on the handlebars of his bike. In some ways we do wish they would marry, because Nan isn't safe to live on her own. She has dizzy spells and keeps swooning. Rheumatics in the head she calls it. Last time she was in with us she fainted twice. I picked her up and carried her to the settee and when she opened her eyes she queried, "Where be I to?"

Nan chides Nelson because he will not have paper on the walls of his bungalow, just gloss paint, and he's got a sack down instead of a doormat.

A few weeks back, Nelson was quite ill with dysentery. "Main dicky he was" Nan said. Nan went in to see him every day instead of the other way round. One day she swept his path and scrubbed his front porch with soapy water. She told him she had ummed and aahed about doing it. She thought it might offend him, but he urged, "Alice, you do whatever you've a mind to."

Once, lying in Nan's bed, I heard him through the door enquire, "Is the babby still sleeping? (Me!!!) I've come in to change her nappy." I smiled into the pillow at his witticism. I heard Nan tell him we were having a piece of chicken for dinner. He told Nan a wonderful story of how he went to his daughter-in-law's for Sunday dinner, and he had to rush from the room when the chicken was carved, because she had left the muck and innards inside, poo and all! He himself boils his kettle and cooks all his meals on the fire. His couple of saucepans and frying pan are black as the ace of spades. He smiled when he informed Aunty Vi and me that he had had a heavy electric bill last quarter, seventeen bob! Nan and Nelson still work in old pounds, shillings and pence.

Aunty Vi told Nelson he is a marvel and a saint, which he thought very whimsical. He said his remedy for a long, happy and healthy life is "Look out to thee stomach, never worry about a thing and take herbs to cure any ailment." He chuckled then and indicated to his pocket watch clipped to his waistcoat (Nan said next Christmas she might knit him a "wescot") and said his two tickers keep time with one another. He had come in singing and dancing, because he was so happy he said. As he left, he told Nan and me not to fight.

Nan snagged her stocking on Tuesday, getting over the fence separating her bungalow from Nelson's – he said she would never do that again. He went out, dug up the posts and cut the wires. Recently he gave her a prop for her washing line.

What was it Nan told Mum on Wednesday (that's Mum's visiting day), as they sat in front of a blazing fire eating tripe and onions? Oh yes, poor Nan had her hot water bottle burst in bed during the Saturday night. She had a gulp of brandy before she got back into bed on the dry side, but she couldn't get comfortable. She couldn't understand why until she realised she had her slippers on. Nelson helped Nan turn the mattress next day. He said she should have bumped the wall and he would have come to help her put her clothes on. Arthritis makes it difficult.

It is all very well going out Nan's for a weekend, but I hate leaving her. Last Sunday evening I left her alone again, as Songs of Praise came on the telly. Nan was singing quietly with the choir "Abide with me" as I closed the door. I stumbled on homeward bound. No lamps to light the way out there. I stood in the doorway of the Butcher's Arms, in an effort to shut out the cold night air. Hilarity could be heard coming from the bar, but my ears were pricked for the familiar trundle of the Bristol bus wheels. I blinked as car headlights flashed by heading into Bristol. They would be home before me. My thoughts returned to solitary little Nan. How long could our Wonder of Wonders survive? My bus came and I sat down to ponder anew. It was pointless looking out of the window, because only my face stared back. Beyond my face was rather monotonous darkness. Yet when I had come to Farmborough the day before, the bus had cruised to an unofficial stop when a pheasant, with beautifully rich colouring, rose up from the wind chilled clods of earth. Possessing great dignity, he strutted bold as brass across our path. He held his head high, wanting us to look at him and we did. Many pheasants are to be seen picking their way through the fields near Marksbury Turnpike, and streaking low in the sky overhead. Mum, as a girl, would walk miles across similar fields to a farm for skimmed milk, and then convey a large, heavy pan home without spilling a drop. "Worth it" she said, "to taste Mam's milk puddings".

Unfailingly, after two days with Nan I'm sent home with more than I go with. Now last time she gave me a serviceable Marks and Sparks roll-on, with short legs, she had acquired and put to one side for me, because she thought it would do my back good. I have worn it, although I wouldn't tell a soul other than family. In this day and age it isn't very feminine attire. It did pull in my tum and bum, but the fat on my thighs pushed and squeezed down through the leg holes, which was a dreadful sight to behold.

How Dave and Al dote on Nan, plague her, lavish love and kisses on her. It's Dave who calls her Rosebud. I have seen Dave go and fetch her from Elsie's, lift her up in his arms and carry her squealing down the street, and Ally declared she was showing her garters. They tease and torment her relentlessly. At mealtimes in our house Dave issues her with a teaspoon, a meat fork, and carving knife to eat with, and a saucer to eat off of. Time and again he removes her cup of tea when her back is turned. While she was with us for Whitsun, Dave yelled at the meal table one day in a Sergeant Major's voice, "Sit up straight Alice, shoulders back, chest out", but Nan was quick to retort, "I've got none to stick out, like Angela". What sauce, and I told her I was finished with her. Dave then wrote Alice in big letters on the steamy window, and when Bloss told him off he said "It weren't I wot did it, t'were Alice". "Hi my man, you're a bad un. Go to hell and pump thunder" Nan said, and gave him a playful tap. He is her man, because he's a second Granfer. Every time she comes down the garden path Dave begins singing in a loud voice, "They're changing guard at Buckingham Palace, Christopher Robin went down with Alice", and so it goes on unceasingly, but Nan laps it up. She has only to sit in the armchair and along comes Dave with a pile of large cushions to cover her with in case she gets cold. Mind you, there is no life in our cushions. Next time Nan is in with us she is going to stuff them with my old tights that I've been saving. I washed them the other day. There was nothing but tights on the line from start to finish. It took me ages to unravel them, because they wound themselves round and round the line. I should have pegged the toes.

I was going to say Mum is shown some mercy if Nan is here, but it isn't always the case. Dave made Nan bandage his head and arm one day and put dollops of strawberry jam on his chin. He was lying moaning and groaning on the settee when Mum came in from shopping, simply to put the wind up her and give Nan a laugh.

Nan is a comic. At Whitsun we were sat watching Neil Diamond singing on the telly. Nan wasn't interested. She was patching sheets. I told Nan I thought Mr. Diamond was sexy, but she wasn't impressed. Her comment was

"Isn't his head ragged, he could do with some of my curlers". Moments passed. We were quiet when out popped "I'd sooner have Best". We wondered whom Nan was referring to, because we knew Nelson's surname wasn't Best. "Who be on about Alice?" Ally quizzed on behalf of us all. "George the football" she said. That reminds me of when the boys were watching an International Soccer Match on telly. Inter-Milan were playing and Dave and Al had Nan believing there were players on the pitch named Cannelloni, Bolognaise, Spaghetti, Macaroni, Tapioca and Semolina. I told Nan we were going to see Neil Diamond live on stage, Dave and I, and she replied she would rather see the Dwarfs. Years back she and Granfer had seen Snow White and the Seven Dwarfs on ice at the Hippodrome. Granfer had been highly amused and called 'em cunning little buggers Nan said. Dave looked up and said "Nan you're 'ooden". That was because she was dozing earlier on and, upon waking, she said she felt 'ooden not wooden. Pop calls Nan kitten, as she goes upstairs on all fours. One thing Nan finds incredible is the amount of food we three kids can devour. Whenever she enters our kitchen she comes upon one or other of us there, chomping. "Grubbing again" smiles Nan.

Nan has to laugh, but we are used to it; before Mum goes to bed she places a dozen pairs of shoes on the mat in front of the back door. She thinks if we have an intruder she will hear him fall over the shoes, and he would automatically panic and bolt. I asked if she would go downstairs to check whether he had gone. She said no, she would call down "Who's there?" She hasn't yet heard Pop go flying over them when he comes home after nights. Dave told Nan, Pops has already had a dozen broken noses so far this year because of Mum and her shoes.

One time Nan stayed with us Mrs. Hewlitt, next door, brought in a lovely gift to cheer her up. It was a dead leaves arrangement, exquisitely done.

Once, when Nan was sat quietly watching the ballet on telly, she suddenly came out with "Look at his bunch". That's not rude if you think about it. Now when I had thrush Ally-boy said "Pange you're a dink, but I'm sorry about your Billies". I told him I thought Billies was rude and he should stick to Wilfrid. That's my word for it, male or female.

I went to bed before Nan one night. She came upstairs at half-ten. I was nearly asleep, but she startled me awake with the words "Damn you, you bad bitch". I thought to myself, what have I done? However, it wasn't me she was damning, but her watch (or herself). She had dropped it in the glass of water beside the bed, and her hand was scrabbling around inside trying to retrieve it as I opened my eyes.

Dave dreamt that Nan ran onto a football pitch with orange segments. Dad too had a funny dream the other night. He dreamt that Granfer came racing down the road doing 100mph on an incredibly powerful motorbike. Granf was crouched low over the bodywork and was wearing a crash helmet and studded leather gear. Little Nan was hanging on to him for dear life and she fainted over our hedge when she got off. These ton-up kids were playing on Dad's mind when he got up for 'earlies', so much so he walked to the end of our road, on his way to work, before turning round and retracing his steps. He realised he had forgotten to put his teeth in.

Dad often has odd dreams and I'm forever hearing him cry out in the middle of the night. His mate Benny is just as bad. The other night he dreamt that both he and Pops were surgeons operating on another one of their mates, Charley. Instead of blood coming out of him, brick dust poured forth. Benny and Dad panicked, and tried to shovel it all back into Charley, but the more they shovelled the more poured out. Benny kept shouting frantically to Dad, "Sew the bugger up Tom, sew him up" and that's when his wife woke him. She had heard enough of his ranting and raving in dreamland. Dad and Benny get called Bill and Ben by the other engine drivers at the sheds.

TASTERS OF FAMILY LIFE

We had a fright this morning. It's Sunday. It was early, 8.30ish I suppose, and only Dad was up. A wood pigeon hurtled through a windowpane in our living room. He had seen himself in the mirror and flew in to investigate, or so we gather. It was like a slaughterhouse with blood dripping from his wounds. There were feathers, broken china and glass splinters scattered about the room. He lay dazed in the armchair, but when Dad tried to pick him up he flew round the room splattering all and sundry. The rest of us took fright and vacated the living room, leaving Dad to somehow or other shoo the bird out. What a commotion.

Dave and Al have got it in for Dad. Dad hardly ever sits down, and Dave tells him stood up he makes the place look untidy. He was outside the kitchen door before lunch, sharpening the carving knife on the step, when a sudden shower soaked him – the brothers at the bathroom window, one armed with a Jiffy lemon and the other with a squeezy washing up liquid bottle. Poor Pop. After a glass of sherry for starters, Dad fell asleep over his dinner and Mum spooned a sprout onto the floor. She picked it up, dusted it off then ate it. As she says, it all goes down the same way. Last Sunday lunchtime Dad had two glasses of sherry before going to work, left the house, walked into the outside privy door and knocked his hat off.

Mum came out with a funny last Sunday. A storm was brewing and gale blowing and she said she wasn't going in the bath because it might blow her out. Can you imagine, a whoosh of wind up the plughole and Bloss does a Mary Poppins swirl around the bathroom, all fourteen stone of her. She insists we listen out for her when she goes in the bath. One day she was up there and we decided to play, loudly, an eerie Canadian record called Loon Noises (the night cries of wild birds and animals). That scared the living daylights out of her, as she wondered what on earth was going on over the golfcourse. She hasn't been sensible this week. She came out with face-tommy (vasectomy), Herb Ashfelt (Alpert) and she stressed that you get warts from inserting hands in boiled egg water. I ask you!

Mum regularly goes missing for hours. We know exactly where she is. Upstairs, woolly bear hunting. Lin's Mum calls them tanks. No bigger than pin-heads they are, often to be found in bedding. In one search Mum never catches more than a couple to flush down the loo, but she believes there are millions in the house, in everyone's house.

Yesterday she had me on a wasted mission, chasing the milkman in pouring rain wearing only my slippers with the toes worn through. She found it in her pinny, the fiver she thought he had mistakenly nicked. What a flap she got into. Mind you, he had grinned at her. She had a huge lipstick smudge on her cheek, planted by me, which she had forgotten about.

I've got a sore throat. It feels fur lined. I've tried gargling, but I'm pretty hopeless at it. I had saline coming out of my nose and gulps of it went down my throat, but none stayed revolving round my tonsils to bathe and soothe them. The noises I made were revolting. Mum said she would show me how it was done. She claimed to be an expert after years of practice on ulcers, but her attempt proved to be a miserable failure. She spluttered, because Al and I made her laugh fit to bust and bust she did. She would have stood in a puddle had she not crossed her legs. Dad would have frowned if he had been here to witness our unsavoury antics. Only yesterday Mum rushed to the loo at bursting point, passing Al on the stairs. He said it was a shame she couldn't tie a knot in it like a man could do at such times. She told him off for making this rude remark, and said he should wash his mouth out with salt water, but later came and whispered to me what he had said, chuckling at the same time. I remember when he had a barking cough and Mum said she would get him a bottle of cough mixture. He was fed up hack hacking and told her, if it wasn't strong enough to make his goolies fall off, it wasn't worth getting and he didn't want it. Mum tittered, but said she wouldn't let him watch Steptoe and Son any more. Bloss thinks she can still protect the boys. She switches off if a sexy programme comes on the telly. Being twenty and twenty-two they stop what they're doing and switch on again.

I'm not elaborating honest, as it wasn't that long ago Dave and Al peeped from their bedroom window when a chap brought me home from a dance. I knew they were there. I got an uncomfortable feeling. In their twenties, and talk about a couple of giggling Gerties. They have, however, recently stopped, because I said at their age they should. They wouldn't like it if I spied on them. Funny thing, whenever I get a nice new boyfriend and Dave or Al acquires a nice new girlfriend, we take them to see Nan before bringing them home to meet Mum and Dad.

Dave is growing a tash. It's coming along nicely. Huh, a little while back he was making rude comments about Al's efforts. Al, at the time, had a scrap of fluff above his mouth barely visible, and Dave went round calling him fungus face and Walrus. I thought Dave's was going to be Mandarin style, but he corrected me by stating it was a Mexican Bandit. Al has kept his whiskers. Nan detests hairy faces, yet admits Granfer wouldn't have been the same without.

On Wednesday Al left a note on the kitchen table for Mum to read when she came home from Nan's. It read "Goono, chips, pancakes or omelette, a four egg one, at quarter to ten please". Cheeky varmint!

Dave keeps pestering me, inferring that Mum has been saying horrible things about me. When I go to tackle her, and tell her I know she has never loved me, she says she hasn't uttered a cheep and it's him, Divid, being a scandalmonger, a wrecker of tranquility and a stirrer causing strife. Him and me will come to blows much more of it. I've got 'em about me anyway, the doldrums. Dad is waving the red-hot poker and threatening to brand the boys who insist on calling him Stoker, because he is always tending the fires in the living room and kitchen.

Dave has now called Al a great outsize Jesse, because he buys gaudy pants without fly fronts, and also on account of him using poof powder (talc). Dave believes there's nothing more manly than a good honest sweat smell. Rish is well aware of this because, after coming back from a run and finding me writing an airmail letter to her, he has wiped a BOey finger on a corner of the page and with it sent his love. A dead fly accompanied his thumbprint once. It had drowned in Dave's sweat. On the quiet Dave uses just as much smelly stuff as Al.

The first thing Dave does when he comes in from a run is to make toast, even before a bath. He requests a cup of tea too if there is somebody close by who can make him one, because he swears he doesn't know how to brew it himself. Oh yes he does. Al doesn't though.

I've quirks myself. The last thing I do before going out, whatever time of day or night, is to help myself to a glass of water. I've also gotten into the habit each night of getting up from my bed several times to check that the immersion heater is switched off. I've never found it on yet. I can't stop myself.

Dave came home at three this morning. He did a jig with me on the landing – I was on my way to spend a penny – because he had smashed his record. Not bad seeing he has had tendon trouble. It must be the result of sitting in soothing bowls of water for hours on end, chopping and changing from hot to cold. When I say sit, I mean he sits in the armchair dangling his feet in the bowls.

Al is better looking now Dad said. He is sporting a black eye and suspected broken nose, acquired when playing football against the police force. He received an elbow jab from an unfair cop. Al preferred not to go to hospital, because he said he would be kept in for a few days, given an injection in the arm, another up the bum, and a surgeon would bang away at his bent and puffy nose with a rubber hammer. Al should be able to do a marvellous high kick due to his height, but he won't for fear of wrenching his hamstring.

I wondered who the devil Dave was speaking to out in the garden when I overheard him say "Hi Jock, what you hanging about for?" Al's jock strap was on the washing line. Then a bit later it was "Begging your pardon Jock" as his head walked into it. Dave talks to the lavvy flush as well. I heard him the other day. It is cantankerous and gentle coaxing got him nowhere. Dave pulled and pulled muttering that he didn't know the right combination, then called it a dang stupid thing, amongst other sordid vehement outbursts, until it obliged him. He gave a wild yahoo when it did deem to flush, and I heard him follow it up with "That's my boy". He probably gave the pipe a fond chuck with his fist too. I heard what went on, because I was sat on the top stair waiting for the loo to become vacant again. I say again, I was in there before Dave, powdering my nose, but got ejected, as his business couldn't wait.

Without fail, Al will come in at one, two or three in the morning, humming to his heart's content, sometimes loud enough to wake us as he climbs the stairs. He's usually happy-go-lucky, even-tempered and loving. Yesterday he wasn't any of those things. He threatened to knock me about the house from room to room when he caught hold of me. (I was in the bathroom at the time. It appears I'm always in the bathroom when he wants to go 'somewhere'. I am when anybody wants to go 'somewhere'. I live in there to hear them talk.) What's wrong with the outside one I'd like to know? He was canoodling with me next minute though, after which I told him off, because he hadn't wiped up a plate he had used, which I had washed. Dad scoffed he wouldn't know how. It's possible. Then I caught him up in my boudoir using my hair-drier. He had a pair of damp trousers lying on my bed, and was only running the drier over them! I'll run over him if I get the pip.

Occasionally Dave and Al call me a turd cake, but I let it pass. Dave has though, a minute ago, called me a stupid great idiot. I came upstairs to find he had swiped 'my' two bar electric fire so I cussed him. I went down and got the other one, only to find the lead was too short for my bedroom, so I went to him again and demanded a swap and got called those words. However, I'm warming nicely now. I should, because I'm wearing brother-in-law's old dressing gown on top of a woolly jumper and trousers. Curses though, I've got the sneezes this morning, gravelly cough and that irritating internal itch in my left lug, which is driving me crazy. Ooh, I would love to have a dig with a knitting needle. The only relief I get is if I rub my tongue back and forth across the roof of my mouth. Mum reckons that my head is wet inside from too many hair washes. Dave says if it's water on the brain I've got he knows the cure. Muggins says, "What's that then?" I ask for what I get, don't I – a tap on it. It is peculiar, but I do think I've got a screw loose. Last night, and there have been others, when doing my few trimming exercises, I noticed every time I did a waist bend to the left something rattled in my napper, like a bean in a doll. I can't go to the Doc's and say I've got an itch in my ear I can't get at, and a bean rattling round in my head. Pru said the itch could be the result of my first wisdom tooth appearing, but I'm not convinced.

My eyes also have felt weary recently, so I did go to Block's, the Optician. Both the receptionist and the optician asked me how Dad's nose was. He has had a break out on his nose caused by new glasses and conjunctivitis tears. More hospital treatment! He now goes for his eyes and nose, his stomach and his feet. Oh yes, his feet as well. The hospital have drilled his shoes and padded them with cork. They gave him injections in the heel too. He did have air in one injection that worried us. Mum enquired, when he came home from work the next day, "You didn't die, did you darling?" Pops answered that he didn't think so.

Pop gets a regular overhauling at the hospital and undergoes murderous tests. He nonetheless comes home smiling from said appointments, never complains, not even the time when the barium meal went right through him, down his trouser legs and into his shoes while he was sat on the bus. He has been put on a pump and blown up like a balloon, wired to a machine like a robot, and has yet more pullings-apart to go through. Still, he does enjoy his nibbles of carrot, shreds of raw cabbage and champs of bran, which is a good thing. When Dave saw a photo of Dad coming out of the water in one of Canada's great lakes, he asked if it was an ad for Oxfam (after he had commented, "Oh look, the Loch Ness Monster"). Now Pops isn't so thin and his weight has gone up and Dave, in a good mood, refers to him as Charles Atlas. In a bad mood it's Mighty Mouse.

I remember Bloss being ill not long before they went to Canada. A week following her smallpox jab it was. I had come home late one night and she called out to me to take in the po, because she felt sick. I rushed into the bedroom (Pops was on nights). Bloss grinned and said she was all right, but next minute she went ghastly white – normally she has a high colouring – and fell back on the pillow. Her mouth dropped open and her irises shot up into her head out of sight, leaving just the whites on show. I shook her, but felt sure she was dead and gave a blood-curdling scream, "Dave". Dave and Al woke simultaneously and came running. I think the three of us were near to tears, as they heaved ho to pull Bloss upright. In a flash the colour flooded back into her cheeks, eyes righted themselves, and there she was beaming at us and saying phew she was hot. I wouldn't leave her and climbed into Pop's vacant place. Impossible to sleep though with that hard bolster, and I was relieved when Dad fished me out next morning at seven o'clock. Dad sometimes wakes up after 'nights' to find the wigged and bespectacled balsa wood head lying on the pillow beside him.

TIME FLIES

I'm off work with tonsillitis. Dave woke me up at 1.30am singing 'I'm not saying that I love you' (one of Gord Lightfoot's). He kissed me, although I was germy, and said "You had better get up in the morning and make me a cup of tea or I'll come up and smash your chesty-wobbles in, if I can find them".

And now, how many years have passed since I began my meandering? I've lost track. It's a long time since I left Wimpeys. I remember the day well. I walked out of the office with a new watch, a travelling alarm clock, tonsillitis, "superseded" stamped on the back of my hand and two left-over cream cakes.

I've now worked for my Mr. H and my Mr. B for three years. We share everything from choc-bars to Granny Smiths. Mr. H is the main boss. He's smashing. If ever I was going to have a crush on a boss he'd be my first choice. For him I even clean the loo and hoover the office. Mr. B is semi-retired and can't seem to pass his driving test. He's had countless goes at it. They're both ever such good listeners and are always ready to lend an ear to my tales of woe and offer advice, especially re my love life. Because Mr. H is thirty and Mr. B is way into his sixties the advice differs tremendously. They're both attractive married men and I do listen to what they have to say. Yesterday, after changing my typewriter ribbon, I typed without thinking 'The Cat sat on the Mat'. I left it in the machine and went off to lunch. On my return I found Mr. H had scribbled 'Really!!!!' beside it. He picked up a girl yesterday lunchtime and went to see her allotment, strictly business. That was the story he gave me on his return to the office at four o'clock. (We're in the Property business.) One day last week I was taking dictation while his little daughter played happily at my feet. He was baby-sitting. Anything goes. It's just that there are days I feel a little bit lonely, with only the three of us, sometimes two and often me by myself, alone for hours on end with nothing but the church clock for company, yet I'm in the heart of Bristol. Not that you would ever realise it. My office is cut off from the rest of the world. It has been my choice though.

The last three years have been quite happy, very full ones, but I've been heading nowhere. I've been one man's sweetheart, even worn his ring. Stupid really, when I knew at the outset there would be no future for us. Sam, what have you done to me? He's a nice man in many many ways, an influential man and an interesting person certainly. Indeed, his photo has appeared on the front of the Sunday Times supplement. That was in his Private Eye days. It didn't matter to me that he's years older than Poppers. The family likes him. My friends frowningly don't. Nan says, "He isn't a messer. He isn't smammy." I have been wined and dined in the best restaurants, taken on a memorable holiday to Greece, met some fascinating people, and I have known a fair proportion of happiness with him. There has though been awful, gut wrenching unhappiness too.

We met by fate. I had gone to the Spa with Pru. She met a magnificent creature, Clive. I had a lousy evening. Pru insisted on taking me home along with Clive who, I don't know for what reason, didn't have his car. We got to Pru's Mini and discovered a puncture. Naturally Clive fixed it, as we looked on. When the task was completed his hands were filthy and he suggested we stop off at his boss's flat, a stone's throw away, so he could wash away the grime. We did and that's how I met Sam – Champagne all the way. Yes, he's quite a man.

But things need to change, and for the better.

Not so long ago a girlfriend saw me in a pub, but from my back view she certainly didn't realise it was me. She thought I was a middle-aged woman until I turned round and realisation dawned. When she told me this it sunk in. I knew it to be the truth. I'm twenty-five, but the last few years have added twenty years. Hopefully, a new wardrobe, new hair-do, in fact a new life altogether can turn the clock back to where it should be. I suppose I must think it's possible.

And what of Sam?

I often wished he was a pea in a pod and not a big shot forever in the limelight, but he likes to be up there with the nobs, and usually I was alongside him. He told me the reason his wife wouldn't divorce him was to prevent him making a fool of himself. Oh yes, I knew he had had a long standing relationship before me with a stunning Malaysian girl, who got tired of waiting and went off and married someone else. There were those who, to my face, called his penthouse the Sin Bin. The times I've spent alone in that flat with orders not to open the door, locked in in fact, and "don't answer the phone". He loved women, I knew that from the start, and flirted outrageously even with my own friends, one in particular. One evening at a restaurant he invited the waitresses back to his place for tea and crumpets. They thought him a "lovely man" and commented how lucky I was. The owner of that restaurant referred to me as Madonna, I don't know why. I was hardly a Madonna when I squeezed Sam's blackheads and cut his toe-nails.

Funny how his two daughters accepted me (one was Greek by his first wife), but his two sons didn't and had no wish to meet me. I've played I Spy with his youngest daughter and was highly amused to discover she had dated Al in the past. She met Nan. I even met his ex mother-in-law in Greece, a barrel of a woman who I could sense took a shine to me although she had no English. It was in Greece his first child, a stunning girl older than me, told me I was too good for her father and gave me both love and worry beads.

Greece was beautiful. We drove there and back in Sam's Rover with a couple of friends. Unfortunately, on the journey there I got prickly heat from head to toe, and Bert had an agonizing boil burst on his private and needed urgent medical treatment on arrival. These things apart Greece was one of the highlights of our relationship. We ate squid in the Plaka tavernas in the shadow of the Acropolis, he paid a fortune for us to go to a Bouzouki evening in Athens to listen to the top singers and throw flowers, we dined more than once at the Hilton on caviar and smoked salmon, and a yacht was chartered to the Islands. It was a blissful existence to be sure and very romantica.

Sam often travelled abroad but wouldn't fly – he saw too much in the war. He was in the Royal Air Force. On one trip he brought me back French perfumes and a suede coat from Turkey. His wife had a £2 candlestick from

Woolies in Palma. There were in addition the little mementoes that perhaps meant more, like the pressed Gardenia and the twig with two balls of cotton attached. For one birthday he bought me an expensive coat. I realise now, an older woman's coat. At the time I felt the bee's knees in it until Dave asked if it was the old grey blanket off my bed. I had a delightful surprise birthday party/dinner that year, which he had arranged unbeknown to me. There we were in one of Bristol's plushy restaurants, surrounded by his special friends (who had become mine), drinking champagne when the band started to play and in came a cake covered in candles. I loved dining there. Who wouldn't! Bernard, the maitre d', gave us preferential treatment, which meant gastronomic sweets not on the menu. Waiters would congregate round us to learn, and other diners would look on enviously. Bernard was a fascinating character. At eighteen he had served Hitler one Tuesday in Berlin and Churchill the following Friday in London. We went to a gourmet dinner at 'his' restaurant once. I've got the menu here somewhere in my diary. Oh yes, to start there was wine tasting (4) followed by oysters, duck and orange soup, woodcock, champagne sorbet, venison in wine sauce, veg of course, cheese covered in walnuts, Queen of Sheba for dessert (Bernard's own concoction of meringue, ice cream, cream, exotic fruits and liqueur), four more wines plus a glass of a rare '47 vintage. I had chronic leg ache after, which I put down to the oysters.

And there were parties, always parties. We went to parties in classy strip joints – my first time in a strip club I sat on the floor, front row, surrounded by men, and had a wink from her out front – gaming clubs in London where a friend lost £600 one night, friends' homes where occasional Blue Movies were shown – they made me feel uncomfortable – and many times we had invites to the Officers' Mess. One party was in a Council Flat in London. In attendance were a high class pro, a pop singer (quite famous years ago, now gone to seed), as well as a crook, a pretty but sad looking forty year old with a very young boyfriend, and a woman (fellow in drag) and 'her' boyfriend. These are just a few who spring to mind. It was Bert's party. He's a London taxi driver, a heavy and goodness knows what else besides. Bert's mistress hated his youngest son who lived with them. She told me so. I thought he was a cutie. He was nine and when he was told I would be sleeping with him, but that it would be in a single bed, he remarked "all the better". Sam's friends were out of my league, but I feel sure they accepted me. They had style and presence: there was a banker, a jeweller, a doctor, a wine merchant, a newspaper editor, singers and a chairman of the board, bigwigs here and bigwigs there. One he introduced me to thought at first I was Sam's daughter. Others may have thought the same initially, but didn't say so. We sometimes had dinner round Dick the Brick's. His wife was the sister of Sam's past Malaysian flame. One day their little boy walked in and said "Mummy, you're a black Sambo". It didn't enter his head that he could be one too. Good friends once asked when we were getting married, and Sam's reply was that we had an understanding. And so I wore the eye-catching engagement ring he gave me, but only for a certain length of time. Eventually it had to be returned to its rightful owner after a debt was paid off. I do know I was wearing it the last time I saw Ben at the Spa and he drove me home.

There were times I didn't even like Sam. Once I got to the flat and found a girl there in a white crochet dress with visible black underwear. I possessed great dignity that evening and was ice itself. On his son's wedding day I attended an RAF dinner/dance with his/my friends. Mid-evening he walked in with the entire wedding party. His wife didn't know me, his sons didn't know me, but some of his relations did and obviously couldn't acknowledge me, like Aunt Lizzie from Nottingham with her twisted feet who had entertained me in her own home, called me Duck, hugged and kissed me. Yes it hurt. I fled out the back way with tears streaming and forgave him the next day. Like he laughingly said on Valentine's Day, what bugger other than me would send him one?

Every Friday was inquisition day, as Thursday evening was my night out with the girls. How my friends begged and implored me to leave him, and how bitterly jealous Sam was of my friendship with the girls. He said my friendships weren't normal. He was even more jealous of men who didn't exist, because faithful I remained through all the nights I lay weeping in bed, asking myself what the bloody hell was I crying about. In work Mr. H would enquire "Trouble?" after a stormy phone call with Sam, which he couldn't help but overhear. His advice was to give Sam competition, advice I never took. Mr. H has found me in tears quite often, always tears shed over Sam.

Yet there was kindness in him. I remember the young waif and stray Katrina, whom he picked up in London, escorted to a hostel, met up with the next morning and saw onto a train bound for home with money in her pocket. I met her at the hostel, a slip of a thing in trouble. She wrote poems. One was about a crab. She wrote to us thanking Sam more than words could say. His generosity, often extreme, earned him the nickname of Godfather in his circle of friends and acquaintances. He liked that.

He spoilt me with his superb cooking, and his family, as most Sundays he cooked lunch at his wife's bungalow. Most evenings, after leaving the office, I would go in the public lavs on the Centre of Bristol, refresh my face before going on to Sam's. Two or three times quite recently a great big fat girl chatted me up in there and showed me her sore bleeding belly button. God knows why. It made my knees go slack. I would then walk up Pipe Lane and see Sam on high, standing on his balcony looking out for me so he knew when to put the kettle on. There awaited me sumptuous meals – real home cooking, like steak and kidney pie and lots of stews with dumplings.

Mum and Dad went only once to his flat, although they had an open invitation. Mum wore his specs to watch the colour telly (a treat as ours is black and white) and poor Nan, who had come with us, had to lie on his bed when the pate upset her.

Rish and Bob didn't take to him. They were over on holiday last year. Yet what a fabulous evening he created for us. Rish, Bob, Des and I had tickets to a Gord Lightfoot concert at the Royal Albert Hall in London. Dave had a ticket too of course, being Gord's greatest fan, but he had to go into hospital, so Sam said rather than waste it, he would come. I didn't want him to, as I knew Gord's singing wouldn't be to his liking and, sure enough, five minutes into the concert he got up from his seat and made for the bar. I glared in his wake. He didn't come back until the intermission and then, what exciting news! He had arranged to take us backstage. He told us to be ready five minutes before the end of the concert. We were. So too were a mother and daughter sat immediately behind us, who had overheard Sam's earlier conversation. And so we all shot backstage and speaking for the female populace, we went well and truly gaga over Gord Lightfoot. He was a thoroughly nice chap. There was wine, and believe it or not Sam smuggled out Gord's glass as a souvenir for Dave. I think the evening ended with Gord propositioning Sam to become his Manager. For sure he could make things happen. I would say he was a bit of a phenomenon. He'd like that.

But somewhere along the way I toppled off the crest of the wave I've been riding. Too many grievances piled up and my thoughts became interminably doom-laden. Did I, or do I love him? No, I don't think so. But get away I must. A fresh start is called for. I need to hoist myself out of this rut I find myself in.

THERE'S NO GOING BACK

Canada beckons and has done for quite a while. Friends have said it's rather extreme and drastic, uprooting and taking myself off to Toronto to live. They say I'm not the type to emigrate. We'll see. After all, Rish, Bob and little Marcus are there so my life should be hunky-dory. God though I'm scared out of my wits thinking about it. Excited too.

Tomorrow I'm going. I've said my goodbyes. My job is no more. Mr. H said if I wanted to come back I could and he would boot the new girl out. Not quite the done thing, but the gesture is most appreciated. I finished work a fortnight ago, and this week have kept up my shorthand by taking down 'Listen with Mother' on the radio. I've had one or two bad panic attacks, but I've dealt with them as and when. Confronted my demons so to speak. They're not nice, these panic attacks that nearly make your legs buckle under you. I can but hope they'll fade away soon. Best foot forward girl and all that.

My friends have been on the phone constantly, even Chris in Kent whom I haven't seen in years. I worry what's going to become of Debbie. Debbie and Rob have got big problems. They have separated. Rob, believe it or not, is now working in Montreal. Deb isn't keen on moving there with the twins. Why oh why was June and Phil's baby born brain damaged? Lin and Ted are all right. They got married a month ago. Happy as Larry they are. Barbie and Russell? I'm puzzled. Married six months ago and now there's talk of an annulment. I can't believe it. Everybody thought they were an ideal couple, so suited, so happy. I was bridesmaid. At the wedding her Dad's new suit tore under the armpit and a wasp went for the roses in my hair. Apparently, Russell had turned up the night before with a monstrous joke pimple on the end of his nose. What on earth could have gone wrong for them? I can't begin to imagine and I've heard both sides. She is back with her Mum and Dad now, and ratty as hell. Russell wants to make a go of their marriage. He called on her one night this week and she screamed at him to get out of her sight. It saddens me. She gave me a choker chain as a going away gift. She is already planning a Canadian visit next year to see me. Des is engaged to Ed. Out of all my friends she deserves the most happiness. I saw what she went through, nursing her dying mother through one of the worst possible hideous, lingering illnesses ever, Motor Neurone Disease. Her mum years back played the piano with such flair. Before she died everything had packed up, except her heart and her brain. I saw Des and Ed this evening at the Town's Talk. George, Ed's brother, was my date. He's a good friend, soon off to Germany to work. He has promised to keep in touch. We had our photo taken, the four of us. We parted at the Town's Talk and Des and I cried. She gave me a piece of fine bone china. She said, engaged or not, she was still coming over to Toronto for a holiday next year on her own. George and I went back to his place for a coffee and, damn me, found Des and Ed ensconced there, so we had to say goodbye all over again. They gave us squatters' rights on the sofa. My dear precious Tritz I saw one evening this week. I'll carry with me a super memory of her. She's very preggy and when I met her she was sat like a squat garden gnome on one of the Nails outside the Corn Exchange, pretty as a picture she looked. We must have looked odd, clutching hold of one another in the city centre come evening's end – she delivered a speech – squashing baby, eyes brimming over, but two gigglers still. She took my photo. She also gave me a lovely powder compact I'll treasure 'til I die.

Sam rang this evening. He called me darling. He sounded sad, but realistic. I honestly don't know what I felt at the end of his call – maybe sad too, but free. Our last date was on Wednesday. We went to the House of Wong, no more to be a regular haunt. He wore a monacle. (Forever the extrovert that man of mine, until today.) We didn't go back to his flat. There would have been too many memories. We drove to the Downs for a short while. He gave me a St Christopher, whom he said would take care of me wherever I roam. I didn't cry then, when we parted, but bawled my eyes out later and blubbed to Mum I may well come back and marry him one day. Pathetic, the hold that man has had over me. I felt relatively calm though after his goodbye phone call this evening.

My little Nan I can't bear to think of. She says she'll not see me again. I feel my going away has broken her heart and caused her infinite sorrow, yet without reproach from her. She said she wouldn't let me see her tears. Saying cheerio to Nan was the bravest I've been so far. She was braver than brave.

Ally, where are you Al? He's staying with a steeplejack family somewhere in the London area for a couple of months while he's learning his rep's job. He comes home weekends and tells us jokes like two lepers playing cards, one threw his hand in, the other laughed his head off. He would cry tomorrow morning if he was home.

Our Dave, Chod, always the joker told me tonight to have a good look at him, because next time I see him he'll be completely bald. Recently, he has even paid a couple of visits to a hair and scalp clinic, but cost and pretty therapists have put him off. Why has God given him such pain this past year, hurt beyond measure? Not only to give him a bad back, but to kill his brilliant running future stone dead. One of England's Olympic hopes, oh yes he was, even beaten Dave Bedford in a race, finished, struck off the list. It's too cruel for words and to witness Dave inwardly suffering makes me both angry and bitter. But still I pray for it all to come right in the end. He's got a serious girlfriend now, Linds, or Lindy Lou as he calls her, but she lives in Cov. They phone each other repeatedly, but obviously don't meet up on a regular basis. The first time I saw her she climbed into my bed alongside me about midnight. We said "Hi" and "Night night" and proper introductions were made in the morning. I like her. Our Dave's besotted certainly. He met her on Bournemouth beach.

And my Mum and Dad? They'll be coming to Heathrow airport with me tomorrow. Mum will say "Go and try and make a new life for yourself". Dad will say, "If you feel unhappy or lonely, you come straight back home". Mum said she would miss me for all the scandal and tittle-tattle I disclose.

I'll stop now and turn out the light, but I won't go to sleep. Thoughts are racing. It isn't just Sam who has driven me to this, oh no. It's a host of things. I'm running away, escaping what has become a discontented, humdrum life, hopeful there will be a better one for me t'other side of the Atlantic. What a let-down I am in the human stakes. Got to stand tall and deliver a few punches – no harm in that. I wonder if I'll have to pay any excess baggage? I am 20lbs overweight (30lbs at first pack), but can't leave behind certain memorabilia and familiar knick-knacks. I found mothballs in the cases when I came to pack, for which Mum got a telling off. Whatever I wear next week in Canada I'll stink. I wanted to go to the Bristol Flower Show, take Mum and Dad as a treat, but ran out of time this week. Now I wish I had made time. Mum wanted me to wash and set her hair, but I didn't get the chance. Sausages are repeating on me. I requested them for my last supper along with Mum's rhubarb tart. I'll have a slice for breakfast plus a bowlful of Kellogg's Country Store. You can't get that cereal in Canada. It's my favourite. Another thing I'll miss, every week Dad brings home from Mac Fisheries, as a special treat, such tasty ham on the bone plus a fresh pineapple and cream roll. My chops are drooling at the thought. You can't get fresh cream in Canada, only that squirty stuff. Lauren dropped by this evening. She had made me a gorgeous flower brooch out of tights. She's a new friend. She said she likes writing letters. Just as well. I received a Bon Voyage card today from Spain. One of Dad's work mates on holiday sent it. I wonder what his wife thought? Will people be as nice in Canada? I'm tired, oh so tired, but up early tomorrow and the start of a new life, new challenges. Put hairs on my chest Dave said.

There were ructions below stairs not long ago. Such jubilation. Our darling Ally boy arrived unexpectedly. I had a deep down gut feeling he would come home if he could, to wave me goodbye. We hugged and hugged, but it felt funny. He was wearing a plaster cast. Back trouble. Both my brothers now have demon backs. Sigh, how am I going to live without the brothers' banter, wit and bonhomie spurring me on each and every day, my Bloss coming out with her 'funnies' and being my confidant, and my Pop the Dop, simply being the very best Dad in the whole wide world. But I'm a big girl now, can stand on my own two feet. Yes damn it, I can! What lies in wait for this girl Pange? Ooh, my body's all of a jangle. Nerves. I need the loo again. Lummy days, at the rate of knots I've been going these past few weeks I'm a mere stripling, a wispy shred of my former self. I give myself the willies, thinking too much.

Blinking heck, I've written reams of drivel, a real hotchpotch. I started my prattling way back when after being dumped by Ben. Quite a lot has happened since. Not all bad. I'm sure there are more highs and lows to come. I'm not a great one for praying, but I do say a silent "Thank you God" when something nice happens. How many times will I say it in the coming months? Or will it be instead "Damn and blast you God!"

Will I continue writing down my thoughts, hopes and dreams in Canada? I expect so. It'll be good therapy to keep me on the straight and narrow, with the odd hiccup here and there to ponder over no doubt. Now stop your wittering girl and douse the light. I've got to pass muster tomorrow. I don't want to be sent back by the authorities with my tail between my legs. All in all it will be a challenging day. A few deep breaths will be called for. Have a practice Pange. You might nod off.